W9-BBX-520

Better Homes and Gardens®

Eat Healthy, Lose Weight

Volume 3

Meredith® Consumer Marketing
Des Moines, Iowa

Better Homes and Gardens®
Eat Healthy, Lose Weight, Volume 3

Meredith Corporation Consumer Marketing
Senior Vice President, Consumer Marketing: David Ball
Consumer Product Marketing Director: Steve Swanson
Consumer Product Marketing Manager: Amanda Werts
Business Director: Ron Clingman
Senior Production Manager: George Susral

Waterbury Publications, Inc.
Editorial Director: Lisa Kingsley
Associate Editors: Tricia Bergman, Mary Williams
Creative Director: Ken Carlson
Associate Design Directors: Doug Samuelson, Bruce Yang
Production Assistant: Mindy Samuelson
Contributing Copy Editors: Terri Fredrickson, Gretchen Kauffman, M. Peg Smith
Contributing Indexer: Elizabeth T. Parson

***Better Homes and Gardens*® Magazine**
Editor in Chief: Gayle Goodson Butler
Deputy Editor, Food and Entertaining: Nancy Wall Hopkins

Meredith Publishing Group
President: Tom Harty
Vice President, Manufacturing: Bruce Heston

Meredith Corporation
President and Chief Executive Officer: Stephen M. Lacy

In Memoriam: E. T. Meredith III (1933–2003)

Printed in the United States of America.
ISSN: 1949-2227
ISBN: 978-0-696-30105-6

All of us at Meredith® Consumer Marketing are dedicated to providing you with the information and ideas you need to create delicious foods. We welcome your comments and suggestions. Write to us at: Meredith Consumer Marketing, 1716 Locust St., Des Moines, IA 50309-3023.

Our seal assures you that every recipe in *Eat Healthy, Lose Weight,* Volume 3 has been tested in the Better Homes and Gardens® Test Kitchen. This means that each recipe is practical and reliable and meets our high standards of taste appeal. We guarantee your satisfaction with this book for as long as you own it.

CONTENTS

Mushroom and Herb Pizza
Page 29

Saucy Meatballs
Page 181

Hazelnut-Mocha Torte
Page 275

FOOD FOR THOUGHT

Simply by picking up this book, you've taken the first step on a journey to weight loss success. A small step like this is what it takes to start you on your way to seeing big changes. In fact, when it comes to weight loss, baby steps are the best way to go for lasting results.

The most obvious way to lose weight is to eat more healthfully. That's what the more than 270 delicious recipes in *Eat Healthy, Lose Weight,* Volume 3 are designed to do. They're made of wholesome, basic ingredients that include whole grains, lean protein, nutrient-rich fruits and vegetables, and healthful fats. All the recipes in this book were developed and tested by registered dietitians in the Better Homes and Gardens® Test Kitchen to ensure that each one is delicious and satisfying. The dishes are so good that many taste testers were surprised these are foods that will help people lose and maintain weight.

In *Eat Healthy, Lose Weight* Vol. 3, there are recipes to suit any need or occasion—from quick, family-friendly weeknight meals to special-occasion appetizers, main dishes, sides, and desserts that taste indulgent but are well within the guidelines of a healthful diet. (How about Chocolate-Peanut Butter Molten Cupcakes?)

Because the holidays are a particularly challenging time for dieters, a special chapter is devoted to recipes that have all of the great tastes of traditional holiday food but are lower in fat and calories than the traditional recipes.

Welcome to *Eat Healthy, Lose Weight,* Volume 3—a dieter's best friend for preparing fresh, wholesome, appetizing dishes. Get cooking, lose weight, and feel great!

Chapter 1

Weight Loss Guide

DETERMINE YOUR HEALTHY WEIGHT

A healthy body weight is one that is right for you. It is a weight that reduces your risk of disease and allows you to look and feel good. There are several ways to determine your healthy weight; one of them is body mass index (BMI). For most people, the BMI provides a fairly accurate estimation of body fat based on height and weight. It's used most commonly to define "overweight" and "obese." To calculate your BMI, turn to the chart on page 8.

Using Our Nutrition Information

These recipes are low in fat and calories and full of flavor. The nutrition information, which is calculated by one serving, helps you keep track of your daily food intake and determine how a dish fits into your meal plan.

At the end of the recipe, you'll find the amounts per serving of calories, fat, saturated fat, cholesterol, sodium, total carbohydrate, fiber, and protein.

Calculating the Nutritional Analysis

Each recipe was tested in the Better Homes and Gardens® Test Kitchen. This means each recipe is practical, reliable, and meets our high standards of taste appeal. Here are the general guidelines used in analyzing our recipes:

- When there's a range in the number of servings (such as 4 to 6 servings), the first (smaller) number is used to calculate calories per serving.
- When ingredient choices appear (such as egg product or eggs), the first one mentioned is analyzed.
- When an ingredient is listed as optional, such as a garnish or flavoring, it is not included in the nutritional analysis.

How Many Calories Do I Need?

Here is a quick and easy way to determine approximately how many calories you need each day.

To Maintain Your Weight: Multiply your weight in pounds by 15 if you're moderately active (you do housework, gardening, or brisk walking for 30 to 60 minutes most days) or by 13 if you're sedentary (you sit all day with no planned exercise). For example: If you're moderately active and weigh 150 pounds, your average intake should be 2,250 calories per day (150 × 15).

To Lose Weight: To drop 1 pound per week, you need to reduce your calories by 500 per day. That's because 3,500 calories (500 calories × 7 days) equals 1 pound of body fat. Losing 1 to 2 pounds a week is considered a healthy rate of weight loss.

If that's too much calculating for you, just consume fewer calories than you do now. Most women lose weight when they eat 1,200 to 1,500 calories per day, while most men lose weight when they eat 1,600 to 1,800 calories per day.

BODY MASS INDEX (BMI)

	Normal						Overweight					Obese										Extremely Obese		
BMI	19	20	21	22	23	24	25	26	27	28	29	30	31	32	33	34	35	36	37	38	39	40	41	42
WEIGHT IN POUNDS																								
4'10"	91	96	100	105	110	115	119	124	129	134	138	143	148	153	158	162	167	172	177	181	186	191	196	201
4'11"	94	99	104	109	114	119	124	128	133	138	143	148	153	158	163	168	173	178	183	188	193	198	203	208
5'0"	97	102	107	112	118	123	128	133	138	143	148	153	158	163	168	174	179	184	189	194	199	204	209	215
5'1"	100	106	111	116	122	127	132	137	143	148	153	158	164	169	174	180	185	190	195	201	206	211	217	222
5'2"	104	109	115	120	126	131	136	142	147	153	158	164	169	175	180	186	191	196	202	207	213	218	224	229
5'3"	107	113	118	124	130	135	141	146	152	158	163	169	175	180	186	191	197	203	208	214	220	225	231	237
5'4"	110	116	122	128	134	140	145	151	157	163	169	174	180	186	192	197	204	209	215	221	227	232	238	244
5'5"	114	120	126	132	138	144	150	156	162	168	174	180	186	192	198	204	210	216	222	228	234	240	246	252
5'6"	118	124	130	136	142	148	155	161	167	173	179	186	192	198	204	210	216	223	229	235	241	247	253	260
5'7"	121	127	134	140	146	153	159	166	172	178	185	191	198	204	211	217	223	230	236	242	249	255	261	268
5'8"	125	131	138	144	151	158	164	171	177	184	190	197	203	210	216	223	230	236	243	249	256	262	269	276
5'9"	128	135	142	149	155	162	169	176	182	189	196	203	209	216	223	230	236	243	250	257	263	270	277	284
5'10"	132	139	146	153	160	167	174	181	188	195	202	209	216	222	229	236	243	250	257	264	271	278	285	292
5'11"	136	143	150	157	165	172	179	186	193	200	208	215	222	229	236	243	250	257	265	272	279	286	293	301
6'0"	140	147	154	162	169	177	184	191	199	206	213	221	228	235	242	250	258	265	272	279	287	294	302	309
6'1"	144	151	159	166	174	182	189	197	204	212	219	227	235	242	250	257	265	272	280	288	295	302	310	318
6'2"	148	155	163	171	179	186	194	202	210	218	225	233	241	249	256	264	272	280	287	295	303	311	319	326
6'3"	152	160	168	176	184	192	200	208	216	224	232	240	248	256	264	272	279	287	295	303	311	319	327	335

SMALL LOSS, BIG IMPACT

10% Slim Down

Losing weight can put pep in your step and add fulfilling years to your life. You don't have to lose a lot to reap the benefits. Losing only 5 to 10 percent of your body weight can give you more energy, lift your mood, and improve your health.

Live a Fuller, More Energized Life

Instead of letting the number on the scale weigh you down, think about the benefit of losing just 10 percent of your weight. It increases vitality, boosts mood, fends off chronic diseases, and might even help you enjoy social activities more.

Defend Against Type 2 Diabetes

Losing a few pounds and getting some exercise fends off type 2 diabetes better than any medication does. In a study of more than 3,000 men and women at high risk for developing type 2 diabetes, losing 5 to 7 percent of body weight and exercising about 20 minutes a day (150 minutes per week) reduced risks of developing the disease by 58 percent.

If you already have type 2 diabetes, trimming a few pounds can help. Losing about 11 pounds lowers fasting blood glucose as well as many drugs can, and losing those pounds might allow you to reduce medications you already take. Bonus: If you control blood glucose with fewer medications or lower doses, you'll save money and dodge some of the side effects of medications.

Halt Heart Disease

One in three adults in the United States has high blood pressure, which is the second biggest chronic health condition (overweight and obesity are No. 1) in this country. Equally disturbing is that the number of deaths from high blood pressure is on the rise. Here's the good news: Dropping 14 pounds or more reduces the long-term risk of developing high blood pressure by 21 to 29 percent in overweight adults who are middle-age and older, say researchers of the Framingham Heart Study.

Don't know your blood pressure numbers? Get them checked at a local pharmacy or your doctor's office—the sooner the better. According to the American Heart Association, nearly 25 percent of people with high blood pressure don't even know they have it. Fortunately, shedding a few pounds can lower elevated blood pressure.

Lowering your cholesterol, especially LDL (bad) cholesterol, is another strategy to safeguard your heart. Losing 10 percent of your weight can reduce both total and LDL cholesterol levels by 15 to 20 percent.

Prevent Cancer

Extra pounds do more than just sit on hips and bellies, making it hard to fit into clothes. Body fat, especially around the waist, pumps out hormones and other compounds that cause chronic inflammation and increased insulin levels; both are risk factors for cancer, type 2 diabetes, and heart disease.

Studies have found that losing 5 to 20 pounds from early adult life to middle age is associated with reduced risks for several cancers, including breast and colon cancers.

Take Action

Ignore strict dieting rules. Instead modify your way of eating. Look carefully at your eating patterns for excesses in calories and portions, then make small changes you can live with. If you and your friends frequently hit the neighborhood coffeehouse for a sugar- and fat-loaded designer drink and a treat, don't give up your friend time to eat bland oatmeal at home alone—it's not a strategy that's likely to last. Instead, continue to enjoy your friends' company, but switch to a trimmed-down breakfast, such as a nonfat latte and a yogurt parfait.

According to the Centers for Disease Control (CDC), women eat about 335 more calories than they did in the 1970s, and men have increased their average daily intake by 168 calories. Much of this comes from expanding portions, which has led to expanding waistlines. To learn how much you're eating—generally people eat more than they think they do—serve your usual portions of food and then measure them. You might be surprised that your portion of cereal, for example, is twice the serving size of the one listed on the box.

A calorie burned in physical activity is a calorie saved. Only about one-third of Americans get regular leisure physical activity, and about one-third get almost none. Work in a bit of activity here and there to help drop a few pounds. Do the housework yourself, stroll around the block before dinner, or walk a loop around the mall before shopping. All these count as activity, and they all burn calories.

Get regular exercise too. Find something you like, such as tennis, water aerobics, or walking. Be sure to prioritize and schedule it—there's less chance something else will interfere with it. Even without weight loss, being active improves blood pressure, back pain, cholesterol, arthritis symptoms, depression, and more.

Don't aim for a magic number on the scale—focus on being healthy and fit. Instead of thinking, *I have to lose weight,* think, *I have a chance to be fit.*

EAT SMART

Get a Grip on Cravings

All efforts to lose weight have one big obstacle: hunger. Serious stomach-growling, headache-inducing hunger can cause overeating. Learn to identify real hunger and plan meals that will keep you full longer so you can outsmart cravings.

STAY FUELED

Be Carb-Smart

Refined carbohydrates, such as white rice, bread, and pasta, might be driving your hunger. Studies suggest that the percentage of calories from fats or carbohydrates is not important in suppressing hunger or weight gain. The form of carbohydrates is important. Highly refined starches, such as white bread and white rice, lead to a fast return of hunger. Whole grain and high-fiber foods satisfy and prevent hunger longer.

Eating sugars and white flour can set you up to feel hungry and mentally unfocused, making you crave more sugar and refined carbs. If you eat primarily refined carbs, you raise your blood sugars. Your body doesn't like spiked blood sugars, so it pumps insulin to bring them down, leaving your brain with less fuel to function. The resulting brain fog is related to diet and lifestyle.

Choose whole grains and avoid white flour and sugar to avoid hunger pangs and the foggy feeling that often lures people to vending machines or poor snack choices.

Eat Filling Foods

Hunger will roar more often throughout the day when you nosh high-calorie foods, such as chips, soda, and fruit snacks that don't offer much staying power.

Here's one simple way to stay full all day: Fill up on nutrient-rich, low-calorie foods. People know they need to eat less to lose weight, but they tend to fill their plates just as full and eat the same number of snacks and meals a day. You can eat your usual amount of food if you choose foods that are lower in caloric density.

Simple steps such as eating a bowl of broth-based soup or a salad to start your meal, allow the water and fiber to fill you up with few calories. Then you can eat a smaller entrée and still feel satisfied. Choosing foods that are less calorie-dense and higher in fiber leads to eating more fruits, vegetables, and whole grains—which most people need to do.

Always Eat Breakfast

Across the board, weight loss experts recommend a satisfying breakfast. A filling, whole grain breakfast with some protein staves off hunger and provides energy all morning.

Skipping breakfast is associated with higher body weight. Good breakfast choices are important. A high-fiber, high-protein breakfast helps control calorie intake later.

Feeling hungry at breakfast is a good way to gauge how well your eating plan went the day before. If you wake up hungry and ready for breakfast, you are eating the right amount.

Portion Properly

Use visual cues, such as an empty bag of crackers, to tell you when you are finished eating. Most people eat more from a large package; it's important to have signals to stop eating.

If you limit access to food in small ways, you will easily eat less without feeling it. Studies show people will eat 20 percent less food and feel equally satisfied by making small changes, such as eating meals from smaller plates. Plating each serving of food and putting the remainder away, instead of serving family style, puts a barrier between you and second servings.

OVERCOME EMOTIONAL EATING

Hunger versus Appetite

Once you eat a well-balanced, fiber-rich diet with adequate calories, hunger should not be an issue. If a candy bar craving hits, you might not be dealing with true hunger. That's when it's time to think about why you feel the need to eat.

Learning to separate hunger from appetite is key to weight loss success. Hunger comes from the stomach; appetite comes from the brain. Caused by stress, boredom, or anxiety, all cravings are psychological. Deal with your emotional state directly rather than using food as a temporary fix.

Curbing cravings might be as simple as focusing on something else. Research shows that if you can distract yourself for 10 minutes, the feeling will go away. It's best if you do something active—take a walk, read a book, or watch a movie.

Sleep Off Hunger

Lifestyle is a trigger for hunger too. Even lack of sleep plays a role. Studies show that getting fewer than five hours of sleep per night is associated with higher BMI. With each hour of deprived sleep, the higher the risk of obesity. Insomnia can cause hormonal changes and cravings for carbohydrates.

Some people even snack to stay awake, especially when driving or working late. The action of eating might help to keep you alert, but a power nap would serve you better.

THINK AWAY CRAVINGS

Distract your mind with a nonfood thought.

Researchers Eva Kemps and Marika Tiggemann at Flinders University in Australia found that inducing a food craving caused subjects to perform poorly on cognitive tests and to have slower reaction times. They discovered a big part of having a craving involved visualizing the desired object. That visualization uses valuable cognitive resources—you truly can't think as well. Such strong cravings can get in the way of performance.

To curb cravings, they asked subjects to visualize something other than food to help eliminate the cravings rather than simply trying to ignore them. So when chocolate is on your mind, try to think of something else, then visualize it fully. You might find that you can concentrate better and no longer need the chocolate.

Getting enough rest will help you keep your resolve to lose weight and eat healthfully. Experts believe that simply feeling fatigued lowers resistance to tempting foods.

What's in a Name?

Is it a snack or a meal? What you call it matters.

A recent study by the Cornell Food and Brand Lab evaluated behavior at buffets. People were sent to a buffet, told they were just having a snack, and were served with paper plates and plastic utensils. A second group was told they were having a meal and sat down to eat with regular dishes, tableware, and tablecloths.

Subjects who thought they were having a snack ate a little less at the buffet, then ate more calories overall because they went in search of a full meal afterward. Subjects who thought the buffet was their meal ate a little more initially but less overall because they didn't seek a meal afterward.

The results of this study show this: If you are going to a party and the food is reasonably healthful, it's better to consider it your dinner. Labeling it as a meal has benefits.

No Forbidden Foods

The psychological aspect of dieting is often the toughest. One mistake many people make is denying themselves the foods they love, such as desserts or bread.

If you deprive yourself of your favorite foods, you crave them, break down, and end up with a loss of control. If you aren't satisfied, you might find yourself binge-eating in a weak moment.

The road to weight loss has the occasional detour, and you won't change overnight. Being patient and kind to yourself goes a long way.

EATING & EXERCISE TIPS

Push Through the Plateau

Have you hit that dreaded diet plateau? These expert tips will help you maximize calorie burn, make food fixes, and get in the right mind-set to recharge your metabolism—which will change your body for good.

MAXIMIZE CALORIE BURN

Get on Your Feet

In terms of calorie-burning, sitting is a disaster. Why? When you stand, your body requires 115 calories every hour simply to keep your body going—to hold your postural muscles in place while enabling your heart, brain, skin, and other vital organs to function. When you sit, the body needs only 80 calories an hour. That's a difference of 35 calories per hour, which seems paltry until you do the math. Add it up: Spend five of your work hours standing at your desk instead of sitting and you burn an extra 175 calories daily. Do it consistently for a year and you'll lose about 18 pounds. So think about putting your laptop on a pile of books or a low shelf. Your office mates might think it's odd, but in a few weeks they'll notice the effects. If you feel weird standing in your cubicle, try staying on your feet while looking through mail, during daily mass transit commute, or while chatting on the phone.

Pull the Plug

Many tools that save physical effort, such as cars and electric mixers, eliminate opportunities to burn extra calories each day. Instead of moving your car every time you go to a different shop in a strip mall, leave it in one spot and walk to each place. Ride a bike to the convenience store. Walk to a nearby coworker's office rather than sending an e-mail. Get down on your hands and knees to clean your floor instead of using a mop. All the calories you burn with these little activities will add up.

Pump It Up

Anyone serious about wanting to lose weight has to strength-train. By adding a single pound of muscle to your body, you can burn an extra 10 to 20 calories a day, which will make a big difference over time. Worried you'll look like a body builder? Don't be. About 99.9 percent of women simply are not physically capable of bulking up unless they lift for hours every day—even then, they'd have to take drugs to get large muscles. Lifting weights simply firms and tightens. Aim for 8 to 15 reps of exercises. Make sure the weight you pump is light enough to do at least eight reps with good form, yet heavy enough to get tough by the time you reach the ninth repetition. Work every big muscle group—chest, upper back, shoulders, stomach, abs, thighs, calves, arms, and butt—at least two or three times a week with a day of rest in between. Weight-train to maintain weight as well as to lose weight.

FOOD FIXES

Write It Down to Drop Pounds

Keep a food journal to get a sense of your eating habits. Take notes about your food intake for a week, then look for ways to cut 100 calories each day, eliminating 700 calories every week and losing weight without feeling deprived. Food journaling is a good habit. Studies show that people who keep a record of food and exercise lose weight faster and keep it off longer because the record helps keep them honest.

Get Seriously Hydrated

Bodies are 60 to 70 percent water. All metabolic processes—including digestion and excretion—require a lot of H_2O; without it, systems don't work well. Experts suggest dividing your weight in half and drinking that many ounces of water daily. (A 140-pound woman would need 70 ounces, or nine 8-ounce glasses.) Juice and milk count toward the total daily fluid intake on a one-to-one ratio, but coffee and tea dehydrate the body. For every one of those beverages, drink two glasses of water to compensate.

Stay Fueled

Eating at regular intervals throughout the day keeps blood sugar—and you—stable. The more frequently you eat, the more physically and emotionally steady you'll feel throughout the day. Studies show that it is especially important to have a bite to eat first thing in the morning. After fasting for several hours during the night, skipping breakfast causes an early crash of energy. An early nosh also can enhance cognitive performance. Research finds that schoolchildren who skipped breakfast showed significant academic improvements after they began eating breakfast regularly. Having something nutritious in the stomach will help you make better, more rational decisions as the day goes on, especially if you're faced with foods that are not the best for you. Studies show that people who don't eat breakfast are more likely to be overweight or obese than those who do eat breakfast.

Fill Up on Fiber

Fiber, an element found naturally in many foods, stays in the system—making you feel full longer—until it passes through. Strive to get 25 to 40 grams of fiber daily. Increase your intake slowly if you're not currently getting that amount to avoid uncomfortable gas.

Most vegetables are full of fiber, particularly dark leafy greens and beans. Fruits, especially berries, are another good source. In the nut family, almonds and whole flaxseeds are healthful choices. For packaged foods, read labels to find products with the most fiber per serving.

THE RIGHT MIND-SET

Baby Steps

Set small weekly weight loss goals for yourself, such as 1 pound a week to feel that you're succeeding. If you lose weight or stick to your exercise regimen, treat yourself, but not with food. Many people don't lose weight initially when they begin exercising more. Many nutrition experts suspect that's because dieters think a workout allows them to eat a muffin or a plate of french fries. They add back all the calories just burned.

A better way to treat yourself: Buy fancy coffee beans or good quality tea. Or put a quarter in a jar for every day you exercise and stick to your diet. Once it adds up, splurge on a nonfood reward. Also set goals beyond the scale. Link your weight loss goals with another achievement, such as getting in shape for a 10-mile charity run. Doing so will prevent you from obsessing about weight. You'll feel good if you finish a race—and great when you raise money for a good cause.

Deal with Stress

Stress can lead to weight gain. If your diet is constantly sabotaged by uncontrollable urges to binge, chill out before you open the fridge door. Under pressure, the level of the hormone cortisol increases. Cortisol increases appetite and causes fat to accumulate in the body, particularly in the abdomen. On top of that, abdomen fat signals the metabolism to slow down more than does fat in other parts of the body.

When you feel stressed, try to work relaxation into your day. Exercising and getting enough sleep counteract some effects of stress. A well-rested brain is better able to understand when your body is full.

Apply these simple tricks to say good-bye to stubborn pounds. Keep your spirits up—and watch your weight go down.

A LITTLE HUNGER IS PART OF ADJUSTING TO A NEW EATING PLAN. ALLOW YOUR BODY TO ADJUST BY FEELING SOME HUNGER.

LOSE THE FAT

Belly Busters

Love handles. Spare tire. Potbelly. Muffin top. All of these playful phrases refer to what medical professionals call abdominal obesity. Unfortunately abdominal obesity is anything but funny. It's downright dangerous.

Research shows that in young and older people alike, a big belly increases risks for chronic diseases, such as cardiovascular disease, stroke, hypertension, insulin resistance, type 2 diabetes, and cancer. More than one-third of U.S. adults are obese, and more than half of all U.S. adults have abdominal obesity. The good news? You can whittle your middle and lower your risk of chronic conditions with lifestyle changes.

Why Belly Fat Is So Bad

Scientists once thought fat cells were just a repository for excess fat. In recent years, researchers discovered that fat cells release hormones and other substances—some bad, some good. Some substances help reduce inflammation while others increase inflammation. The more excess fat you have, though, the more harmful chemicals the fat produces.

Fat cells are endocrine factories that produce a wide array of hormones and other compounds that pour into the blood.

There are two kinds of belly fat: subcutaneous fat, which accumulates around the middle, and visceral fat, hidden beneath abdominal muscles. Subcutaneous fat contributes to inflammation and cardiovascular disease.

Visceral fat plays an important role in the immune system. It is filled with white blood cells that mop up microbes and other toxic substances that may escape through the intestinal wall.

But too much visceral fat secretes inflammatory chemicals—much more than fat cells in other parts of your body. Inflammation is what researchers believe leads to chronic diseases. Excessive visceral fat also dumps free fatty acids into the bloodstream, which carries them to the liver. Over time this overflow of fat to the liver causes high cholesterol, high triglycerides, and insulin resistance. Excess visceral fat has also been linked to fat accumulating around organs such as the heart and liver, impairing their ability to function well.

Fat-Causing Factors

Genes influence where each body stores extra fat. Even if you are genetically inclined to store fat around your waist, you are not necessarily doomed to look like your portly relatives. Research and common sense prove that behaviors such as smoking, drinking alcohol, and being a couch potato lead to less-healthy lifestyles, which often lead to a big stomach. When

you manage your calorie intake and engage in daily exercise, you may still have your family's blue eyes—without the belly.

Chronic stress may also play a role. When your body is stressed, it produces cortisol, a hormone that places your body on alert. Research suggests that this hormone can lead to an increase in belly fat in adults and children. Stress is also linked to behaviors such as increased eating, drinking, and smoking—and less exercise.

Middle Management

You don't have to be stuck with a big gut. The solution comes as no surprise: Eat right and exercise regularly.

In the 2006 STRIDDE study, walking the equivalent of 11 miles a week prevented accumulation of visceral fat. More exercise resulted in a loss of ab flab. Subjects who did not exercise gained a significant amount of abdominal fat, including visceral fat, in only six months.

A 2006 study published in the *International Journal of Sport Nutrition and Exercise Metabolism* evaluated the most efficient way to eat and exercise to blast abdominal fat. Researchers divided subjects into two groups. Group One followed a diet higher in protein (about 40 percent of calories) and lower in fat and carbohydrates while incorporating high-intensity strength and cardiovascular exercise. Group Two followed a traditional food guide pyramid diet (50 to 55 percent carbohydrate, 15 to 20 percent protein, less than 30 percent fat) while incorporating moderate-intensity cardiovascular exercise.

After 12 weeks those in Group One lost about twice as much weight overall than those in Group Two. Group One also lost 26.4 percent abdominal fat compared with 13.5 percent in Group Two. Based on these results, the most effective way of beating ab flab may be to include more protein in your diet while incorporating regular high-intensity cardio and strength exercise.

GUT BUSTERS

Take these simple steps to good health and healthy weight.

- **Control portion size** by using smaller plates and bowls.
- **Stop drinking sugar-sweetened beverages,** such as regular sodas and fruit drinks.
- **Include vegetables** with every lunch and dinner. Besides being nutritious, they help fill you up.
- **See a registered dietitian** to help you create a healthful eating plan. Visit eatright.org to find a registered dietitian in your area.
- **Use only low-fat or fat-free** milk, cheese, and yogurt.
- **Go meatless** a few nights a week. Try a whole wheat pasta primavera with lots of vegetables instead of a steak and potato.
- **Stop eating after dinner** while watching TV or in front of the computer. Most people needlessly consume hundreds more calories while mindlessly munching.
- **Exercise daily.** Adults need two hours and 30 minutes a week of moderate-intensity aerobic activity, such as brisk walking, and muscle-strengthening activities two or more days a week, says the Centers for Disease Control and Prevention's exercise guidelines.
- **Limit your intake of saturated fats.** Scientific evidence suggests you can reduce belly fat by eating less saturated fat. Saturated fat is found in butter, cheese, meat, and ice cream.
- **Drink less alcohol and quit smoking.**
- **Manage your stress.** Take time to destress and relax when you can. A few deep breaths in a frustrating moment can work wonders.
- **Add whole grains to your diet.** A study in the *American Journal of Clinical Nutrition* found that consuming whole grains decreased abdominal fat in obese men and women.

Chapter 2

Breakfast

On the opener: Mexican-Style Scrambled Eggs *(see recipe, page 25)*

EGGS & CHEESE

FRUIT

PANCAKES & FRENCH TOAST

Banana-Stuffed French Toast

PREP 20 minutes **BAKE** 10 minutes
OVEN 500°F **MAKES** 4 servings

NUTRITION FACTS per serving

CALORIES 210
TOTAL FAT 4 g (1 g sat. fat)
CHOLESTEROL 107 mg
SODIUM 352 mg
CARBOHYDRATE 34 g
FIBER 2 g
PROTEIN 9 g
EXCHANGES 1½ Starch, ½ Other Carbo., ½ Medium-Fat Meat

Nonstick cooking spray
2 eggs
½ cup fat-free milk
½ teaspoon vanilla
⅛ teaspoon ground cinnamon
4 1-inch slices French bread
⅔ cup thinly sliced banana
Sifted powdered sugar, light pancake and waffle syrup product, or maple syrup (optional)

1 Preheat oven to 500°F. Line a baking sheet with foil; lightly coat foil with cooking spray. In a shallow bowl combine eggs, milk, vanilla, and cinnamon. Beat with a wire whisk or rotary beater until well mixed. Set aside.

2 Using a knife, cut a pocket in each bread slice, cutting horizontally from the top crust almost to, but not through, the bottom crust. Fill bread pockets with banana.

3 Dip bread slices into egg mixture, coating both sides of each slice. Place on the prepared baking sheet. Bake for 10 to 12 minutes or until golden, turning once. If desired, sprinkle with powdered sugar or serve with syrup.

Blueberry Buckwheat Pancakes

START TO FINISH 30 minutes
MAKES six 2-pancake servings

NUTRITION FACTS per serving

CALORIES 132
TOTAL FAT 3 g (1 g sat. fat)
CHOLESTEROL 2 mg
SODIUM 244 mg
CARBOHYDRATE 22 g
FIBER 3 g
PROTEIN 6 g
EXCHANGES 1 Starch, ½ Other Carbo., ½ Fat

- ½ cup buckwheat flour
- ½ cup whole wheat flour
- 1 tablespoon sugar
- ½ teaspoon baking powder
- ¼ teaspoon baking soda
- ¼ teaspoon salt
- 1¼ cups buttermilk or sour milk*
- ¼ cup refrigerated or frozen egg product, thawed, or 1 egg, lightly beaten
- 1 tablespoon vegetable oil
- ¼ teaspoon vanilla
- ¾ cup fresh or frozen blueberries

1 In a medium bowl stir together buckwheat flour, whole wheat flour, sugar, baking powder, baking soda, and salt. Make a well in center of flour mixture; set aside. In a small bowl combine buttermilk, egg product, oil, and vanilla. Add buttermilk mixture all at once to flour mixture. Stir just until combined but slightly lumpy. Stir in blueberries.

2 Heat a lightly greased griddle or heavy skillet over medium heat until a few drops of water sprinkled on griddle dance across the surface. For each pancake, pour a scant ¼ cup of the batter onto hot griddle. Spread batter into a circle about 4 inches in diameter.

3 Cook over medium heat until pancakes are browned, turning to cook second sides when pancake surfaces are bubbly and edges are slightly dry (1 to 2 minutes per side). Serve immediately or keep warm in a loosely covered ovenproof dish in a 300°F oven.

***Note:** To make 1¼ cups sour milk, place 4 teaspoons lemon juice or vinegar in a 2-cup glass measuring cup. Add enough milk to equal 1¼ cups total liquid; stir. Let the mixture stand for 5 minutes before using.

Zucchini Pancakes

PREP 20 minutes **COOK** 4 minutes per batch
STAND 30 minutes
MAKES 10 pancakes

NUTRITION FACTS per pancake

CALORIES 69
TOTAL FAT 3 g (1 g sat. fat)
CHOLESTEROL 3 mg
SODIUM 154 mg
CARBOHYDRATE 7 g
FIBER 1 g
PROTEIN 4 g
EXCHANGES 1 Vegetable, ½ Lean Meat, ½ Fat

- 1 pound zucchini, shredded
- ¼ teaspoon salt
- ½ cup finely chopped red onion (1 medium)
- ½ cup finely shredded Parmesan cheese (2 ounces)
- ½ cup white whole wheat flour or all-purpose flour
- ½ cup refrigerated or frozen egg product, thawed, or 2 lightly beaten eggs
- 1 tablespoon extra virgin olive oil
- ¼ teaspoon garlic powder
- ¼ teaspoon black pepper
- Nonstick cooking spray
- 1 teaspoon extra virgin olive oil
- ¼ cup light sour cream (optional)
- Chopped red onion (optional)
- Shredded or bite-size sticks zucchini (optional)

1 In a large bowl combine the 1 pound zucchini and the salt. Let stand for 30 minutes. Place zucchini in a strainer and press firmly with a rubber spatula to force out water.

2 Return the zucchini to the bowl. Stir in the ½ cup red onion, the Parmesan cheese, flour, egg product, the 1 tablespoon olive oil, the garlic powder, and pepper. If the batter is not thick enough to hold together, add a little more flour, 1 tablespoon at a time, until the mixture is the right consistency.

3 Lightly coat a large skillet or griddle with cooking spray. Add 1 teaspoon olive oil to skillet and heat over medium heat. Using ¼ cup zucchini mixture per pancake, drop zucchini mixture onto hot skillet, leaving 2 to 3 inches between mounds. Flatten mounds to about ½-inch thickness. Cook pancakes about 4 minutes or until golden brown, carefully turning once halfway through cooking.

4 Keep pancakes warm in a 300°F oven while cooking the remaining pancakes. If desired, top pancakes with sour cream and sprinkle with additional chopped red onion and shredded zucchini to serve.

Scrambled Eggs with Tomatoes and Peppers

START TO FINISH 20 minutes
MAKES 4 servings

NUTRITION FACTS per serving

CALORIES 114
TOTAL FAT 4 g (1 g sat. fat)
CHOLESTEROL 0 mg
SODIUM 386 mg
CARBOHYDRATE 7 g
FIBER 1 g
PROTEIN 13 g
EXCHANGES ½ Vegetable, 2 Lean Meat, 1 Fat

- 1 tablespoon olive oil
- ½ cup chopped onion (1 medium)
- ½ cup chopped red or green sweet pepper
- ½ cup chopped, seeded tomato (1 medium)
- 2 cups refrigerated or frozen egg product, thawed, or 8 eggs
- ⅓ cup fat-free milk
- ¼ teaspoon salt
- ⅛ teaspoon black pepper

1. In a large skillet heat olive oil over medium heat. Add onion and sweet pepper; cook for 4 to 6 minutes or until tender, stirring occasionally. Stir in tomato.

2. Meanwhile, in a medium bowl beat together egg product, milk, salt, and black pepper. Add egg mixture to onion mixture in skillet. Cook over medium heat, without stirring, until mixture begins to set on the bottom and around the edges.

3. With a spatula or a large spoon, lift and fold the partially cooked egg mixture so the uncooked portion flows underneath. Continue cooking over medium heat for 2 to 3 minutes or until the egg mixture is cooked through but is still glossy and moist. Remove skillet from heat. Serve immediately.

Mexican-Style Scrambled Eggs

START TO FINISH 30 minutes
OVEN 350°F **MAKES** 4 servings

- 1 cup water
- ¼ cup thinly sliced green onions (2)
- ¼ cup chopped red or green sweet pepper
- 1 8-ounce carton refrigerated or frozen egg product, thawed
- ¼ cup fat-free milk
- ⅛ teaspoon black pepper
- 4 7-inch whole wheat tortillas
- 1 teaspoon butter
- ½ cup shredded reduced-fat cheddar cheese (2 ounces)
- ⅓ cup purchased fresh salsa
- ¼ cup light sour cream (optional)

1 In a small saucepan combine the water, green onions, and sweet pepper. Bring to boiling; reduce heat. Simmer, uncovered, for 5 to 7 minutes or until vegetables are tender. Drain well. In a medium bowl stir together egg product, milk, and black pepper. Stir in cooked vegetables.

2 Preheat oven to 350°F. Stack tortillas; wrap in foil. Bake about 10 minutes or until warm. (Or just before serving, cover and microwave tortillas on high about 1 minute.)

3 Meanwhile, in a large skillet melt butter over medium heat. Pour in egg mixture. Cook, without stirring, until mixture begins to set on the bottom and around edges. Using a spatula or large spoon, lift and fold partially cooked eggs so uncooked portion flows underneath. Sprinkle with cheese. Continue cooking for 2 to 3 minutes or until eggs are cooked through but still glossy and moist.

4 To serve, immediately spoon egg mixture along the center of each warm tortilla. Fold tortilla in half or roll up. Top with salsa and, if desired, sour cream.

NUTRITION FACTS per serving

CALORIES 228
TOTAL FAT 8 g (4 g sat. fat)
CHOLESTEROL 13 mg
SODIUM 608 mg
CARBOHYDRATE 20 g
FIBER 11 g
PROTEIN 18 g
EXCHANGES 1 Starch, 2 Lean Meat, 1½ Fat

Spinach and Cheese Omelet

PREP 10 minutes **COOK** 8 minutes
MAKES 4 servings

NUTRITION FACTS per serving

CALORIES 120
TOTAL FAT 3 g (2 g sat. fat)
CHOLESTEROL 10 mg
SODIUM 438 mg
CARBOHYDRATE 5 g
FIBER 1 g
PROTEIN 16 g
EXCHANGES ½ Vegetable, 2 Lean Meat, ½ Fat

- Nonstick cooking spray
- 2 cups refrigerated or frozen egg product, thawed, or 8 eggs
- 2 tablespoons snipped fresh chives, Italian (flat-leaf) parsley, or chervil
- ⅛ teaspoon salt
- ⅛ teaspoon cayenne pepper
- ½ cup shredded reduced-fat sharp cheddar cheese (2 ounces)
- 2 cups fresh baby spinach leaves or torn fresh spinach
- 1 recipe Red Pepper Relish

1 Coat a large nonstick skillet with flared sides with cooking spray. Heat skillet over medium heat.

2 Meanwhile, in a large bowl beat egg product, chives, salt, and cayenne pepper with a rotary beater or wire whisk until frothy. Pour egg mixture into hot skillet. Immediately begin stirring the eggs gently and continuously with a wooden or plastic spatula until mixture resembles small pieces of cooked egg surrounded by liquid egg. Stop stirring. Cook for 30 to 60 seconds more or until egg is set but shiny.

3 When egg is set but still shiny, sprinkle with cheese. Top with 1 cup of the spinach and ¼ cup of the Red Pepper Relish. With a spatula, lift and fold 1 side of omelet partially over filling. Transfer omelet to platter. Top with remaining spinach and Red Pepper Relish.

Red Pepper Relish: In a small bowl combine ⅔ cup chopped red sweet pepper, 2 tablespoons finely chopped green onion or onion, 1 tablespoon cider vinegar, and ¼ teaspoon black pepper.

Tomato-Broccoli Frittata

PREP 20 minutes **BROIL** 5 minutes
STAND 5 minutes **MAKES** 4 servings

NUTRITION FACTS per serving

CALORIES 134
TOTAL FAT 6 g (2 g sat. fat)
CHOLESTEROL 161 mg
SODIUM 416 mg
CARBOHYDRATE 7 g
FIBER 2 g
PROTEIN 14 g
EXCHANGES 1 Vegetable, 2 Lean Meat

- 6 egg whites
- 3 eggs
- ¼ teaspoon salt
- ¼ teaspoon black pepper
- ¼ cup crumbled reduced-fat feta cheese or regular feta cheese
- 1 teaspoon olive oil
- 2 cups small broccoli florets
- 2 tablespoons finely chopped shallots
- 1¼ cups cherry tomatoes, quartered

1 Preheat broiler. In a medium bowl whisk together egg whites, eggs, salt, and pepper. Stir in cheese; set aside.

2 In a large broilerproof skillet heat oil over medium heat. Add broccoli and shallots; cook for 8 to 10 minutes or just until tender, stirring occasionally. Pour egg mixture over the broccoli mixture in skillet. Cook over medium-low heat. As mixture sets, run a spatula around the edge of the skillet, lifting egg mixture so uncooked portion flows underneath. Continue cooking and lifting edges until egg mixture is almost set (surface will be moist). Arrange tomatoes on top of egg mixture.

3 Broil 4 to 5 inches from the heat about 5 minutes or until center is set. Let stand for 5 minutes before serving. Cut into wedges.

Super Breakfast Burritos

START TO FINISH 30 minutes
MAKES 6 burritos

NUTRITION FACTS per serving

CALORIES 297
TOTAL FAT 12 g (4 g sat. fat)
CHOLESTEROL 216 mg
SODIUM 602 mg
CARBOHYDRATE 29 g
FIBER 12 g
PROTEIN 20 g
EXCHANGES 2 Starch, 2 Medium-Fat Meat

- 2 teaspoons olive oil
- 2 medium fresh poblano chile peppers, seeded and chopped*
- ¾ cup canned black beans, rinsed and drained
- ¾ cup frozen corn, thawed
- ⅓ cup purchased tomato salsa or green salsa
- ½ teaspoon ground cumin
- ½ teaspoon chili powder
- 6 eggs
- 6 8-inch whole grain tortillas, warmed
- 4 ounces queso fresco, crumbled, or reduced-fat Monterey Jack cheese, shredded (¾ cup)
- ¼ cup snipped fresh cilantro

1 In a large skillet heat 1 teaspoon of the oil over medium heat. Add poblano peppers; cook about 3 minutes or just until tender. Stir in beans, corn, the ⅓ cup salsa, the cumin, and chili powder. Cook and stir about 2 minutes or until hot. Remove vegetable mixture from skillet.

2 In a medium bowl whisk together eggs, a dash of *salt,* and a dash of *black pepper.* In same skillet heat remaining 1 teaspoon oil over medium heat. Pour in egg mixture. Cook, without stirring, until mixture begins to set on the bottom and around edges. Using a spatula, lift and fold the partially cooked eggs so uncooked portion flows underneath. Continue cooking for 2 to 3 minutes or until egg mixture is cooked through but is still glossy and moist. Remove from heat. Gently fold in vegetable mixture. Spoon about ⅔ cup of the egg mixture along the center of each tortilla. Top with cheese and cilantro. Fold sides of tortillas over filling. Roll up tortillas starting at 1 end. If desired, serve with additional salsa.

***Note:** Because chile peppers contain volatile oils that can burn your skin and eyes, avoid direct contact with them as much as possible. When working with chile peppers, wear plastic or rubber gloves. If your bare hands do touch the peppers, wash your hands and fingernails well with soap and warm water.

Mushroom and Herb Pizza

PREP 40 minutes **BAKE** 22 minutes
OVEN 425°F **MAKES** 8 servings

NUTRITION FACTS per serving

CALORIES 274
TOTAL FAT 11 g (3 g sat. fat)
CHOLESTEROL 170 mg
SODIUM 575 mg
CARBOHYDRATE 30 g
FIBER 3 g
PROTEIN 17 g
EXCHANGES ½ Vegetable, 2 Starch, 1½ Medium-Fat Meat

- 1 16-ounce loaf frozen honey-wheat bread dough, thawed
- 6 eggs
- ⅓ cup fat-free milk
- Nonstick cooking spray
- 1 tablespoon olive oil
- 3 cups sliced fresh mushrooms
- ⅓ cup snipped fresh basil and/or parsley or 2 teaspoons dried Italian seasoning, crushed
- 1 tablespoon snipped fresh oregano
- 3 cloves garlic, minced
- ¼ teaspoon salt
- 1 cup shredded part-skim mozzarella cheese (4 ounces)
- ¼ cup finely shredded Parmesan cheese

1. Preheat oven to 425°F. Lightly grease a 15×10×1-inch baking pan. On a floured surface roll bread dough to a 15×10-inch rectangle. If dough is difficult to roll, let it rest a few minutes. Press dough into prepared pan, building up edges slightly. Prick generously with a fork. Let stand for 5 minutes. Bake about 10 minutes or until lightly browned. Cool for 5 minutes.

2. Meanwhile, in a medium bowl whisk together eggs and milk. Coat an unheated large nonstick skillet with cooking spray. Preheat over medium heat. Pour in egg mixture. Cook, without stirring, until mixture begins to set on bottom and around edges. Using a spatula, lift and fold partially cooked egg mixture so uncooked portion flows underneath. Cook for 2 to 3 minutes or until egg mixture is cooked through but still glossy and moist. Transfer eggs to a bowl; set aside.

3. In the same skillet heat oil over medium heat. Add mushrooms, basil, oregano, garlic, and salt; cook for 5 to 7 minutes or just until mushrooms are tender, stirring occasionally. Fold cooked eggs into mushroom mixture.

4. Sprinkle mozzarella cheese over partially baked crust. Top with egg mixture and Parmesan cheese. Bake for 12 to 15 minutes or until edges are golden brown. If desired, sprinkle with freshly ground *black pepper.*

Mushroom, Asparagus, and Tofu Quiches

PREP 20 minutes **COOK** 5 minutes
BAKE 20 minutes **OVEN** 350°F
MAKES 6 servings

NUTRITION FACTS per serving

CALORIES 108
TOTAL FAT 6 g (1 g sat. fat)
CHOLESTEROL 0 mg
SODIUM 319 mg
CARBOHYDRATE 5 g
FIBER 1 g
PROTEIN 10 g
EXCHANGES ½ Vegetable, 1½ Medium-Fat Meat

- 1 12.3-ounce package light firm silken-style tofu (fresh bean curd)
- ½ cup refrigerated or frozen egg product, thawed, or 2 eggs
- 3 ounces cheddar-flavor soy cheese, finely shredded (¾ cup)
- 2 tablespoons snipped fresh basil
- ¼ teaspoon black pepper
- ⅛ teaspoon salt
- 2 teaspoons olive oil
- 1½ cups sliced fresh assorted mushrooms (such as cremini, stemmed shiitake, morel, and/or button)
- 12 ounces fresh asparagus spears, trimmed and cut into 1-inch pieces
- ¼ cup finely chopped shallots

1 Preheat oven to 350°F. In a food processor or blender combine tofu and eggs. Cover and process or blend just until combined. Transfer to a large bowl; stir in soy cheese, 1 tablespoon of the basil, the pepper, and salt. Set aside.

2 In a large skillet heat olive oil over medium-high heat. Add mushrooms, asparagus, and shallots. Cook and stir for 5 to 8 minutes or just until tender; cool slightly. Stir vegetable mixture into tofu mixture, stirring until well mixed.

3 Divide mixture among six 6-ounce ramekins or au gratin dishes. Place filled ramekins in a 15×10×1-inch baking pan.

4 Bake, uncovered, about 20 minutes or until set and edges are bubbly. Sprinkle with the remaining 1 tablespoon basil. Serve warm.

Cheesy Mushroom Casserole

PREP 30 minutes **BAKE** 25 minutes
STAND 5 minutes **OVEN** 350°F
MAKES 6 servings

Nonstick cooking spray
3 cups water
1 cup quick-cooking (hominy) grits
¾ cup shredded reduced-fat cheddar cheese
⅛ teaspoon salt
1 8-ounce package sliced fresh button mushrooms
1 6-ounce package sliced fresh portobello mushrooms or two 3-ounce portobello mushrooms, cleaned and sliced
¼ teaspoon black pepper
4 ounces thinly sliced prosciutto, chopped
2 cloves garlic, minced
4 egg whites, lightly beaten
2 eggs, lightly beaten
Snipped fresh parsley (optional)

1 Preheat oven to 350°F. Coat a 2-quart rectangular baking dish with cooking spray; set aside. In a large saucepan bring the water to boiling. Gradually stir in grits. Reduce heat to low. Cook, uncovered, for 5 to 7 minutes or until thick, stirring frequently. Remove from heat. Stir in ¼ cup of the cheese and the salt. Spread evenly in the prepared dish.

2 Coat an unheated large nonstick skillet with cooking spray. Preheat skillet over medium heat. Add mushrooms and pepper. Cook about 5 minutes or until mushrooms are tender and any liquid is evaporated, stirring occasionally. Add prosciutto and garlic. Cook and stir for 1 minute more. Cool slightly.

3 Add egg whites and eggs to the mushroom mixture; stir to combine. Spread egg mixture over grits in dish. Sprinkle with the remaining ½ cup cheese.

4 Bake, uncovered, for 25 to 30 minutes or until heated through and egg mixture is set in center. Let stand for 5 minutes before serving. If desired, sprinkle with parsley.

NUTRITION FACTS per serving

CALORIES 235
TOTAL FAT 10 g (2 g sat. fat)
CHOLESTEROL 81 mg
SODIUM 571 mg
CARBOHYDRATE 23 g
FIBER 2 g
PROTEIN 17 g
EXCHANGES ½ Vegetable, 1½ Starch, 1½ Medium-Fat Meat

Tomato, Spinach, and Feta Strata

PREP 30 minutes **CHILL** 4 to 24 hours
BAKE 1 hour 10 minutes **STAND** 10 minutes
OVEN 325°F **MAKES** 6 servings

NUTRITION FACTS per serving

CALORIES 247
TOTAL FAT 9 g (3 g sat. fat)
CHOLESTEROL 216 mg
SODIUM 419 mg
CARBOHYDRATE 27 g
FIBER 7 g
PROTEIN 18 g
EXCHANGES 1 Vegetable, 1½ Starch, 1½ Medium-Fat Meat

Nonstick cooking spray
4 cups cubed whole grain bread
1 pound fresh asparagus, trimmed and cut into 1-inch pieces
1 cup chopped onion (1 large)
2 cups fresh baby spinach
6 eggs
1 cup fat-free milk
⅛ teaspoon sea salt or kosher salt
⅛ teaspoon freshly ground black pepper
2 plum tomatoes, thinly sliced
½ cup reduced-fat feta cheese
¼ cup snipped fresh basil

1 Coat a 2-quart rectangular baking dish with cooking spray. Arrange half the bread cubes in the prepared baking dish.

2 In a covered medium saucepan cook asparagus and onion in a small amount of boiling water for 2 to 3 minutes or just until tender; stir in spinach. Immediately drain well. Spoon half the asparagus mixture on bread in baking dish. Top with the remaining bread cubes and the remaining asparagus mixture. Set aside.

3 In a large bowl whisk together eggs, milk, salt, and pepper. Pour evenly over mixture in baking dish. Using the back of a large spoon, lightly press down layers. Arrange tomato slices on top. Top with feta cheese and basil. Cover with foil; chill for 4 to 24 hours.

4 Preheat oven to 325°F. Bake, covered, for 30 minutes. Uncover; bake about 40 minutes more or until center registers 180°F when tested with an instant-read thermometer (there will be some liquid in center that will be absorbed during standing). Let stand on a wire rack for 10 minutes before serving.

Broccoli Soy Strata

PREP 15 minutes **CHILL** 8 to 24 hours
BAKE 50 minutes **STAND** 10 minutes
OVEN 325°F **MAKES** 6 servings

NUTRITION FACTS per serving

CALORIES 210
TOTAL FAT 7 g (4 g sat. fat)
CHOLESTEROL 17 mg
SODIUM 581 mg
CARBOHYDRATE 21 g
FIBER 2 g
PROTEIN 15 g
EXCHANGES ½ Vegetable, 1 Starch, 2 Lean Meat, ½ Fat

- 2 cups cut-up fresh broccoli or 2 cups frozen broccoli cuts, thawed
- 4 cups 1-inch cubes country or crusty Italian bread cubes
- 4 ounces process Gruyère cheese, cut up
- 1½ cups refrigerated or frozen egg product, thawed, or 6 eggs, lightly beaten
- 1½ cups light plain soy milk or fat-free milk
- 1 tablespoon honey mustard
- ½ teaspoon salt
- ¼ teaspoon black pepper
- ¼ teaspoon ground nutmeg
- ½ cup thinly sliced green onions (4)

1. In a medium saucepan cook broccoli, covered, in a small amount of boiling salted water for 3 minutes; drain. Rinse with cold running water until cool; drain again.

2. In a greased 2-quart square baking dish spread half the bread cubes. Top with broccoli and cheese. Add remaining bread cubes.

3. In a medium bowl combine eggs, soy milk, mustard, salt, pepper, and nutmeg. Pour egg mixture over mixture in baking dish. Sprinkle with green onions. Cover and chill for 8 to 24 hours.

4. Preheat oven to 325°F. Bake, uncovered, for 50 to 55 minutes or until an instant-read thermometer inserted in center registers 170°F. Let stand for 10 minutes before serving.

Lemon Breakfast Parfaits

PREP 30 minutes **MAKES** 6 servings

NUTRITION FACTS per serving

CALORIES 147
TOTAL FAT 3 g (1 g sat. fat)
CHOLESTEROL 7 mg
SODIUM 61 mg
CARBOHYDRATE 28 g
FIBER 4 g
PROTEIN 5 g
EXCHANGES ½ Fruit, 1 Starch, ½ Fat

¾ cup fat-free milk
Dash salt
⅓ cup whole wheat or regular couscous
½ cup lemon low-fat yogurt
½ cup light sour cream
1 tablespoon honey
¼ teaspoon finely shredded lemon peel
3 cups assorted fresh fruit, such as sliced strawberries, kiwifruit, nectarine, or star fruit (carambola); and/or blueberries or raspberries
Chopped crystallized ginger (optional)
Fresh mint (optional)

1 In a medium saucepan bring milk and salt to boiling; stir in the couscous. Simmer, covered, for 1 minute. Remove from heat; let stand for 5 minutes. Stir with a fork until fluffy. Let cool.

2 In a small bowl combine yogurt, sour cream, honey, and lemon peel. Stir yogurt mixture into couscous. In another bowl combine assorted fruit.

3 To serve, divide half the fruit mixture among 6 parfait glasses or dessert dishes. Spoon couscous mixture over fruit. Top with remaining fruit mixture. If desired, sprinkle with crystallized ginger and garnish with mint.

Tropical Ambrosia Salad

START TO FINISH 20 minutes
MAKES 10 servings

- 1 24-ounce jar refrigerated mango slices, drained and coarsely chopped
- 1 24-ounce jar refrigerated grapefruit sections, drained
- 1 20-ounce can pineapple chunks (juice pack), drained
- 1 recipe Sour Cream-Orange Dressing
- ½ cup large flaked coconut or dried coconut chips, toasted*
- 1 to 2 tablespoons pomegranate seeds

1 In a large bowl stir together mango, grapefruit, and pineapple. Add Sour Cream-Orange Dressing, stirring gently to coat. Spoon into a serving dish. Sprinkle with coconut and pomegranate seeds. Serve immediately.

Sour Cream-Orange Dressing: In a small bowl stir together ½ cup light sour cream; 2 tablespoons frozen orange juice concentrate, thawed; and 1 tablespoon packed brown sugar.

***Note:** To toast coconut, preheat oven to 350°F. Spread coconut in a single layer in a shallow baking pan. Bake for 5 to 10 minutes or until golden brown, stirring once or twice. Watch carefully so coconut does not burn.

NUTRITION FACTS per serving

CALORIES 158
TOTAL FAT 3 g (2 g sat. fat)
CHOLESTEROL 3 mg
SODIUM 40 mg
CARBOHYDRATE 33 g
FIBER 1 g
PROTEIN 2 g
EXCHANGES 1½ Fruit, ½ Other Carbo., ½ Fat

Honey-Ginger Compote

PREP 20 minutes **CHILL** 4 to 48 hours
MAKES 2 (3/4-cup) servings

NUTRITION FACTS per serving

CALORIES 103
TOTAL FAT 0 g
CHOLESTEROL 0 mg
SODIUM 10 mg
CARBOHYDRATE 27 g
FIBER 1 g
PROTEIN 1 g
EXCHANGES 1 Fruit, 1/2 Other Carbo.

- 1/4 cup apple juice, apple cider, or unsweetened pineapple juice
- 2 teaspoons honey
- 1 teaspoon finely chopped crystallized ginger
- 1 teaspoon lemon juice
- 1 1/2 cups assorted fruit, such as cubed melon, sliced star fruit (carambola), halved grapes, raspberries, pitted sweet cherries, cubed peaches, cubed pears, cubed mango, sliced kiwifruit, and/or chopped pineapple)
- 2 tablespoons low-fat vanilla yogurt (optional)

1 In a small saucepan combine apple juice, honey, crystallized ginger, and lemon juice. Cook and stir over medium heat until boiling. Transfer to a small bowl; cover and chill for 4 to 48 hours.

2 To serve, toss together assorted fruit. Spoon into tall stemmed glasses or dessert dishes. Pour apple juice mixture over fruit. If desired, spoon yogurt on top of fruit mixture.

Chapter 3

Breads

On the opener: Orange-Rye Spirals *(see recipe, page 56)*

QUICK BREADS

YEAST BREADS

Mango Coffee Cake

PREP 25 minutes **BAKE** 35 minutes
COOL 30 minutes **OVEN** 375°F
MAKES 10 servings

NUTRITION FACTS per serving

CALORIES 208
TOTAL FAT 6 g (1 g sat. fat)
CHOLESTEROL 0 mg
SODIUM 73 mg
CARBOHYDRATE 35 g
FIBER 3 g
PROTEIN 4 g
EXCHANGES 1 Starch, 1½ Other Carbo., 1 Fat

- Nonstick cooking spray
- 2 mangoes
- ½ cup sugar
- ¼ cup vegetable oil
- ¾ cup fat-free milk
- ⅓ cup refrigerated or frozen egg product, thawed, or 2 egg whites
- ⅔ cup all-purpose flour
- ½ cup whole wheat flour
- 2 teaspoons baking powder
- ½ teaspoon finely shredded lime peel
- ¼ teaspoon ground cardamom or allspice
- 1¼ cups quick-cooking rolled oats

1 Preheat oven to 375°F. Lightly coat a 9×1½-inch round baking pan with cooking spray; set aside. Seed, peel, and chop one of the mangoes; set aside. Seed, peel, and slice the remaining mango; set aside.

2 In a large mixing bowl stir together sugar and oil. Add milk and egg. Beat with an electric mixer on medium for 1 minute.

3 In a small bowl combine all-purpose flour, whole wheat flour, baking powder, lime peel, and cardamom. Add to beaten mixture; beat until combined. Stir in oats and chopped mango. Spoon into prepared pan. Arrange sliced mango on top of batter.

4 Bake for 35 to 40 minutes or until a wooden toothpick inserted near the center of the cake portion comes out clean. Cool in pan on a wire rack for 30 minutes. Serve warm.

Apple-Pumpkin Muffins

PREP 20 minutes **BAKE** 25 minutes
COOL 5 minutes **OVEN** 375°F
MAKES 12 muffins

NUTRITION FACTS per muffin

CALORIES 127
TOTAL FAT 3 g (1 g sat. fat)
CHOLESTEROL 1 mg
SODIUM 192 mg
CARBOHYDRATE 22 g
FIBER 2 g
PROTEIN 4 g
EXCHANGES 1 Starch, ½ Other Carbo., ½ Fat

Nonstick cooking spray
1¼ cups all-purpose flour
½ cup whole wheat flour
3 tablespoons toasted wheat germ
2 teaspoons pumpkin pie spice or apple pie spice
1½ teaspoons baking powder
½ teaspoon salt
¼ teaspoon baking soda
½ cup refrigerated or frozen egg product, thawed, or 2 eggs, lightly beaten
1 cup canned pumpkin
¾ cup buttermilk or fat-free sour milk*
⅓ cup unsweetened applesauce
¼ cup packed brown sugar
2 tablespoons vegetable oil

1 Preheat oven to 375°F. Lightly coat twelve 2½-inch muffin cups with cooking spray; set aside. In a large bowl stir together all-purpose flour, whole wheat flour, wheat germ, pumpkin pie spice, baking powder, salt, and baking soda; set aside.

2 In a medium bowl combine egg product, pumpkin, buttermilk, applesauce, brown sugar, and oil; add pumpkin mixture all at once to flour mixture. Stir just until moistened. Divide batter evenly among prepared muffin cups, filling each about two-thirds full.

3 Bake about 25 minutes or until golden brown and a wooden toothpick inserted near centers comes out clean.

4 Cool in muffin cups on a wire rack for 5 minutes. Remove from muffin cups; serve warm.

***Note:** To make ¾ cup fat-free sour milk, place 2¼ teaspoons lemon juice or vinegar in a glass measuring cup. Add enough fat-free milk to equal ¾ cup total liquid; stir. Let mixture stand for 5 minutes before using.

Lemon-Poppy Seed Muffins

PREP 15 minutes **BAKE** 20 minutes
COOL 5 minutes **OVEN** 375°F
MAKES 12 muffins

NUTRITION FACTS per muffin

CALORIES 150
TOTAL FAT 5 g (0 g sat. fat)
CHOLESTEROL 0 mg
SODIUM 153 mg
CARBOHYDRATE 24 g
FIBER 1 g
PROTEIN 3 g
EXCHANGES 1½ Other Carbo., ½ Fat

- Nonstick cooking spray
- 1¾ cups all-purpose flour
- ½ cup granulated sugar
- 1 tablespoon poppy seeds
- 1 tablespoon finely shredded lemon peel
- 2 teaspoons baking powder
- ½ teaspoon salt
- ¾ cup fat-free milk
- ¼ cup refrigerated or frozen egg product, thawed, or 1 egg, lightly beaten
- ¼ cup canola oil
- 2 teaspoons coarse sugar

1 Preheat oven to 375°F. Lightly coat twelve 2½-inch muffin cups with cooking spray or line with paper bake cups. Spray insides of paper bake cups, if using, with cooking spray. Set muffin cups aside.

2 In a medium bowl stir together flour, granulated sugar, poppy seeds, lemon peel, baking powder, and salt. Make a well in the center of flour mixture.

3 In another medium bowl combine milk, egg product, and oil. Add egg mixture all at once to flour mixture. Stir just until moistened (batter will be lumpy). Spoon batter evenly into the prepared muffin cups, filling each two-thirds full. Sprinkle tops with coarse sugar.

4 Bake for 20 to 25 minutes or until golden. Cool in muffin cups on a wire rack for 5 minutes. Remove from pans. Serve warm.

Raisin-Carrot Muffins

PREP 25 minutes **BAKE** 18 minutes
COOL 5 minutes **OVEN** 400°F
MAKES 16 muffins

NUTRITION FACTS per muffin

CALORIES 146
TOTAL FAT 4 g (1 g sat. fat)
CHOLESTEROL 14 mg
SODIUM 168 mg
CARBOHYDRATE 24 g
FIBER 2 g
PROTEIN 4 g
EXCHANGES 1 Starch, ½ Other Carbo., ½ Fat

- ⅔ cup golden raisins or dried currants
- ½ cup boiling water
- Nonstick cooking spray
- 1½ cups all-purpose flour
- ½ cup whole wheat flour
- ⅓ cup toasted wheat germ
- 1½ teaspoons baking powder
- ½ teaspoon baking soda
- ½ teaspoon salt
- ½ teaspoon ground cinnamon
- 1 egg
- 1¼ cups buttermilk*
- ⅓ cup packed brown sugar
- ¼ cup vegetable oil
- 1 cup finely shredded carrots (2 medium)
- Ground cinnamon

1 Preheat oven to 400°F. In a small bowl combine raisins and boiling water; set aside. Coat sixteen 2½-inch muffin cups with cooking spray or line with paper bake cups; set aside.

2 In a medium bowl stir together all-purpose flour, whole wheat flour, wheat germ, baking powder, baking soda, salt, and the ½ teaspoon cinnamon. Make a well in the center of flour mixture.

3 In a small bowl beat egg lightly; stir in buttermilk, brown sugar, and oil. Add all at once to flour mixture; stir just until moistened (batter should be lumpy). Drain raisins. Gently fold raisins and carrots into batter.

4 Spoon batter evenly into prepared muffin cups, filling each two-thirds full. Sprinkle with additional cinnamon.

5 Bake for 18 to 20 minutes or until golden. Cool in muffin cups on a wire rack for 5 minutes. Remove from cups. Serve warm.

***Note:** To make 1¼ cups fat-free buttermilk, place 4½ teaspoons lemon juice or vinegar in a glass measuring cup. Add enough fat-free milk to equal 1¼ cups total liquid; stir. Let mixture stand for 5 minutes before using.

Ginger-Pear Muffins

PREP 25 minutes **BAKE** 18 minutes
COOL 5 minutes **OVEN** 400°F
MAKES 12 muffins

NUTRITION FACTS per muffin

CALORIES 149
TOTAL FAT 7 g (1 g sat. fat)
CHOLESTEROL 0 mg
SODIUM 96 mg
CARBOHYDRATE 19 g
FIBER 2 g
PROTEIN 3 g
EXCHANGES 1 Starch, 1½ Fat

Nonstick cooking spray
1 cup all-purpose flour
1 cup quick-cooking rolled oats
3 tablespoons packed brown sugar
1½ teaspoons baking powder
½ teaspoon ground ginger
¼ teaspoon salt
⅔ cup fat-free milk
⅓ cup vegetable oil
¼ cup refrigerated or frozen egg product, thawed, or 1 egg, lightly beaten
¾ cup chopped, cored pear
¼ cup chopped walnuts (optional)
1 tablespoon oat bran
¼ teaspoon ground ginger

1 Preheat oven to 400°F. Lightly coat twelve 2½-inch muffin cups with cooking spray. Set aside.

2 In a large bowl combine flour, oats, brown sugar, baking powder, the ½ teaspoon ginger, and the salt. Make a well in the center of the flour mixture. In a small bowl combine milk, oil, and egg product; add all at once to flour mixture. Stir just until moistened. Fold in pear and, if desired, walnuts.

3 Spoon batter evenly into prepared muffin cups. Combine oat bran and the ¼ teaspoon ginger; sprinkle over muffins.

4 Bake for 18 to 20 minutes or until tops are brown. Cool in muffin cups on wire rack for 5 minutes. Remove from muffin cups; serve warm.

Pineapple-Glazed Banana-Blueberry Muffins

PREP 20 minutes **BAKE** 15 minutes
COOL 5 minutes **OVEN** 400°F
MAKES 12 muffins

NUTRITION FACTS per muffin

CALORIES 172
TOTAL FAT 4 g (3 g sat. fat)
CHOLESTEROL 11 mg
SODIUM 135 mg
CARBOHYDRATE 31 g
FIBER 2 g
PROTEIN 3 g
EXCHANGES 2 Other Carbo., ½ Fat

Nonstick cooking spray
1¾ cups all-purpose flour
⅓ cup packed brown sugar
2 teaspoons baking powder
½ teaspoon ground cinnamon
¼ teaspoon salt
¾ cup mashed ripe banana
½ cup fat-free milk
¼ cup butter, melted
¼ cup refrigerated or frozen egg product, thawed, or 1 egg, lightly beaten
1 teaspoon vanilla
¾ cup fresh blueberries
¼ cup pineapple preserves

1 Preheat oven to 400°F. Coat twelve 2½-inch muffin cups with cooking spray or line with paper bake cups; set aside.

2 In a large bowl combine flour, brown sugar, baking powder, cinnamon, and salt. Make a well in center of flour mixture; set aside.

3 In a medium bowl combine banana, milk, melted butter, egg product, and vanilla. Add banana mixture all at once to flour mixture. Stir just until moistened (batter should be lumpy). Fold in blueberries.

4 Spoon batter evenly into prepared muffin cups, filling each about three-fourths full. Spoon 1 teaspoon pineapple preserves on top of batter in each muffin cup.

5 Bake for 15 to 20 minutes or until golden and a wooden toothpick inserted in centers comes out clean. Cool in muffin cups on wire rack for 5 minutes. Remove from muffin cups; serve warm.

Upside-Down Tomato Corn Bread Muffins

PREP 25 minutes **ROAST** 30 minutes
BAKE 15 minutes **COOL** 10 minutes
OVEN 350°F/400°F **MAKES** 12 muffins

NUTRITION FACTS per serving

CALORIES 162
TOTAL FAT 8 g (2 g sat. fat)
CHOLESTEROL 8 mg
SODIUM 264 mg
CARBOHYDRATE 18 g
FIBER 1 g
PROTEIN 5 g
EXCHANGES 1 Starch, 1½ Fat

- 4 medium plum tomatoes
- 1 cup chopped onion (1 large)
- 3 tablespoons olive oil
- 1 teaspoon garlic powder
- ½ teaspoon black pepper
- 1 8.5-ounce package corn muffin mix
- 1 cup shredded reduced-fat cheddar cheese (4 ounces)
- 1 4-ounce can diced green chile peppers, drained
- ¼ cup fat-free milk
- ¼ cup light sour cream
- ¼ cup refrigerated or frozen egg product, thawed, or 1 egg, lightly beaten
- Nonstick cooking spray

1 Preheat oven to 350°F. Trim ends off tomatoes and remove cores. Cut each tomato crosswise into three ¾-inch slices (12 slices total). Line a 15×10×1-inch baking pan with parchment paper. Place tomato slices and chopped onion in the prepared pan. Drizzle with olive oil. Sprinkle with garlic powder and black pepper. Roast for 30 minutes. Remove from oven. Increase oven temperature to 400°F.

2 Meanwhile, in a large bowl combine corn muffin mix, cheese, chile peppers, milk, sour cream, and egg product. Stir just until combined; set aside.

3 Coat twelve 2½-inch muffin cups with cooking spray. Place a tomato slice and some of the onions in the bottom of each muffin cup. Spoon corn muffin mixture on tomato slices, filling muffin cups nearly full.

4 Bake for 15 minutes or until tops are golden brown and a wooden toothpick inserted into muffins comes out clean. Let muffins cool in cups on wire racks for 10 minutes. Run a thin metal spatula around edges of muffins to loosen from sides of pan. Invert muffins onto a serving plate. Serve warm.

Spiced Fan Biscuits

PREP 20 minutes **BAKE** 10 minutes
OVEN 450°F **MAKES** 12 biscuits

NUTRITION FACTS per biscuit

CALORIES 121
TOTAL FAT 4 g (1 g sat. fat)
CHOLESTEROL 0 mg
SODIUM 190 mg
CARBOHYDRATE 18 g
FIBER 1 g
PROTEIN 3 g
EXCHANGES 1 Starch, 1 Fat

- 2 cups all-purpose flour
- 4 teaspoons baking powder
- ½ teaspoon cream of tartar
- ¼ teaspoon salt
- ¼ cup shortening
- ¾ cup fat-free milk
- 2 tablespoons sugar
- 1 teaspoon ground cinnamon

1 Preheat oven to 450°F. Grease twelve 2½-inch muffin cups; set aside. In a large bowl stir together flour, baking powder, cream of tartar, and salt. Using a pastry blender, cut in shortening until mixture resembles coarse crumbs. Make a well in the center; add milk. Stir just until dough clings together.

2 Turn out dough onto a lightly floured surface. Knead by folding and gently pressing dough for 10 to 12 strokes or until dough is nearly smooth. Divide dough in half. Roll 1 half in a 12×10-inch rectangle. In a small bowl combine sugar and cinnamon. Sprinkle half the sugar mixture on the rectangle.

3 Cut rectangle into five 12×2-inch strips. Stack the strips on top of each other; cut into six 2-inch-square stacks. Place each stack, cut side down, in a prepared muffin cup. Repeat with remaining dough and sugar mixture.

4 Bake for 10 to 12 minutes or until golden brown. Serve warm.

Cranberry-Whole Wheat Scones

PREP 20 minutes **BAKE** 13 minutes
OVEN 400°F **MAKES** 12 scones

NUTRITION FACTS per scone

CALORIES 167
TOTAL FAT 5 g (3 g sat. fat)
CHOLESTEROL 14 mg
SODIUM 169 mg
CARBOHYDRATE 26 g
FIBER 1 g
PROTEIN 4 g
EXCHANGES ½ Fruit, 1 Starch, 1 Fat

- 1½ cups all-purpose flour
- ½ cup whole wheat flour
- 3 tablespoons sugar
- 1½ teaspoons baking powder
- 1 teaspoon ground ginger or cinnamon
- ¼ teaspoon baking soda
- ¼ teaspoon salt
- ⅓ cup butter
- ½ cup refrigerated or frozen egg product, thawed, or 2 eggs, lightly beaten
- ⅓ cup buttermilk or fat-free sour milk*
- ¾ cup dried cranberries or dried currants
- Buttermilk or fat-free milk*
- 3 tablespoons rolled oats

1 Preheat oven to 400°F. In a large bowl stir together all-purpose flour, whole wheat flour, sugar, baking powder, ginger, baking soda, and salt. Using a pastry blender, cut in butter until mixture resembles coarse crumbs. Make a well in the center of the flour mixture.

2 In a small bowl combine egg product and the ⅓ cup buttermilk; stir in dried cranberries. Add the buttermilk mixture all at once to the flour mixture. Using a fork, stir just until moistened (some of the dough may look dry).

3 Turn out dough onto a floured surface. Quickly knead dough by gently folding and pressing for 10 to 12 strokes or until nearly smooth. Pat or lightly roll the dough to a circle 8 inches in diameter. Lightly brush top with additional buttermilk; sprinkle with oats, pressing gently into dough. Cut into 12 wedges.

4 Place wedges 1 inch apart on an ungreased baking sheet. Bake for 13 to 15 minutes or until edges are lightly browned. Serve warm.

***Note:** To make ⅓ cup fat-free sour milk, place 1 teaspoon lemon juice or vinegar in a glass measuring cup. Add enough fat-free milk to equal ⅓ cup total liquid; stir. Let the mixture stand for 5 minutes before using.

Blueberry-Oat Scones With Flaxseeds

PREP 20 minutes **BAKE** 16 minutes
OVEN 400°F **MAKES** 12 scones

NUTRITION FACTS per scone

CALORIES 148
TOTAL FAT 5 g (3 g sat. fat)
CHOLESTEROL 11 mg
SODIUM 133 mg
CARBOHYDRATE 22 g
FIBER 2 g
PROTEIN 4 g
EXCHANGES 1½ Starch, 1 Fat

- 2 tablespoons flaxseeds, toasted*
- 1½ cups all-purpose flour
- ½ cup rolled oats
- ¼ cup sugar
- 2 teaspoons baking powder
- ¼ teaspoon salt
- ¼ cup cold butter, cut into pieces
- 1 6-ounce carton plain fat-free or low-fat yogurt
- 1 egg white, lightly beaten
- 1¼ cups fresh blueberries
- Fat-free milk
- Rolled oats and/or flax seeds (optional)

1 Preheat oven to 400°F. Line a baking sheet with foil or parchment paper; set aside. Place toasted flaxseeds in a spice grinder and pulse until ground to a fine powder.

2 In a medium bowl combine ground flaxseeds, flour, the ½ cup oats, the sugar, baking powder, and salt. Using a pastry blender, cut in butter until mixture resembles coarse crumbs. Make a well in the center of the flour mixture; set aside.

3 In a medium bowl combine yogurt and egg white. Gently fold in blueberries. Add yogurt mixture all at once to flour mixture. Using a fork, stir just until moistened.

4 Turn out dough onto a lightly floured surface. Knead by folding and gently pressing dough for 10 to 12 strokes or until dough is nearly smooth. Pat or lightly roll dough into a 10-inch circle. Cut into 12 wedges.

5 Place wedges 1 inch apart on the prepared baking sheet. Brush tops of scones with milk. If desired, sprinkle lightly with additional oats. Bake for 16 to 18 minutes or until golden brown. Serve warm.

***Note:** To toast flaxseeds, place in a small dry skillet over medium heat. Cook and stir until the seeds are fragrant and begin to pop.

Lemon-Nutmeg Scones

PREP 20 minutes **BAKE** 12 minutes
COOL 5 minutes **OVEN** 400°F
MAKES 8 scones

NUTRITION FACTS per scone

CALORIES 173
TOTAL FAT 7 g (3 g sat. fat)
CHOLESTEROL 16 mg
SODIUM 206 mg
CARBOHYDRATE 26 g
FIBER 2 g
PROTEIN 5 g
EXCHANGES 1 Starch, 1 Other Carbo., 1 Fat

- Nonstick cooking spray
- 1¼ cups all-purpose flour
- ¾ cup oat bran
- 3 tablespoons sugar
- 2 teaspoons baking powder
- ¼ teaspoon baking soda
- ¼ teaspoon ground nutmeg
- ⅛ teaspoon salt
- ¼ cup butter
- 1 6-ounce carton lemon low-fat yogurt with no-calorie sweetener
- ¼ cup refrigerated or frozen egg product, thawed, or 1 egg

1. Preheat oven to 400°F. Lightly coat a baking sheet with cooking spray. Set aside.

2. In a medium bowl combine flour, oat bran, sugar, baking powder, baking soda, nutmeg, and salt. Using a pastry blender, cut in butter until mixture resembles coarse crumbs. In a small bowl combine yogurt and egg product; add all at once to flour mixture. Stir just until moistened.

3. Turn out dough onto a floured surface. Knead dough by folding and gently pressing dough for 10 strokes. Lightly pat dough into a circle 6 inches in diameter. Cut dough into 8 wedges. Carefully separate wedges; place wedges about 2 inches apart on the prepared baking sheet.

4. Bake about 12 minutes or until golden brown. Cool on baking sheet on a wire rack for 5 minutes. Serve warm.

Goat Cheese and Onion Scones

PREP 20 minutes **BAKE** 15 minutes
OVEN 400°F **MAKES** 12 scones

NUTRITION FACTS per scone

CALORIES 106
TOTAL FAT 3 g (2 g sat. fat)
CHOLESTEROL 22 mg
SODIUM 193 mg
CARBOHYDRATE 15 g
FIBER 1 g
PROTEIN 5 g
EXCHANGES 1 Starch, ½ Fat

- 2 cups all-purpose flour
- 2 tablespoons finely chopped green onion (1)
- 2 teaspoons baking powder
- ¼ teaspoon baking soda
- ¼ teaspoon salt
- ¼ teaspoon freshly ground black pepper
- 1 egg, lightly beaten
- 4 ounces semisoft goat cheese (chèvre), crumbled or cut into small cubes
- ½ cup buttermilk or fat-free sour milk*

1 Preheat oven to 400°F. In a medium bowl combine flour, green onion, baking powder, baking soda, salt, and pepper. Make a well in the center of flour mixture; set aside.

2 In a small bowl stir together the egg, goat cheese, and buttermilk. Add egg mixture all at once to flour mixture. Using a fork, stir just until moistened.

3 Turn out dough onto a lightly floured surface. Knead dough by folding and gently pressing dough for 10 to 12 strokes or until dough is nearly smooth. Divide dough in half. Pat or lightly roll half the dough into a 5-inch circle. Cut into 6 wedges. Repeat with remaining dough. Place wedges 1 inch apart on an ungreased baking sheet.

4 Bake for 15 to 18 minutes or until golden. Serve warm.

***Note:** To make ½ cup fat-free sour milk, place 1½ teaspoons lemon juice or vinegar in a glass measuring cup. Add enough milk to equal ½ cup total liquid; stir. Let mixture stand for 5 minutes before using.

Pear-Cheddar Quick Bread

PREP 30 minutes **BAKE** 50 minutes
COOL 10 minutes **CHILL** overnight
STAND 1 hour **OVEN** 350°F
MAKES 1 loaf (16 slices)

NUTRITION FACTS per slice

CALORIES 164
TOTAL FAT 6 g (1 g sat. fat)
CHOLESTEROL 4 mg
SODIUM 107 mg
CARBOHYDRATE 24 g
FIBER 2 g
PROTEIN 4 g
EXCHANGES 1½ Other Carbo., 1 Fat

- 1⅓ cups all-purpose flour
- ½ cup whole wheat pastry flour or whole wheat flour
- ¼ cup flaxseed meal or toasted wheat germ
- 2 teaspoons baking powder
- ¼ teaspoon salt
- 1½ cups shredded, cored, unpeeled pears (about 1½ medium pears)
- ½ cup refrigerated or frozen egg product, thawed, or 2 eggs, lightly beaten
- ½ cup sugar
- ⅓ cup canola oil
- ¼ cup buttermilk or fat-free sour milk*
- ¼ cup honey
- 1 teaspoon vanilla
- ½ cup shredded white cheddar cheese (2 ounces)

1 Preheat oven to 350°F. Grease the bottom and ½ inch up the sides of one 9×5×3-inch loaf pan or two 7×3½×2-inch loaf pans; set aside. In a large bowl combine all-purpose flour, whole wheat pastry flour, flaxseed meal, baking powder, and salt. Make a well in the center of flour mixture; set aside.

2 In a medium bowl combine pears, egg product, sugar, oil, buttermilk, honey, and vanilla. Add pear mixture all at once to flour mixture. Stir just until combined. Fold in cheese. Spoon batter into prepared pan.

3 Bake for 50 to 55 minutes (45 to 50 minutes for the smaller pans) or until a wooden toothpick inserted near center comes out clean. Cool in pan on a wire rack for 10 minutes. Remove from pan. Cool completely on wire rack. Wrap and store overnight in the refrigerator; let stand at room temperature for 1 hour before slicing.

***Note:** To make ¼ cup fat-free sour milk, place ¾ teaspoon lemon juice or vinegar in a glass measuring cup. Add enough milk to equal ¼ cup total liquid; stir. Let mixture stand for 5 minutes before using.

Brandied Apricot Loaves

PREP 30 minutes **STAND** 15 minutes
BAKE 40 minutes **COOL** 10 minutes
STAND overnight **OVEN** 350°F
MAKES 2 loaves (12 slices each)

NUTRITION FACTS per slice

CALORIES 141
TOTAL FAT 4 g (2 g sat. fat)
CHOLESTEROL 7 mg
SODIUM 97 mg
CARBOHYDRATE 24 g
FIBER 1 g
PROTEIN 2 g
EXCHANGES 1½ Other Carbo., 1 Fat

- ¼ cup snipped dried apricots
- ¼ cup golden raisins
- ¼ cup apricot brandy or apricot nectar
- 2 cups all-purpose flour
- 1 cup sugar
- 2 teaspoons baking powder
- ½ teaspoon salt
- ¼ teaspoon ground cinnamon
- ¼ teaspoon ground mace
- 1 cup apricot nectar
- ½ cup refrigerated or frozen egg product, thawed, or 2 eggs, lightly beaten
- ⅓ cup butter, melted
- ½ cup sliced almonds, toasted (see note, page 35)
- 1 recipe Apricot Icing

1 Grease bottoms and ½ inch up the sides of two 7½×3½×2-inch loaf pans; set aside. In a bowl combine the ¼ cup apricots, the raisins, and apricot brandy; let stand for 15 minutes.

2 Preheat oven to 350°F. In a large bowl stir together flour, sugar, baking powder, salt, cinnamon, and mace. Make a well in the center of flour mixture. Set aside.

3 In a bowl mix nectar, egg product, and butter. Add egg mixture all at once to flour mixture. Stir just until moistened (batter should be lumpy). Fold in fruit mixture and the ½ cup almonds. Spoon evenly into prepared pans.

4 Bake for 40 to 45 minutes or until a wooden toothpick inserted near centers comes out clean. Cool loaves in pans on wire racks for 10 minutes. Remove from pans. Cool on wire racks. Wrap each loaf in foil; store overnight. To serve, drizzle Apricot Icing over bread. If desired, sprinkle with additional snipped dried apricots and toasted sliced almonds.

Apricot Icing: In a small bowl combine ½ cup powdered sugar, 2 teaspoons apricot nectar, and ⅛ teaspoon vanilla. Stir in additional apricot nectar, 1 teaspoon at a time, until icing reaches drizzling consistency.

Chocolate-Cherry Banana Bread

PREP 25 minutes **BAKE** 35 minutes
COOL 1 hour **OVEN** 350°F
MAKES 1 loaf (16 slices)

- Nonstick cooking spray
- 1½ cups all-purpose flour
- ⅔ cup sugar
- 2 teaspoons baking powder
- ¼ teaspoon baking soda
- ¼ cup fat-free sour cream
- ¼ cup fat-free milk
- ¼ cup refrigerated or frozen egg product, thawed, or 1 egg, lightly beaten
- 2 teaspoons vegetable oil
- ⅔ cup mashed bananas (about 2 medium bananas)
- 1 teaspoon vanilla
- 8 maraschino cherries, drained and chopped
- ¼ cup chopped walnuts
- 2 tablespoons miniature semisweet chocolate pieces

1 Preheat oven to 350°F. Lightly coat the bottom and ½ inch up the sides of a 9×5×3-inch loaf pan with cooking spray; set aside.

2 In a large bowl stir together flour, sugar, baking powder, and baking soda. Make a well in the center of flour mixture; set aside.

3 In a medium bowl combine sour cream, milk, egg product, and oil. Stir in mashed bananas and vanilla.

4 Add sour cream mixture all at once to flour mixture; stir just until moistened (batter should be lumpy). Fold in chopped cherries, walnuts, and chocolate chips.

5 Spoon batter into prepared pan. Bake for 35 to 40 minutes or until a wooden toothpick inserted near the center comes out clean. Cool in pan on a wire rack for 10 minutes. Remove bread from pan. Cool completely on wire rack.

NUTRITION FACTS per slice

CALORIES 119
TOTAL FAT 2 g (0 g sat. fat)
CHOLESTEROL 0 mg
SODIUM 61 mg
CARBOHYDRATE 23 g
FIBER 1 g
PROTEIN 2 g
EXCHANGES ½ Starch, 1 Other Carbo., ½ Fat

Orange-Date Pumpkin Bread

PREP 20 minutes **BAKE** 50 minutes
COOL 1 hour **OVEN** 350°F
MAKES 2 loaves (32 slices)

NUTRITION FACTS per slice

CALORIES 126
TOTAL FAT 4 g (1 g sat. fat)
CHOLESTEROL 0 mg
SODIUM 87 mg
CARBOHYDRATE 22 g
FIBER 2 g
PROTEIN 3 g
EXCHANGES ½ Starch, 1 Other Carbo., ½ Fat

- 2 cups all-purpose flour
- 1⅓ cups whole wheat flour
- 2 teaspoons baking powder
- 1 teaspoon ground nutmeg
- ½ teaspoon salt
- ½ teaspoon baking soda
- 1 15-ounce can pumpkin
- ¾ cup sugar
- 1 cup refrigerated or frozen egg product, thawed, or 4 eggs, lightly beaten
- ½ cup honey
- ⅓ cup vegetable oil
- 1 teaspoon finely shredded orange peel
- ⅓ cup orange juice
- ½ cup chopped walnuts or pecans
- ½ cup snipped pitted dates or raisins

1 Preheat oven to 350°F. Grease the bottom and ½ inch up the sides of two 8×4×2-inch loaf pans; set aside. In a large bowl stir together all-purpose flour, whole wheat flour, baking powder, nutmeg, salt, and baking soda. Set aside.

2 In a medium bowl stir together pumpkin, sugar, egg product, honey, oil, orange peel, and orange juice. Using a wooden spoon, stir pumpkin mixture into flour mixture just until combined. Stir in nuts and dates. Divide mixture between the prepared pans.

3 Bake about 50 minutes or until a toothpick inserted near centers comes out clean. Cool in pans on wire racks for 10 minutes. Remove from pans. Cool completely on wire racks.

Make-Ahead Directions: Prepare as directed. Place each loaf of bread in a freezer container or bag. Seal, label, and freeze up to 3 months. To serve, thaw the wrapped bread at room temperature.

Parmesan Corn Bread

PREP 25 minutes **BAKE** 45 minutes
COOL 40 minutes **OVEN** 375°F
MAKES 1 loaf (12 slices)

- 1 cup boiling water
- ¼ cup bulgur
- 1 cup coarse-ground or regular yellow cornmeal
- 1 cup all-purpose flour
- ½ cup grated Parmesan cheese
- 2 tablespoons sugar
- 1 tablespoon baking powder
- ½ teaspoon salt
- 1 cup fat-free milk
- ½ cup refrigerated or frozen egg product, thawed, or 2 eggs, lightly beaten
- 3 tablespoons olive oil
- ⅓ cup sliced green onions
- 2 tablespoons snipped fresh basil or 2 teaspoons dried basil, crushed
- Olive oil or vegetable oil (optional)
- Coarse-ground or regular yellow cornmeal (optional)

1 Preheat oven to 375°F. In a bowl pour the boiling water over bulgur; let stand for 5 minutes; drain. Generously grease and flour a 1½-quart soufflé dish or a 9×5×3-inch loaf pan. Set aside.

2 In a large bowl combine the 1 cup cornmeal, the flour, Parmesan cheese, sugar, baking powder, and salt. Make a well in the center of flour mixture.

3 In a bowl stir together milk, egg product, and the 3 tablespoons oil. Stir in drained bulgur, onions, and basil. Add bulgur mixture all at once to flour mixture. Stir just until moistened (batter should be lumpy). Pour batter into prepared dish or pan.

4 Bake for 45 to 50 minutes for the soufflé dish, 40 to 45 minutes for the loaf pan, or until a wooden toothpick inserted near the center comes out clean. If necessary to prevent overbrowning, cover loosely with foil the last 10 to 15 minutes of baking. Let cool in dish or pan on wire rack for 10 minutes. If desired, brush top with oil and sprinkle with cornmeal. Remove corn bread from dish or pan. Cool on a wire rack for 30 minutes. Serve warm.

NUTRITION FACTS per slice

CALORIES 150
TOTAL FAT 5 g (1 g sat. fat)
CHOLESTEROL 3 mg
SODIUM 241 mg
CARBOHYDRATE 22 g
FIBER 2 g
PROTEIN 5 g
EXCHANGES 1½ Starch, ½ Fat

Orange-Rye Spirals

PREP 50 minutes **RISE** 1 hour 30 minutes
BAKE 14 minutes **OVEN** 375°F
MAKES 16 rolls

NUTRITION FACTS per roll

CALORIES 164
TOTAL FAT 4 g (0 g sat. fat)
CHOLESTEROL 0 mg
SODIUM 390 mg
CARBOHYDRATE 29 g
FIBER 2 g
PROTEIN 4 g
EXCHANGES 1 Starch, 1 Other Carbo., ½ Fat

2¾ to 3¼ cups all-purpose flour
1 package active dry yeast
1 cup water
¼ cup sugar
¼ cup vegetable oil
¾ teaspoon salt
2 egg whites
1¼ cups rye flour
¼ cup finely chopped candied orange peel
1 teaspoon caraway seeds, crushed
Nonstick cooking spray
¼ cup low-sugar orange marmalade or orange marmalade, melted

1 In a large bowl stir together 2 cups all-purpose flour and yeast. In a medium saucepan heat and stir the water, sugar, oil, and salt just until warm (120°F to 130°F). Add water mixture and egg whites to flour mixture. Beat with an electric mixer on low to medium for 30 seconds, scraping sides of bowl occasionally. Beat on high for 3 minutes. Using a wooden spoon, stir in rye flour, orange peel, caraway seeds, and as much of the remaining all-purpose flour as you can.

2 Turn dough out onto a lightly floured surface. Knead in enough of the remaining all-purpose flour to make a moderately stiff dough that is smooth and elastic (6 to 8 minutes total). Shape dough into a ball. Place in a lightly greased bowl; turn once. Cover; let rise in a warm place until double in size (1 to 1½ hours).

3 Punch dough down. Turn out dough onto a lightly floured surface. Divide dough in half. Cover; let rest for 10 minutes. Meanwhile, lightly coat 2 baking sheets with cooking spray.

4 Divide each half of the dough into 8 pieces. On a lightly floured surface roll each piece into a 12-inch-long rope. Form each rope into an "S" shape, coiling each end snugly. Place rolls on prepared baking sheets. Cover; let rise in a warm place until nearly double in size (30 minutes).

5 Preheat oven to 375°F. Bake about 14 minutes or until golden brown. Transfer to a wire rack. Cool slightly. Brush rolls with orange marmalade while warm. Serve warm.

Cranberry-Walnut Whole Wheat Rolls

PREP 45 minutes **RISE** 1 hour 30 minutes
BAKE 12 minutes **OVEN** 375°F
MAKES 24 rolls

NUTRITION FACTS per roll

CALORIES 119
TOTAL FAT 3 g (1 g sat. fat)
CHOLESTEROL 6 mg
SODIUM 127 mg
CARBOHYDRATE 19 g
FIBER 1 g
PROTEIN 3 g
EXCHANGES 1 Starch, ½ Fat

- 2¾ to 3¼ cups all-purpose flour
- 1 package active dry yeast
- 1 cup fat-free milk
- ¼ cup butter, margarine, or shortening
- 2 tablespoons sugar
- 1 teaspoon salt
- ½ cup refrigerated or frozen egg product, thawed, or 2 eggs
- 1¼ cups whole wheat flour
- ⅔ cup snipped dried cranberries
- ⅓ cup finely chopped walnuts or pecans, toasted (see note, page 275)
- 2 teaspoons finely shredded orange peel

1 In a large mixing bowl stir together 2 cups of the all-purpose flour and the yeast. In a medium saucepan heat and stir milk, butter, sugar, and salt just until warm (120°F to 130°F) and butter is almost melted. Add milk mixture and egg product to flour mixture. Beat with an electric mixer on low to medium for 30 seconds, scraping sides of bowl constantly. Beat on high for 3 minutes. Using a wooden spoon, stir in whole wheat flour, cranberries, nuts, orange peel, and as much of the remaining all-purpose flour as you can.

2 Turn out dough onto a lightly floured surface. Knead in enough of the remaining all-purpose flour to make a moderately stiff dough that is smooth and elastic (6 to 8 minutes total). Shape the dough into a ball. Place in a lightly greased bowl, turning once to grease surface. Cover; let rise in a warm place until double in size (about 1 hour).

3 Punch dough down. Turn out dough onto a lightly floured surface. Divide dough in half. Cover; let rest for 10 minutes. Grease twenty-four 2½-inch muffin cups. Divide each portion of dough into 36 pieces. Shape each piece in a ball, pulling edges underneath to make a smooth top. Place 3 balls in each prepared muffin cup, smooth sides up. Cover; let rise in a warm place until nearly double in size (30 minutes).

5 Preheat oven to 375°F. Bake 12 to 15 minutes or until golden brown. Immediately remove rolls from muffin cups. Cool on wire racks.

Multigrain Rolls

PREP 45 minutes **RISE** 1 hour 30 minutes
BAKE 12 minutes **COOL** 10 minutes
OVEN 375°F **MAKES** 24 rolls

NUTRITION FACTS per roll

CALORIES 153
TOTAL FAT 4 g (2 g sat. fat)
CHOLESTEROL 32 mg
SODIUM 224 mg
CARBOHYDRATE 26 g
FIBER 2 g
PROTEIN 5 g
EXCHANGES 1½ Starch, ½ Fat

- 3¾ to 4¼ cups all-purpose flour
- 2 packages active dry yeast
- 1½ cups fat-free milk
- ¼ cup honey
- ¼ cup butter
- 2 teaspoons salt
- 2 eggs
- ⅔ cup whole wheat flour
- ½ cup rye flour
- ½ cup quick-cooking rolled oats
- ⅓ cup toasted wheat germ
- 1 tablespoon cornmeal
- 1 egg, lightly beaten

1 In a large mixing bowl combine 2 cups of the all-purpose flour and the yeast; set aside. Heat and stir milk, honey, butter, and salt just until warm (120°F to 130°F). Add milk mixture and eggs to flour mixture. Beat with electric mixer on medium for 30 seconds, scraping bowl frequently. Beat on high for 3 minutes, scraping bowl occasionally. Stir in whole wheat and rye flours, ½ cup oats, wheat germ, and 1 tablespoon cornmeal. Stir in as much of the remaining all-purpose flour as possible. Turn out dough onto floured surface. Knead in enough remaining flour to make a moderately stiff dough (6 to 8 minutes total). Shape in a ball. Place in a greased large bowl, turning once to grease surface. Cover; let rise in a warm place until double (1 to 1½ hours).

2 Punch dough down. Turn out onto floured surface. Divide dough into 6 portions. Cover; let rest for 10 minutes. Meanwhile, grease 2 large baking sheets and sprinkle with additional cornmeal. Divide each portion of dough into 4 portions (24 total). Shape each portion into a 4x1½-inch oval. Place on prepared baking sheets. Using kitchen shears, cut 3 slanted cuts about ¾ inch deep on both long sides of each oval. Cover; let rise in a warm place until double in size (30 to 45 minutes).

3 Preheat oven to 375°F. Combine the beaten egg and 1 tablespoon *water.* Brush on rolls. If desired, sprinkle with *sesame* or *poppy seeds.* Bake for 12 to 14 minutes or until golden. Remove from pans. Cool on wire racks.

Onion and Olive Focaccia

PREP 30 minutes **RISE** 1 hour 20 minutes
BAKE 25 minutes **OVEN** 375°F
MAKES 2 rounds (24 servings)

NUTRITION FACTS per serving

CALORIES 94
TOTAL FAT 3 g (0 g sat. fat)
CHOLESTEROL 0 mg
SODIUM 147 mg
CARBOHYDRATE 15 g
FIBER 1 g
PROTEIN 3 g
EXCHANGES 1 Starch, ½ Fat

- 3¼ to 3¾ cups bread flour or all-purpose flour
- 1 package active dry yeast
- 1¼ cups warm water (120°F to 130°F)
- 2 tablespoons olive oil or vegetable oil
- 1 teaspoon salt
- 1½ cups chopped onion
- 2 cloves garlic, minced
- 1 cup sliced pitted ripe olives and/or snipped oil-packed dried tomatoes, drained
- 2 tablespoons snipped fresh rosemary

1 In a large mixing bowl combine 1¼ cups of the flour and the yeast. Add the warm water, 1 tablespoon of the oil, and the salt. Beat with electric mixer on low to medium for 30 seconds, scraping bowl frequently. Beat on high for 3 minutes. Stir in as much of the remaining flour as you can.

2 Turn dough out onto floured surface. Knead in enough remaining flour to make a stiff dough that is smooth and elastic (8 to 10 minutes total). Shape into a ball. Place in a greased bowl, turning once to grease surface. Cover; let rise in warm place until double (1 hour).

3 Punch dough down. Turn out onto floured surface. Divide in half. Shape each portion in a ball. Place on 2 lightly greased baking sheets. Cover; let rest for 10 minutes.

4 Meanwhile, in a covered medium skillet cook onion and garlic in the remaining 1 tablespoon oil over low heat for 3 to 5 minutes or until onion is tender, stirring occasionally. Uncover; cook and stir just until onion begins to brown. Stir in olives; set aside.

5 Flatten each ball to 10 inches in diameter. Make ½-inch-deep indentations every 2 inches. Spoon onion mixture on dough. Sprinkle with rosemary. Cover and let rise in a warm place for 20 minutes. Preheat oven to 375°F. Bake about 25 minutes or until golden. If using dried tomatoes, sprinkle on bread the last 5 minutes of baking. Remove from baking sheet; cool on wire racks.

Flaxseed and Rye Breadsticks

PREP 25 minutes **RISE** 1 hour 30 minutes
BAKE 12 minutes **COOL** 10 minutes
OVEN 425°F **MAKES** 16 breadsticks

NUTRITION FACTS per breadstick

CALORIES 132
TOTAL FAT 4 g (0 g sat. fat)
CHOLESTEROL 0 mg
SODIUM 185 mg
CARBOHYDRATE 21 g
FIBER 2 g
PROTEIN 4 g
EXCHANGES 1½ Starch, ½ Fat

- ⅓ cup flaxseeds
- 2¼ to 2¾ cups all-purpose flour
- 1 cup rye flour
- 1 package active dry yeast
- 1½ cups warm water (120°F to 130°F)
- 2 tablespoons olive oil
- 1 tablespoon honey
- 1¼ teaspoons salt
- 2 tablespoons flaxseeds

1 Heat a large skillet over medium-low heat. Add the ⅓ cup flaxseeds. Cook, stirring with a wooden spoon, for 5 to 7 minutes or until the seeds pop gently; cool. Place seeds in a blender. Cover and blend until seeds are finely ground (should have about ½ cup).

2 In a mixing bowl stir together 1 cup of the all-purpose flour, the rye flour, and yeast. Add the warm water, oil, honey, and salt. Beat with electric mixer on low to medium for 30 seconds, scraping bowl. Beat on high for 3 minutes. Stir in the ground flaxseeds and as much of the remaining all-purpose flour as you can.

3 Turn dough out onto a lightly floured surface. Knead in enough of the remaining all-purpose flour to make a moderately stiff dough that is smooth and elastic (6 to 8 minutes total). Shape dough in a ball. Place in a greased bowl. Turn once to grease surface of the dough. Cover; let rise in a warm place until nearly double in size (about 1 hour).

4 Punch dough down. Turn out onto floured surface. Cover; let rest for 10 minutes. Coat 2 baking sheets with *nonstick cooking spray;* set aside. Roll dough to a 16×8-inch rectangle. Brush generously with water. Sprinkle with the 2 tablespoons flaxseeds. Gently pat into dough. Cut crosswise into 1-inch strips.

6 Place strips 1 inch apart on prepared baking sheets, twisting breadsticks two to three times. Cover; let rise in a warm place until nearly double in size (about 30 minutes).

7 Preheat oven to 425°F. Bake breadsticks for 12 to 15 minutes or until golden brown. Remove from baking sheet. Cool on wire racks.

Cheddar Batter Bread

PREP 20 minutes **RISE** 30 minutes
BAKE 40 minutes **OVEN** 350°F
MAKES 1 loaf (12 slices)

NUTRITION FACTS per slice

CALORIES 164
TOTAL FAT 4 g (2 g sat. fat)
CHOLESTEROL 28 mg
SODIUM 186 mg
CARBOHYDRATE 27 g
FIBER 1 g
PROTEIN 6 g
EXCHANGES 1½ Starch, 1 Fat

- 1 tablespoon cornmeal
- 2 cups all-purpose flour
- 1 package fast-rising active dry yeast
- ¼ teaspoon onion powder
- ¼ teaspoon black pepper
- 1 cup fat-free milk
- 2 tablespoons sugar
- 2 tablespoons butter
- ½ teaspoon salt
- 1 egg
- ¾ cup shredded reduced-fat cheddar cheese (3 ounces)
- ½ cup cornmeal

1 Grease bottom and sides of an 8×4×2-inch loaf pan. Sprinkle with the 1 tablespoon cornmeal, tilting pan to coat sides and bottom; set aside. In a large mixing bowl stir together 1½ cups of the flour, the yeast, onion powder, and pepper; set aside.

2 In a small saucepan combine milk, sugar, butter, and salt; heat and stir over medium heat just until mixture is warm (120°F to 130°F) and butter is almost melted. Add milk mixture and egg to flour mixture. Beat with an electric mixer on low to medium for 30 seconds, scraping bowl. Beat on high for 3 minutes. Stir in cheese and the ½ cup cornmeal. Stir in remaining flour (batter will be soft and sticky). Spoon batter evenly into prepared pan. Cover and let rise in a warm place until nearly double (about 30 minutes).

3 Preheat oven to 350°F. Bake, uncovered, about 40 minutes or until bread sounds hollow when lightly tapped. If necessary, cover with foil during the last 15 minutes of baking to prevent overbrowning. Loosen edges of bread from the pan using a small sharp knife or thin spatula. Remove bread from pan. Cool on a wire rack. Serve slightly warm.

Reheating Directions: Wrap bread in foil and heat in a 350°F oven for 20 minutes or until warmed through.

Make-Ahead Directions: Wrap and freeze bread up to 3 months. Thaw before serving or reheating.

Hearty Oat and Grain Bread

PREP 50 minutes **RISE** 1 hour 30 minutes
BAKE 30 minutes **COOL** 10 minutes
OVEN 375°F **MAKES** 1 loaf (20 slices)

NUTRITION FACTS per slice

CALORIES 115
TOTAL FAT 2 g (0 g sat. fat)
CHOLESTEROL 0 mg
SODIUM 124 mg
CARBOHYDRATE 21 g
FIBER 3 g
PROTEIN 4 g
EXCHANGES 1½ Starch

- 2 cups water
- ⅓ cup cracked wheat
- 2 tablespoons vegetable oil
- 2 tablespoons molasses
- 1 package active dry yeast
- 1 cup rolled oats
- ¼ cup nonfat dry milk powder
- ¼ cup oat bran or toasted wheat germ
- 1 teaspoon salt
- 1½ cups whole wheat flour
- 1½ to 2 cups all-purpose flour
- Water
- 1 tablespoon rolled oats

1 In a small saucepan bring the 2 cups water to boiling; add cracked wheat. Reduce heat. Simmer, covered, for 5 minutes. Remove from heat; transfer mixture to a large bowl. Stir in oil and molasses. Cool to lukewarm (105°F to 115°F). Stir in yeast until dissolved. Add the 1 cup rolled oats, the dry milk powder, oat bran, and salt.

2 Using a wooden spoon, stir in the whole wheat flour; stir in as much of the all-purpose flour as you can. Turn out dough onto a lightly floured surface. Knead in enough of the remaining all-purpose flour to make a moderately stiff dough that is smooth and elastic (6 to 8 minutes total). Shape in a ball. Place in a lightly greased bowl, turning once to grease surface. Cover and let rise in a warm place until double in size (about 1 hour).

3 Punch dough down; cover and let rest for 10 minutes. Meanwhile, grease a baking sheet. Shape dough in an 8-inch round loaf; place on baking sheet. Cover and let rise in a warm place until nearly double in size (30 to 45 minutes).

4 Preheat oven to 375°F. Make 3 diagonal shallow slits across the top of the loaf. Brush lightly with water; sprinkle with the 1 tablespoon rolled oats.

5 Bake for 30 to 35 minutes or until loaf sounds hollow when tapped. Remove from baking sheet; cool on wire rack.

Wild Rice and Oat Bran Bread

PREP 35 minutes **RISE** 1 hour 30 minutes
BAKE 35 minutes **OVEN** 375°F
MAKES 1 loaf (16 slices)

NUTRITION FACTS per slice

CALORIES 105
TOTAL FAT 2 g (1 g sat. fat)
CHOLESTEROL 4 mg
SODIUM 128 mg
CARBOHYDRATE 19 g
FIBER 2 g
PROTEIN 4 g
EXCHANGES 1 Starch, ½ Fat

1¼ to 1¾ cups bread flour
1 package active dry yeast
1 cup fat-free milk
2 tablespoons honey
2 tablespoons butter or shortening
¾ teaspoon salt
1 cup whole wheat flour
¾ cup cooked wild rice
⅓ cup oat bran

1 In a large mixing bowl combine 1 cup of the bread flour and the yeast; set aside. In a small saucepan heat and stir milk, honey, butter, and salt just until warm (120°F to 130°F) and butter is almost melted. Add milk mixture to flour mixture. Beat with an electric mixer on low to medium for 30 seconds, scraping bowl constantly. Beat on high for 3 minutes. Stir in whole wheat flour, cooked wild rice, oat bran, and as much of the remaining bread flour as you can.

2 Turn out dough onto a lightly floured surface. Knead in enough of the remaining bread flour to make a moderately stiff dough that is smooth and elastic (3 to 5 minutes total). Shape dough in a ball. Place dough in a greased large bowl, turning once to grease surface. Cover; let rise in a warm place until double in size (about 1 hour).

3 Punch dough down. Turn out dough onto a lightly floured surface. Cover; let rest for 10 minutes. Meanwhile, grease an 8×4×2-inch loaf pan; set aside.

4 Shape dough by patting and pinching into a loaf shape, tucking edges beneath. Place shaped dough in prepared pan. Cover and let rise in a warm place until nearly double in size (about 30 minutes).

6 Preheat oven to 375°F. Bake about 35 minutes or until bread sounds hollow when lightly tapped. (If necessary to prevent overbrowning, cover loosely with foil for the last 10 minutes of baking.) Immediately remove bread from pan. Cool on wire rack.

Two-Tone Balsamic-Onion Spiral Rolls

PREP 35 minutes **RISE** 45 minutes
BAKE 25 minutes **COOL** 15 minutes
OVEN 375°F **MAKES** 16 rolls

NUTRITION FACTS per roll

CALORIES 189
TOTAL FAT 4 g (1 g sat. fat)
CHOLESTEROL 18 mg
SODIUM 237 mg
CARBOHYDRATE 29 g
FIBER 1 g
PROTEIN 7 g
EXCHANGES 2 Starch, ½ Fat

- 2 slices bacon
- 2 cups chopped onions (2 large)
- ¼ cup balsamic vinegar
- ½ cup grated Parmesan cheese
- ¼ teaspoon black pepper
- 1 1-pound loaf frozen white bread dough, thawed
- 1 1-pound loaf frozen whole wheat bread dough, thawed
- 1 egg yolk, lightly beaten
- 1 tablespoon fat-free milk

1 Grease a 15×10×1-inch baking pan; set aside. In a large skillet cook bacon until crisp. Remove bacon, reserving drippings in skillet. Drain bacon on paper towels; crumble bacon and set aside. Cook onions in bacon drippings over medium heat for 5 minutes or until onions are tender. Carefully stir in vinegar. Simmer, uncovered, over medium-low heat for 1 to 2 minutes or until most of the liquid has evaporated. Remove from heat. Stir in Parmesan cheese and pepper. Cool completely.

2 Meanwhile, on a lightly floured surface roll each loaf of bread dough in a 16×10-inch rectangle. Spread onion mixture on white dough rectangle; sprinkle with bacon. Top with wheat dough rectangle. Roll up rectangles together, starting from a long side. Seal seam. Slice roll crosswise into 16 pieces. Place rolls, cut sides down, in prepared pan.

3 Cover loosely and let dough rise in a warm place until nearly double in size (about 45 minutes). Preheat oven to 375°F. In a small bowl beat together egg yolk and milk. Brush dough with egg mixture.

4 Bake about 25 minutes or until roll tops are light brown. Remove from oven. Invert onto a wire rack. Cool slightly. Invert again onto a serving platter. Serve warm.

Chapter 4

Sandwiches & Wraps

On the opener: Cannellini-Tuna Wraps *(see recipe, page 85)*

Grilled Beef and Avocado Pitas

PREP 20 minutes **MARINATE** 24 hours
GRILL 17 minutes **MAKES** 6 sandwiches

NUTRITION FACTS per sandwich

CALORIES 254
TOTAL FAT 11 g (3 g sat. fat)
CHOLESTEROL 23 mg
SODIUM 425 mg
CARBOHYDRATE 24 g
FIBER 5 g
PROTEIN 17 g
EXCHANGES 1 Starch, 2 Lean Meat, 1 Vegetable, ½ Fat

- 12 ounces beef flank steak
- ½ cup bottled light clear Italian salad dressing
- ½ teaspoon finely shredded lime peel
- ¼ cup lime juice
- 2 tablespoons snipped fresh cilantro
- ¼ cup finely chopped onion
- 4 cups spring baby salad greens
- 1 medium red sweet pepper, seeded and cut into bite-size strips
- 1 medium avocado, halved, seeded, peeled, and thinly sliced
- 3 whole wheat pita bread rounds, halved

1 Trim fat from steak. Score both sides of steak in a diamond pattern by making shallow diagonal cuts at 1-inch intervals. Place steak in a resealable plastic bag set in a shallow dish. For marinade, in a screw-top jar combine salad dressing, lime peel, lime juice, and cilantro. Cover; shake well. Pour half the marinade into a small bowl and add onion; cover and chill. Pour the remaining marinade over steak in bag. Seal; turn to coat steak. Marinate in the refrigerator for 24 hours, turning bag occasionally.

2 Drain beef, discarding marinade. Sprinkle with ¼ teaspoon *salt* and ¼ teaspoon *black pepper.* For a charcoal grill, place steak on the rack of an uncovered grill directly over medium coals. Grill for 17 to 21 minutes for medium doneness (160°F), turning once halfway through grilling. (For a gas grill, preheat grill. Reduce heat to medium. Place steak on grill rack over heat. Cover and grill as above.) To serve, thinly slice beef across grain. In a large bowl toss together beef, salad greens, red pepper, avocado, and reserved dressing mixture. Fill each pita half with beef mixture.

Broiling Directions: Place steak on unheated rack of a broiler pan. Broil 3 to 4 inches from the heat for 15 to 18 minutes for medium doneness (160°F), turning once halfway through broiling.

Five-Spice Steak Wraps

START TO FINISH 25 minutes
MAKES 4 wraps

NUTRITION FACTS per wrap

CALORIES 237
TOTAL FAT 7 g (2 g sat. fat)
CHOLESTEROL 51 mg
SODIUM 329 mg
CARBOHYDRATE 20 g
FIBER 2 g
PROTEIN 22 g
EXCHANGES 1 Vegetable, 1 Starch, 2 Medium-Fat Meat

- 12 ounces boneless beef round steak
- 2 cups packaged shredded cabbage with carrot (coleslaw mix)
- ¼ cup red and/or green sweet pepper cut into thin bite-size strips
- ¼ cup carrot cut into thin bite-size strips
- ¼ cup snipped fresh chives
- 2 tablespoons rice vinegar
- ½ teaspoon toasted sesame oil
- ½ teaspoon five-spice powder
- ¼ teaspoon salt
- Nonstick cooking spray
- ¼ cup plain low-fat yogurt or light sour cream
- 4 8-inch flour tortillas

1 If desired, partially freeze steak for easier slicing. In a medium bowl combine coleslaw mix, sweet pepper, carrot, and chives. In a small bowl combine vinegar and sesame oil. Pour vinegar mixture over coleslaw mixture; toss to coat. Set aside.

2 Trim fat from steak. Thinly slice steak across the grain into bite-size strips. Sprinkle steak with five-spice powder and salt. Coat an unheated large nonstick skillet with cooking spray. Preheat over medium-high heat. Add steak strips; stir-fry for 3 to 4 minutes or until brown.

3 To assemble, spread 1 tablespoon of the yogurt along the center of each tortilla. Top with steak strips. Stir coleslaw mixture; spoon over steak. Fold in sides of tortillas. If desired, secure with wooden toothpicks.

Bagel Beef Sandwiches

PREP 15 minutes **STAND** 15 minutes
BROIL 12 minutes **MAKES** 4 sandwiches

NUTRITION FACTS per sandwich

CALORIES 294
TOTAL FAT 9 g (2 g sat. fat)
CHOLESTEROL 38 mg
SODIUM 293 mg
CARBOHYDRATE 28 g
FIBER 4 g
PROTEIN 25 g
EXCHANGES 1 Vegetable, 1½ Starch, 2½ Lean Meat, 1 Fat

- ¼ cup sliced dried tomatoes (not oil-packed)
- 2 teaspoons olive oil
- 12 ounces beef sirloin steak, about ¾ inch thick
- ¼ teaspoon garlic salt
- ¼ teaspoon black pepper
- 1 medium onion, sliced
- 2 tablespoons light mayonnaise
- 1 tablespoon yellow mustard
- 2 small whole wheat bagels, split and toasted (3 to 4 ounces total)
- 2 cups finely shredded romaine lettuce

1 Preheat broiler. Place tomatoes in a small bowl; cover with water. Microwave on high for 1 minute. Let stand for 15 minutes.

2 Meanwhile, brush oil on onion slices. Arrange steak and onions on the unheated rack of a broiler pan; sprinkle with garlic salt and pepper. Broil 3 to 4 inches from heat for 12 to 16 minutes or until desired doneness, turning once. Thinly slice beef across the grain into bite-size pieces. Chop onion.

3 Meanwhile, drain tomatoes. Finely chop tomatoes. In a bowl combine tomatoes, onion, mayonnaise, and mustard. Top bagel halves with steak, romaine, and tomato mixture.

Beef and Cabbage Wraps

START TO FINISH 20 minutes
OVEN 350°F **MAKES** 4 wraps

NUTRITION FACTS per wrap

CALORIES 356
TOTAL FAT 12 g (5 g sat. fat)
CHOLESTEROL 55 mg
SODIUM 561 mg
CARBOHYDRATE 33 g
FIBER 12 g
PROTEIN 27 g
EXCHANGES ½ Vegetable, 2 Starch, 3 Lean Meat, 1 Fat

- 4 8-inch whole wheat or regular flour tortillas
- 12 ounces lean ground beef
- ½ cup chopped onion (1 medium)
- 1 cup frozen whole kernel corn
- ¼ cup bottled barbecue sauce
- 2 cups packaged shredded cabbage with carrot (coleslaw mix)
- Bottled barbecue sauce (optional)

1 Preheat oven to 350°F. Wrap tortillas tightly in foil; place on a baking sheet. Heat in oven about 10 minutes or until heated through.

2 Meanwhile, for filling, in a large skillet cook meat and onion until meat is browned and onion is tender. Drain off fat. Stir in corn. Cover and cook about 4 minutes or until corn is tender, stirring once. Stir in the barbecue sauce. Cook and stir until heated through.

3 To serve, spoon about ⅓ cup of the filling onto 1 side of each tortilla; top with cabbage. Fold tortillas in half over filling. If desired, serve with additional barbecue sauce.

Italian-Style Sloppy Joes

PREP 15 minutes **COOK** 15 minutes
MAKES 6 sandwiches

- 12 ounces lean ground beef
- ½ cup chopped onion (1 medium)
- 1 8-ounce can tomato sauce
- ¼ teaspoon dried oregano, crushed
- ¼ teaspoon dried basil, crushed
- 6 crusty dinner rolls, split, or whole wheat or white hamburger buns, split and toasted
- ½ cup shredded reduced-fat mozzarella cheese (2 ounces)
- ¼ cup finely shredded Parmesan cheese (1 ounce)

1 In a large skillet cook ground beef and onion over medium-high heat until meat is browned and onion is tender. Drain off fat. Stir in tomato sauce, oregano, and basil. Bring mixture to boiling; reduce heat. Simmer, covered, for 15 minutes.

2 Divide beef mixture among roll bottoms; sprinkle with mozzarella and Parmesan cheese. Add roll tops.

NUTRITION FACTS per sandwich

CALORIES 281
TOTAL FAT 10 g (5 g sat. fat)
CHOLESTEROL 50 mg
SODIUM 583 mg
CARBOHYDRATE 25 g
FIBER 3 g
PROTEIN 20 g
EXCHANGES 1½ Starch, 2½ Lean Meat, 1 Fat

Beef and Basil Wraps

START TO FINISH 20 minutes
MAKES 4 wraps

NUTRITION FACTS per wrap

CALORIES 200
TOTAL FAT 7 g (3 g sat. fat)
CHOLESTEROL 25 mg
SODIUM 586 mg
CARBOHYDRATE 18 g
FIBER 10 g
PROTEIN 15 g
EXCHANGES 1 Starch, 2 Lean Meat, 1 Fat

- 4 7- or 8-inch whole wheat tortillas
- ¼ cup light cream cheese with chive and onion or roasted garlic
- 16 fresh basil leaves
- ½ of a 7-ounce jar roasted red sweet peppers, well drained and cut into ¼-inch-wide strips
- 4 ounces lower-sodium thinly sliced cooked roast beef, ham, and/or turkey
- Fresh basil leaves (optional)

1 For each wrap, spread a tortilla with one-fourth of the cream cheese. Cover cream cheese with 4 basil leaves, leaving a 1-inch border. Arrange roasted red peppers on basil leaves. Top with sliced meat.

2 Roll up each tortilla tightly into a spiral. Cut each tortilla roll in half crosswise. If desired, garnish with additional basil.

Smoky-Sweet Pork Planks

PREP 25 minutes **COOK** 1 hour 30 minutes
MAKES 8 sandwiches

NUTRITION FACTS per sandwich

CALORIES 261
TOTAL FAT 5 g (1 g sat. fat)
CHOLESTEROL 53 mg
SODIUM 610 mg
CARBOHYDRATE 29 g
FIBER 2 g
PROTEIN 22 g
EXCHANGES 1 Starch, 1 Other Carbo., 2½ Lean Meat

- 1½ pounds boneless pork top loin roast (single loin) or boneless pork blade roast
- 2 teaspoons vegetable oil
- 1½ cups water
- ½ cup ketchup
- ½ cup bottled low-calorie barbecue sauce
- 1 cup chopped red onion (1 large)
- ½ cup chopped celery (1 stalk)
- ¼ cup snipped pitted dates
- 2 tablespoons packed brown sugar
- 2 tablespoons finely chopped canned chipotle peppers in adobo sauce (see note, page 80)
- 1 teaspoon dry mustard
- 2 cloves garlic, minced
- 8 1-inch slices bread
- 8 lettuce leaves (optional)

1 Trim fat from roast. In a large saucepan heat oil over medium-high heat. Add roast; brown roast on all sides. Drain off fat. Add the water, ketchup, barbecue sauce, onion, celery, dates, brown sugar, chipotle peppers, mustard, and garlic. Bring to boiling; reduce heat. Simmer, covered, for 1½ to 2 hours or until meat is fork-tender, stirring sauce occasionally.

2 Remove meat from sauce. Pour sauce into a large glass measure or bowl; set aside. Using 2 forks, pull meat apart into shreds. Skim fat from sauce if necessary. Return meat to saucepan; stir in enough of the sauce for desired consistency. Heat through.

3 If desired, top bread slices with lettuce. Spoon meat mixture onto bread slices.

Pork Primavera Sandwiches

PREP 25 minutes
COOK 6 to 7 hours (low) or 3 to 3½ hours (high)
MAKES 10 sandwiches

NUTRITION FACTS per sandwich

CALORIES 258
TOTAL FAT 5 g (1 g sat. fat)
CHOLESTEROL 57 mg
SODIUM 418 mg
CARBOHYDRATE 28 g
FIBER 3 g
PROTEIN 24 g
EXCHANGES 2 Starch, 2½ Medium-Fat Meat

- 1 cup shredded carrots (2 medium)
- 1 cup coarsely chopped red sweet pepper (1 large)
- 1 medium onion, cut into thin wedges
- 2 tablespoons quick-cooking tapioca, crushed
- 2 to 2½ pounds boneless pork sirloin roast or boneless pork loin roast
- ¾ cup bottled reduced-sodium, fat-free barbecue sauce
- 10 whole wheat hamburger buns, split and toasted

1 In a 3½- or 4-quart slow cooker combine carrots, sweet pepper, and onion. Sprinkle with tapioca. Trim fat from pork roast. Place roast on top of vegetables. Pour barbecue sauce over meat. Cover and cook on low-heat setting for 6 to 7 hours or on high-heat setting for 3 to 3½ hours.

2 Remove meat from slow cooker, reserving juices. Thinly slice meat. Return sliced meat to slow cooker; stir to coat with sauce. Serve meat on hamburger buns.

Italian Turkey Sandwiches

START TO FINISH 20 minutes
MAKES 4 sandwiches

- ⅓ cup fine dry bread crumbs
- 2 teaspoons dried Italian seasoning, crushed
- 2 turkey tenderloins (about 1 pound total)
- 2 teaspoons olive oil
- 3 tablespoons light mayonnaise or salad dressing
- 2 tablespoons snipped fresh basil
- 8 ½-inch slices Italian bread, toasted
- Fresh basil leaves (optional)
- 1 cup bottled roasted red and/or yellow sweet peppers, well drained and cut into thin strips

1 In a large resealable plastic bag combine the bread crumbs and Italian seasoning. Split each turkey tenderloin in half horizontally to make ½-inch-thick steaks. Place a turkey tenderloin steak in the bag; seal and shake to coat. Repeat with remaining steaks.

2 In a very large nonstick skillet heat oil over medium heat. Add turkey steaks; cook about 10 minutes or until tender and no longer pink (170°F), turning once.

3 In a small bowl stir together mayonnaise and snipped basil. Spread mayonnaise mixture on 1 side of bread slices. Top 4 of the bread slices with basil leaves (if using), turkey steaks, sweet pepper strips, and the snipped remaining basil. Top with remaining bread slices, spread sides down. If desired, garnish with additional basil leaves.

NUTRITION FACTS per sandwich

CALORIES 384
TOTAL FAT 9 g (2 g sat. fat)
CHOLESTEROL 74 mg
SODIUM 522 mg
CARBOHYDRATE 39 g
FIBER 3 g
PROTEIN 35 g
EXCHANGES ½ Vegetable, 2½ Starch, 4 Lean Meat

Greek Fusion Burgers

PREP 25 minutes **GRILL** 10 minutes
MAKES 4 burgers

NUTRITION FACTS per burger

CALORIES 272
TOTAL FAT 6 g (3 g sat. fat)
CHOLESTEROL 58 mg
SODIUM 473 mg
CARBOHYDRATE 22 g
FIBER 3 g
PROTEIN 33 g
EXCHANGES 1 Vegetable, 1 Starch, 4 Lean Meat, ½ Fat

- 1 pound uncooked ground turkey breast
- 2 teaspoons finely chopped canned chipotle chile peppers in adobo sauce (see note, page 80)
- 1 teaspoon dried oregano, crushed
- ¼ cup light tub-style cream cheese, softened
- ¼ cup shredded reduced-fat cheddar cheese
- 1 tablespoon finely chopped green onion
- ⅛ teaspoon salt
- 2 large whole wheat pita bread rounds, halved crosswise
- ½ of a medium cucumber, cut into thin bite-size strips
- 8 small slices tomato

1 In a medium bowl combine turkey, 1 teaspoon of the chipotle peppers, and the oregano. Shape mixture into four ½-inch-thick oval patties.

2 For a charcoal grill, place patties on the greased rack of an uncovered grill directly over medium coals. Grill for 10 to 13 minutes or until an instant-read thermometer inserted into side of each patty registers 165°F, turning once halfway through grilling. (For a gas grill, preheat grill. Reduce heat to medium. Place patties on grill rack over heat. Cover and grill as above.)

3 Meanwhile, in a small bowl stir together the remaining 1 teaspoon chipotle pepper, the cream cheese, cheddar cheese, green onion, and salt; mix well.

4 Open cut sides of halved pita bread rounds to make pockets. Spread cream cheese mixture into pockets. Add cucumber, grilled patties, and tomato slices.

Thai Turkey Burgers

PREP 20 minutes **GRILL** 14 minutes
MAKES 6 burgers

- ¼ cup refrigerated or frozen egg product, thawed, or 1 egg, lightly beaten
- ¼ cup fine dry bread crumbs
- 1 teaspoon Thai seasoning or curry powder
- 1 pound uncooked ground turkey breast
- 6 whole grain cocktail-size hamburger buns, split and toasted
- ¾ cup fresh basil leaves
- 2 tablespoons bottled peanut sauce
- 1 medium mango, seeded, peeled, and sliced

1 In a medium bowl combine egg product, bread crumbs, and Thai seasoning. Add ground turkey breast; mix well. Shape into six ¾-inch-thick patties.

2 For a charcoal grill, place patties on the greased rack of an uncovered grill directly over medium coals. Grill for 14 to 18 minutes or until an instant-read thermometer inserted into side of each patty registers 165°F, turning once halfway through grilling. (For a gas grill, preheat grill. Reduce heat to medium. Place patties on grill rack over heat. Cover and grill as above.)

3 To serve burgers, top bottom half of each bun with some of the basil. Add patties. Spoon peanut dipping sauce over patties; add mango slices and bun tops.

NUTRITION FACTS per burger

CALORIES 213
TOTAL FAT 4 g (1 g sat. fat)
CHOLESTEROL 30 mg
SODIUM 438 mg
CARBOHYDRATE 23 g
FIBER 2 g
PROTEIN 22 g
EXCHANGES ½ Fruit, 1 Starch, 3 Lean Meat

Chicken Focaccia Sandwiches

START TO FINISH 15 minutes
MAKES 6 sandwiches

NUTRITION FACTS per sandwich

CALORIES 246
TOTAL FAT 7 g (1 g sat. fat)
CHOLESTEROL 49 mg
SODIUM 335 mg
CARBOHYDRATE 27 g
FIBER 0 g
PROTEIN 20 g
EXCHANGES 2 Starch, 2 Lean Meat

- 1 8-inch tomato or onion Italian flatbread (focaccia) or 12 slices whole grain bread*
- ⅓ cup light mayonnaise or salad dressing
- 1 cup lightly packed fresh basil leaves
- 2 cups sliced or shredded cooked chicken breast
- ½ of a 7-ounce jar roasted red sweet peppers, drained and cut into strips (about ½ cup)

1 If using focaccia bread, use a long serrated knife to split in half horizontally.

2 Spread cut sides of bread halves with mayonnaise. Layer basil leaves, chicken, and roasted sweet peppers between bread halves. Cut into wedges.

***Note:** If using the whole grain bread, toast bread and spread mayonnaise on 1 side of each bread slice. Assemble sandwiches between the spread sides of the bread slices. Cut each sandwich in half to serve.

Curried Chicken Salad Wraps

PREP 20 minutes **CHILL** 2 to 24 hours
MAKES 4 wraps

- ½ cup fat-free or light mayonnaise or salad dressing
- ½ teaspoon curry powder
- ⅛ teaspoon black pepper
- 2 cups chopped cooked chicken breast (about 10 ounces)
- ¼ cup sliced green onions (2)
- 4 romaine leaves or 8 fresh spinach leaves
- 4 7-inch whole wheat flour tortillas
- ½ cup chopped tomato (1 medium)

1. For curried chicken salad, in a medium bowl combine mayonnaise, curry powder, and pepper. Stir in chicken and green onions. Cover and chill for 2 to 24 hours.

2. To assemble, place 1 romaine leaf or 2 spinach leaves on each tortilla. Top with chicken mixture and tomatoes. Roll up. If desired, cut in half to serve.

NUTRITION FACTS per wrap

CALORIES 246
TOTAL FAT 5 g (1 g sat. fat)
CHOLESTEROL 60 mg
SODIUM 537 mg
CARBOHYDRATE 18 g
FIBER 9 g
PROTEIN 28 g
EXCHANGES 1 Vegetable, 1 Starch, 3 Lean Meat, ½ Fat

Bacon, Lettuce, and Tomato Salsa Wraps

START TO FINISH 25 minutes
MAKES 4 wraps

NUTRITION FACTS per wrap

CALORIES 227
TOTAL FAT 9 g (3 g sat. fat)
CHOLESTEROL 30 mg
SODIUM 625 mg
CARBOHYDRATE 27 g
FIBER 2 g
PROTEIN 8 g
EXCHANGES 1 Vegetable, 1½ Starch, ½ Medium-Fat Meat, 1½ Fat

- 1¾ cups seeded, coarsely chopped tomatoes (2 large)
- ¼ cup finely chopped red onion
- ¼ cup chopped fresh cilantro
- 1 tablespoon finely chopped fresh jalapeño*
- 1 tablespoon lime juice
- ⅛ teaspoon kosher salt
- 8 slices turkey bacon or reduced-sodium turkey bacon
- 4 10-inch vegetable-flavor flour tortillas or flour tortillas
- ¼ cup light mayonnaise or salad dressing
- 2 cups fresh baby spinach

1 For tomato salsa, in a medium bowl combine tomatoes, red onion, cilantro, and jalapeño. Stir in lime juice and kosher salt. Set aside.

2 Cook bacon according to package directions. Drain well on paper towels; cut bacon into large pieces.

3 To assemble wraps, spread mayonnaise on tortillas; top with spinach. Using a slotted spoon, spoon tomato salsa on spinach. Top with bacon. Roll up tortillas; cut in half.

***Note:** Because chile peppers contain volatile oils that can burn your skin and eyes, avoid direct contact with them as much as possible. When working with chile peppers, wear plastic or rubber gloves. If your bare hands do touch the peppers, wash your hands and fingernails well with soap and water.

Turkey-Tomato Wraps

START TO FINISH 20 minutes
MAKES 4 wraps

NUTRITION FACTS per wrap

CALORIES 233
TOTAL FAT 6 g (1 g sat. fat)
CHOLESTEROL 19 mg
SODIUM 559 mg
CARBOHYDRATE 34 g
FIBER 5 g
PROTEIN 15 g
EXCHANGES 1 Vegetable, 2 Starch, 1½ Lean Meat

- ½ cup purchased hummus
- 4 7- to 8-inch tomato-basil flour tortillas or whole wheat tortillas
- 6 ounces thinly sliced, cooked peppered turkey breast
- 4 romaine lettuce leaves, ribs removed
- 3 small tomatoes, thinly sliced
- 3 thin slices red onion, separated into rings

1 Spread hummus evenly on tortillas. Layer turkey, romaine leaves, tomato slices, and red onion near 1 edge. Roll up tortillas, starting from the edge with the turkey. Cut into fourths to serve.

Po'Boys

PREP 25 minutes
BAKE 4 to 6 minutes per ½-inch thickness
OVEN 400°F **MAKES** 4 sandwiches

NUTRITION FACTS per sandwich

CALORIES 345
TOTAL FAT 13 g (2 g sat. fat)
CHOLESTEROL 112 mg
SODIUM 610 mg
CARBOHYDRATE 32 g
FIBER 4 g
PROTEIN 25 g
EXCHANGES 1 Starch, 3½ Lean Meat, 1 Vegetable, ½ Fat

- 4 4-ounce fresh or frozen gray sole, flounder, or other thin fish fillets
- ⅓ cup light mayonnaise
- 1 tablespoon vinegar
- 1 tablespoon prepared horseradish
- 1 teaspoon sugar
- 3 cups packaged shredded cabbage with carrot (coleslaw mix)
- ½ cup finely chopped celery (1 stalk)
- 3 tablespoons snipped fresh parsley
- Nonstick cooking spray
- 1 egg, lightly beaten
- 1 tablespoon fat-free milk
- ¼ cup yellow cornmeal
- ¼ cup fine dry bread crumbs
- ¼ teaspoon salt
- ¼ teaspoon black pepper
- 2 teaspoons olive oil
- 4 whole grain rolls, split

1 Thaw fish, if frozen. Preheat oven to 400°F. In a medium bowl whisk together mayonnaise, vinegar, horseradish, and sugar. Remove and set aside 2 tablespoons of the mixture. Add coleslaw mix, celery, and parsley to the mayonnaise mixture in the bowl; stir to coat.

2 Rinse fish; pat dry with paper towels. Measure the thickness of fillets. Lightly coat a shallow foil-lined baking pan with cooking spray. In a shallow dish combine egg and milk. In another shallow dish combine cornmeal, bread crumbs, salt, and pepper; stir in olive oil until well mixed. Dip fish into egg mixture, then into cornmeal mixture, turning to coat both sides.

3 Place fish in prepared pan. Bake for 4 to 6 minutes per ½-inch thickness or until fish flakes easily when tested with a fork. Hollow out some of the insides of the top halves of rolls; discard crumbs. Spread the reserved 2 tablespoons mayonnaise mixture on roll bottoms. Top with fish. Layer with coleslaw mixture and roll tops.

Open-Face Barbecue Tilapia Sandwiches

PREP 15 minutes
GRILL 4 to 6 minutes per ½-inch thickness
MAKES 4 sandwiches

4 4- to 5-ounce fresh or frozen skinless tilapia or flounder fillets
Nonstick cooking spray
2 tablespoons light mayonnaise
2 teaspoons lemon juice
2 cups packaged shredded cabbage with carrot (coleslaw mix)
4 slices whole wheat bread, toasted
2 tablespoons bottled low-calorie barbecue sauce

1 Thaw fish, if frozen. Rinse fish; pat dry with paper towels. Measure thickness of fish. Lightly coat both sides of each fish fillet with cooking spray.

2 For a charcoal grill, place fish on the greased rack of an uncovered grill directly over medium coals. Grill for 4 to 6 minutes per ½-inch thickness or until fish flakes easily when tested with a fork. (For a gas grill, preheat grill. Reduce heat to medium. Place fish on greased grill rack over heat. Cover and grill as above.)

3 In a medium bowl stir together mayonnaise and lemon juice. Add cabbage; toss to coat.

4 To assemble, spoon cabbage mixture onto bread slices. Top with fish fillets. Drizzle fish with barbecue sauce.

NUTRITION FACTS per sandwich

CALORIES 206
TOTAL FAT 5 g (1 g sat. fat)
CHOLESTEROL 59 mg
SODIUM 339 mg
CARBOHYDRATE 13 g
FIBER 2 g
PROTEIN 26 g
EXCHANGES ½ Vegetable, 1 Starch, 3 Lean Meat

Grilled Jamaican Jerk Fish Wraps

PREP 30 minutes
GRILL 4 to 6 minutes per ½-inch thickness
MAKES 4 wraps

NUTRITION FACTS per wrap

CALORIES 254
TOTAL FAT 4 g (1 g sat. fat)
CHOLESTEROL 48 mg
SODIUM 509 mg
CARBOHYDRATE 23 g
FIBER 11 g
PROTEIN 29 g
EXCHANGES 1 Vegetable, 1 Starch, 3½ Lean Meat

- 1 pound fresh or frozen skinless flounder, cod, or sole fillets
- 1½ teaspoons Jamaican jerk seasoning
- 4 7- to 8-inch whole grain flour tortillas
- 2 cups packaged fresh baby spinach
- ¾ cup chopped, seeded tomato
- ¾ cup chopped fresh mango or pineapple
- 2 tablespoons snipped fresh cilantro
- 1 tablespoon finely chopped seeded fresh jalapeño (See note, page 80)
- 1 tablespoon lime juice

1 Thaw fish, if frozen. Rinse fish; pat dry with paper towels. Sprinkle Jamaican jerk seasoning on both sides of each fillet; rub in with your fingers. Measure thickness of fish.

2 For a charcoal grill, place tortillas on the greased rack of an uncovered grill directly over medium coals; grill for 1 minute or until bottoms of tortillas have grill marks. Remove from grill and set aside. Place fish on the grill rack directly over the coals. Grill fish for 4 to 6 minutes per ½-inch thickness or until fish flakes easily when tested with a fork, turning once halfway through grilling. (For a gas grill, preheat grill. Reduce heat to medium. Place tortillas on greased grill rack over heat. Cover; grill as above. Remove tortillas from the grill and add fish; cover and grill as above.) Coarsely flake the fish.

3 Meanwhile, in a medium bowl toss together spinach, tomato, mango, cilantro, chile pepper, and lime juice.

4 To assemble, place tortillas, grilled sides down, on a work surface. Top tortillas with spinach mixture and flaked fish. Roll up tortillas to enclose filling; cut each tortilla in half to serve.

Cannellini-Tuna Wraps

START TO FINISH 15 minutes
MAKES 6 wraps

NUTRITION FACTS per wrap

CALORIES 297
TOTAL FAT 7 g (1 g sat. fat)
CHOLESTEROL 33 mg
SODIUM 402 mg
CARBOHYDRATE 28 g
FIBER 14 g
PROTEIN 29 g
EXCHANGES 2 Starch, 3 Lean Meat

- ¼ cup finely chopped red onion
- 2 tablespoons lemon juice
- ⅛ teaspoon black pepper
- Dash salt
- 1 tablespoon olive oil
- 1 15-ounce can organic no-salt-added white kidney (cannellini) beans, rinsed and drained
- 12 ounces cooked tuna, broken into chunks, or two 6-ounce cans very low-sodium chunk white tuna, drained
- 1 cup cherry tomatoes, quartered
- ¼ cup snipped fresh parsley
- 6 8-inch whole wheat, tomato, or spinach flour tortillas
- ½ cup julienned carrot

1 In a small bowl combine red onion, lemon juice, black pepper, and salt. Whisk in olive oil; set aside.

2 In a large bowl slightly mash beans.* Add tuna, tomatoes, and parsley. Pour dressing over bean and tuna mixture; stir gently.

3 Divide bean mixture among tortillas. Top with carrot. Roll up tightly. Serve immediately or cover and chill up to 6 hours.

***Note:** The more the beans are mashed, the more the mixture will hold together.

Seasoned Tuna Sandwiches

START TO FINISH 10 minutes
MAKES 4 sandwiches

NUTRITION FACTS per sandwich

CALORIES 277
TOTAL FAT 8 g (1 g sat. fat)
CHOLESTEROL 48 mg
SODIUM 446 mg
CARBOHYDRATE 23 g
FIBER 4 g
PROTEIN 28 g
EXCHANGES ½ Vegetable, 1½ Starch, 3 Lean Meat, ½ Fat

- 2 6-ounce cans low-sodium chunk (light or white) tuna, drained
- 2 teaspoons lemon juice
- 1 tablespoon olive oil
- 1 teaspoon capers, drained
- ⅛ teaspoon black pepper
- 2 tablespoons light mayonnaise or salad dressing
- 8 slices whole wheat bread
- 4 romaine lettuce leaves, ribs removed
- 4 large tomato slices

1 In a small bowl combine tuna, lemon juice, oil, capers, and pepper.

2 To assemble, spread mayonnaise on 4 bread slices. Top with lettuce, tomato, tuna mixture, and remaining bread slices.

Tomato and Edamame Grilled Cheese

PREP 25 minutes **ROAST** 15 minutes
OVEN 425°F **MAKES** 4 sandwiches

NUTRITION FACTS per sandwich

CALORIES 226
TOTAL FAT 10 g (4 g sat. fat)
CHOLESTEROL 20 mg
SODIUM 619 mg
CARBOHYDRATE 21 g
FIBER 5 g
PROTEIN 15 g
EXCHANGES 1½ Starch, 2 Lean Meat, ½ Fat

- 1 bulb garlic
- 1 teaspoon canola oil
- 1 12-ounce package frozen shelled sweet soybeans (edamame)
- ¼ cup lemon juice
- ¼ cup water
- ½ teaspoon salt
- ½ teaspoon ground cumin
- ⅓ cup snipped fresh Italian (flat-leaf) parsley
- 8 very thin slices firm-textured whole wheat bread
- 4 ounces reduced-fat Monterey Jack cheese, cut into 4 slices
- 1 medium tomato, thinly sliced

1 Preheat oven to 425°F. Slice off top ½ inch of garlic bulb. Leaving bulb whole, remove loose outer layers. Place bulb, cut side up, in custard cup. Drizzle with oil. Cover with foil; roast about 15 minutes or until soft. Cool.

2 Meanwhile, cook soybeans according to package directions. Drain; rinse with cold water.

3 Squeeze 3 garlic cloves from bulb and place in a food processor. (Wrap and refrigerate remaining garlic cloves for another use.) Add cooled soybeans, lemon juice, the water, salt, and cumin to garlic in food processor. Cover and process until smooth. Transfer to a small bowl. Stir in parsley.

4 For sandwiches, spread 1 side of each bread slice with 2 tablespoons soybean mixture. Top the spread sides of 4 bread slices with cheese and tomato. Top with remaining bread, spread sides down.

5 Place sandwiches on a nonstick griddle or very large nonstick skillet over medium to medium-high heat. Cook for 5 to 6 minutes or until bread is golden and cheese is melted, turning once.

All-Wrapped-Up Salad

PREP 20 minutes **CHILL** up to 6 hours
MAKES 4 wraps

NUTRITION FACTS per wrap

CALORIES 248
TOTAL FAT 13 g (4 g sat. fat)
CHOLESTEROL 13 mg
SODIUM 401 mg
CARBOHYDRATE 20 g
FIBER 12 g
PROTEIN 13 g
EXCHANGES ½ Vegetable, 1 Starch, 1 High-Fat Meat, 1 Fat

- 4 8-inch whole grain, whole wheat, or flour tortillas
- 1½ cups shredded romaine lettuce and/or fresh spinach
- 1 avocado, halved, seeded, peeled, and sliced
- ½ of a cucumber, halved lengthwise, seeded, and thinly sliced
- ½ cup shredded Monterey Jack cheese with jalapeño peppers, (2 ounces)
- Purchased salsa (optional)

1 On each tortilla layer romaine lettuce, avocado, cucumber, and cheese. Roll up tightly. Wrap each with plastic wrap. Refrigerate up to 6 hours.

2 To serve, cut tortillas diagonally into halves. If desired, serve with salsa.

Chapter 5

Salads

On the opener: Lemon-Sage Pork Taco Salad *(see recipe, page 93)*

BEEF AND PORK

CHICKEN AND TURKEY

FISH & SEAFOOD

MEATLESS

Beef and Fruit Salad

PREP 20 minutes **MARINATE** 2 to 8 hours
BROIL 15 minutes **MAKES** 4 servings

NUTRITION FACTS per serving

CALORIES 207
TOTAL FAT 7 g (2 g sat. fat)
CHOLESTEROL 52 mg
SODIUM 380 mg
CARBOHYDRATE 17 g
FIBER 3 g
PROTEIN 21 g
EXCHANGES 1 Vegetable, 1 Fruit, 2½ Medium-Fat Meat

- 12 ounces boneless beef top sirloin steak, cut 1 inch thick
- ⅓ cup bottled reduced-sodium teriyaki sauce or reduced-sodium soy sauce
- ¼ cup lemon juice
- ¼ cup water
- 2 teaspoons toasted sesame oil
- ⅛ teaspoon bottled hot pepper sauce
- 3 cups shredded napa cabbage
- 1 cup torn or shredded fresh sorrel or fresh spinach
- 2 cups fresh fruit (such as sliced kiwifruit, plums, or nectarines; halved strawberries or seedless grapes; raspberries; and/or blueberries)

1 Trim fat from steak. Place steak in a resealable plastic bag set in a shallow dish. For marinade, in a small bowl combine teriyaki sauce, lemon juice, the water, sesame oil, and hot pepper sauce; reserve ⅓ cup for dressing. Pour remaining marinade over steak; close bag. Marinate in the refrigerator for 2 to 8 hours.

2 Drain steak, reserving marinade. Place steak on the unheated rack of a broiler pan. Broil 3 to 4 inches from heat to desired doneness, turning once and brushing occasionally with reserved marinade up to the last 5 minutes of broiling time. Allow 15 to 17 minutes for medium rare (145°F) or 20 to 22 minutes for medium (160°F). Discard any remaining marinade.

3 To serve, divide cabbage and sorrel among 4 dinner plates. Thinly slice steak diagonally. Arrange steak and fruit on greens. Drizzle with the reserved dressing.

Middle Eastern Beef Salad

PREP 20 minutes **GRILL** 10 minutes
MAKES 4 servings

NUTRITION FACTS per serving

CALORIES 282
TOTAL FAT 9 g (3 g sat. fat)
CHOLESTEROL 58 mg
SODIUM 542 mg
CARBOHYDRATE 25 g
FIBER 6 g
PROTEIN 27 g
EXCHANGES 2 Vegetable, 1 Starch, 3 Lean Meat, ½ Fat

- 12 ounces beef tenderloin steaks, cut 1 inch thick
- ⅛ teaspoon salt
- ⅛ teaspoon black pepper
- 6 cups packaged fresh baby spinach
- 2 medium yellow or red tomatoes, cut into wedges
- 1 small cucumber, coarsely chopped
- 1 15-ounce can garbanzo beans (chickpeas), rinsed and drained
- ¼ cup snipped fresh parsley
- ¼ cup snipped fresh mint
- 3 cloves garlic, minced
- 1 teaspoon olive oil
- 1 teaspoon honey
- 6 tablespoons plain low-fat or fat-free yogurt

1 Trim fat from steaks. Sprinkle steaks with salt and pepper. For a charcoal grill, place steaks on the grill rack directly over medium coals. Grill, uncovered, until desired doneness, turning once halfway through. Allow 10 to 12 minutes for medium rare (145°F) or 12 to 15 minutes for medium (160°F). (For a gas grill, preheat grill. Reduce heat to medium. Place steaks on grill rack over heat. Cover and grill as above.)

2 Meanwhile, on a large serving platter arrange spinach, tomatoes, cucumber, and garbanzo beans. Set aside.

3 For dressing, in a small bowl combine parsley, mint, garlic, oil, and honey. Stir in yogurt until well combined.

4 Thinly slice the grilled steak and place on top of salad. Serve with dressing.

Lemon-Sage Pork Taco Salad

START TO FINISH 40 minutes
MAKES 6 servings

NUTRITION FACTS per serving

CALORIES 266
TOTAL FAT 14 g (2 g sat. fat)
CHOLESTEROL 49 mg
SODIUM 269 mg
CARBOHYDRATE 17 g
FIBER 7 g
PROTEIN 21 g
EXCHANGES 1½ Vegetable, ½ Starch, 2½ Lean Meat, 2½ Fat

- 1 1-pound pork tenderloin, cut into ¼-inch slices
- 1 tablespoon finely shredded lemon peel
- 6 leaves fresh sage, thinly sliced
- ½ teaspoon ground cumin
- 1 tablespoon olive oil
- 1 head green leaf lettuce, torn
- 1½ cups chopped tomatoes
- 1 avocado, halved, seeded, peeled, and chopped
- 1 cup canned black beans, rinsed and drained
- ½ cup chopped green onions (4)
- 1 recipe Red Hot Pepper Vinaigrette

1 Place pork in a large bowl. Toss with lemon peel, sage, cumin, ¼ teaspoon *black pepper*, and ⅛ teaspoon *salt*. Let stand for 10 minutes.

2 In a very large skillet heat oil over medium-high heat. Cook pork, half at a time, in hot oil for 2 to 3 minutes or until slightly pink in center, turning once. Remove pork from skillet.

3 Place lettuce on a serving platter. Top with tomatoes, avocado, black beans, and green onions. Arrange pork on salad. Drizzle with some Red Hot Pepper Vinaigrette; pass remaining vinaigrette.

Red Hot Pepper Vinaigrette: Halve 1 red sweet pepper and 1 fresh jalepeño* lengthwise. Remove stems, seeds, and membranes. Place peppers, cut sides down, on foil-lined baking sheet. Bake in 425°F oven for 20 to 25 minutes or until charred. Enclose peppers in foil. Let stand for 15 minutes. Use a sharp knife to pull off skin; discard. Place peppers in blender. Add 2 tablespoons lime juice, 2 tablespoons balsamic vinegar, 2 tablespoons olive oil, and ⅛ teaspoon salt. Cover; blend until smooth.

***Note:** Because hot chile peppers contain volatile oils that can burn your skin and eyes, avoid direct contact with chiles as much as possible. When working with chile peppers, wear plastic or rubber gloves. If your bare hands do touch the chile peppers, wash your hands and fingernails well with soap and water.

Grilled Pork and Pear Salad

PREP 20 minutes **GRILL** 9 minutes
MAKES 4 servings

NUTRITION FACTS per serving

CALORIES 251
TOTAL FAT 10 g (3 g sat. fat)
CHOLESTEROL 50 mg
SODIUM 368 mg
CARBOHYDRATE 20 g
FIBER 4 g
PROTEIN 21 g
EXCHANGES 1 Vegetable, 1 Fruit, 3 Lean Meat, 1½ Fat

- 2 boneless pork loin chops, cut ¾ inch thick (about 12 ounces total)
- 2 teaspoons olive oil
- 2 teaspoons snipped fresh sage or thyme, or 1 teaspoon dried sage or thyme, crushed
- ¼ teaspoon salt
- ¼ teaspoon black pepper
- 8 cups torn mixed salad greens
- 2 medium pears or apples, cored and thinly sliced
- 1 recipe Creamy Apple Dressing
- ¼ cup broken walnuts, toasted (optional)

1 Trim fat from chops; brush chops with oil. In a small bowl stir together sage, salt, and pepper. Sprinkle sage mixture evenly on all sides of pork chops; rub in with your fingers.

2 For a charcoal grill, place chops on the rack of an uncovered grill directly over medium coals for 9 to 11 minutes or until done (160°F) and juices run clear, turning chops once halfway through grilling. (For a gas grill, preheat grill. Reduce heat to medium. Place chops on grill rack over heat. Cover and grill as above.)

3 To serve, slice chops. Divide greens among 4 serving plates. Top with pear slices and pork slices. Stir Creamy Apple Dressing; pour over salads. If desired, sprinkle with walnuts.

Broiling Directions: Preheat broiler. Prepare chops as directed in Step 1. Arrange on the unheated rack of a broiler pan. Broil 3 to 4 inches from the heat for 9 to 11 minutes or until done (160°F), turning once. Serve as directed.

Creamy Apple Dressing: In a small bowl stir together ½ cup buttermilk; 2 tablespoons light mayonnaise; 1 tablespoon frozen apple juice concentrate or frozen orange juice concentrate, thawed; 1 teaspoon Dijon mustard; 2 tablespoons chopped green onion; 1 teaspoon snipped fresh sage or thyme or ¼ teaspoon dried sage or thyme, crushed; ⅛ teaspoon salt; and ⅛ teaspoon black pepper. Cover and chill up to 24 hours.

Southwest Chicken Salad with Mango Salsa

PREP 30 minutes **GRILL** 12 minutes
CHILL 30 minutes **MAKES** 6 servings

- 2 tablespoons chili powder
- 1 teaspoon salt
- 1 teaspoon garlic powder
- 1 teaspoon ground cumin
- ½ teaspoon black pepper
- ¼ teaspoon cayenne pepper
- 3 tablespoons olive oil or canola oil
- 6 skinless, boneless chicken breast halves
- 3 medium mangoes, seeded, peeled, and cubed
- 1 cup blueberries
- ⅓ cup finely chopped red onion
- 3 tablespoons lime juice
- 2 tablespoons snipped fresh mint
- 2 tablespoons honey
- ¼ teaspoon crushed red pepper
- 8 cups torn mixed greens
- Fresh mint sprigs (optional)

1. In a small bowl stir together chili powder, salt, garlic powder, cumin, black pepper, and cayenne pepper. Stir in oil. Brush mixture on both sides of chicken breasts. Place chicken in a shallow dish; cover and chill for 30 minutes.

2. Meanwhile, for mango salsa, in a medium bowl combine mangoes, blueberries, red onion, lime juice, mint, honey, and crushed red pepper.

3. For a charcoal grill, place chicken on the rack of an uncovered grill directly over medium coals. Grill for 12 to 15 minutes or until chicken is no longer pink (170°F), turning once halfway through grilling. (For a gas grill, preheat grill. Reduce heat to medium. Place chicken on grill rack over heat. Cover and grill as above.)

4. Slice chicken in strips. In a large bowl top greens with chicken and salsa. If desired, garnish with fresh mint sprigs.

NUTRITION FACTS per serving

CALORIES 335
TOTAL FAT 10 g (2 g sat. fat)
CHOLESTEROL 77 mg
SODIUM 497 mg
CARBOHYDRATE 31 g
FIBER 5 g
PROTEIN 33 g
EXCHANGES 1½ Vegetable, 1 Fruit, ½ Other Carbo., 4 Lean Meat, ½ Fat

Sesame and Ginger Chicken Salad

START TO FINISH 20 minutes
MAKES 4 servings

NUTRITION FACTS per serving

CALORIES 231
TOTAL FAT 7 g (1 g sat. fat)
CHOLESTEROL 66 mg
SODIUM 436 mg
CARBOHYDRATE 12 g
FIBER 3 g
PROTEIN 29 g
EXCHANGES 1½ Vegetable, 4 Lean Meat

- 1 pound skinless, boneless chicken breast halves, cut into strips
- Salt and black pepper
- Nonstick cooking spray
- ¼ cup bottled light Asian-style salad dressing with sesame and ginger
- 2 cups packaged julienned or shredded fresh carrots
- ⅛ teaspoon crushed red pepper
- 1 head Boston or Bibb lettuce, leaves separated
- ¼ cup chopped honey-roasted peanuts
- Lime wedges (optional)

1 Lightly sprinkle chicken with salt and black pepper. Lightly coat a large skillet with cooking spray; heat over medium-high heat. Add chicken; cook and stir for 3 minutes. Add 1 tablespoon of the dressing and the carrots to skillet; cook and stir for 2 to 3 minutes more or until carrots are crisp-tender and chicken is no longer pink. Stir in crushed red pepper.

2 On a large platter or 4 plates arrange lettuce leaves. Spoon chicken mixture into lettuce leaves. Sprinkle with peanuts. Serve with remaining dressing and, if desired, lime wedges.

Curried Chicken Salad

PREP 15 minutes **COOK** 8 minutes
CHILL 1 hour **MAKES** 4 servings

NUTRITION FACTS per serving

CALORIES 209
TOTAL FAT 6 g (2 g sat. fat)
CHOLESTEROL 41 mg
SODIUM 69 mg
CARBOHYDRATE 24 g
FIBER 3 g
PROTEIN 16 g
EXCHANGES 1 Vegetable, 1 Fruit, 2 Lean Meat, ½ Fat

- 2 skinless, boneless chicken breast halves (about 8 ounces total)
- Nonstick cooking spray
- Dash onion powder
- Dash garlic powder
- 1 Gala or Fuji apple, cored and chopped
- ½ cup chopped green onions (4)
- ½ cup chopped celery (1 stalk)
- ⅓ cup seedless golden raisins
- ¼ cup unsalted sliced almonds*
- 1 recipe Curried Salad Dressing
- 8 Boston or bibb lettuce leaves
- Unsalted sliced almonds (optional)

1 Heat a medium nonstick skillet over medium heat. Coat chicken with cooking spray. Sprinkle with onion powder and garlic powder. Cook for 8 to 10 minutes or until chicken is no longer pink (170°F), turning once. Cool slightly; cut chicken into bite-size pieces.

2 In a medium bowl combine apple, green onions, and celery. Add the cooked chicken, raisins, and the ¼ cup almonds. Spoon Curried Salad Dressing over the salad and stir to coat. Cover and chill for 1 hour.

3 To serve, spoon ½ cup salad into each lettuce leaf. If desired, sprinkle with additional almonds.

Curried Salad Dressing: In a small bowl combine ½ cup light sour cream, 1 to 2 teaspoons curry, 1 teaspoon honey, ½ teaspoon ground ginger, and a dash of cayenne pepper. Stir until smooth. Cover and chill.

***Note:** Unsalted cashews may be substituted for the almonds.

Chicken and Spinach Salad with Avocado Dressing

START TO FINISH 40 minutes
MAKES 8 servings

NUTRITION FACTS per serving

CALORIES 214
TOTAL FAT 10 g (3 g sat. fat)
CHOLESTEROL 68 mg
SODIUM 241 mg
CARBOHYDRATE 9 g
FIBER 3 g
PROTEIN 23 g
EXCHANGES 1½ Vegetable, 3 Lean Meat, 1 Fat

- 1 6-ounce package fresh baby spinach (about 6 cups)
- 4 cups chopped or shredded cooked chicken
- 1 medium cucumber, halved lengthwise, seeded, and sliced
- 1 cup cherry tomatoes, halved
- 2 medium red, yellow, and/or green sweet peppers, cut into thin strips
- 1 small red onion, thinly sliced
- ¼ cup snipped fresh cilantro
- 1 large ripe avocado, halved, seeded, peeled, and cut up
- 2 cloves garlic, minced
- 2 teaspoons finely shredded lime peel (set aside)
- 2 tablespoons lime juice
- ⅔ cup light sour cream
- 2 tablespoons snipped fresh cilantro
- ½ teaspoon salt
- ⅛ teaspoon black pepper
- Bottled hot pepper sauce

1 In a large serving bowl toss together spinach, chicken, cucumber, cherry tomatoes, sweet peppers, half the sliced red onion, and cilantro. Set aside.

2 For dressing, in a food processor* combine avocado, the remaining red onion, the garlic, and lime juice. Cover and process until mixture is smooth. Stir in lime peel, sour cream, cilantro, salt, black pepper, and bottled hot pepper sauce. If necessary, stir in 1 to 2 tablespoons water to make dressing desired consistency.

3 Spoon dressing over spinach mixture. Toss gently to combine.

***Note:** If you don't have a food processor, mash avocado with a fork or potato masher. Finely chop the onion. Stir ingredients together.

Turkey-Broccoli Salad with Grapes

START TO FINISH 20 minutes
MAKES 6 servings

- 1/3 cup white balsamic vinegar
- 2 tablespoons olive oil
- 2 teaspoons sugar
- 1/8 teaspoon salt
- 1 12-ounce package shredded broccoli (broccoli slaw mix)
- 1 pound cooked turkey breast, shredded
- 1 1/2 cups seedless red grapes, halved
- 1 cup coarsely shredded carrots (2)
- 1/4 cup sliced or slivered almonds, toasted (see note, page 275), or sunflower kernels
- 1/8 teaspoon coarsely ground black pepper

1 For vinaigrette, in a screw-top jar combine vinegar, olive oil, sugar, and salt. Cover and shake well.

2 In a very large bowl combine shredded broccoli, turkey, grapes, and carrots. Add dressing; toss to coat. Serve immediately or cover and chill up to 24 hours. Sprinkle with almonds and pepper just before serving.

NUTRITION FACTS per serving

CALORIES 226
TOTAL FAT 7 g (1 g sat. fat)
CHOLESTEROL 63 mg
SODIUM 120 mg
CARBOHYDRATE 14 g
FIBER 3 g
PROTEIN 25 g
EXCHANGES 1 Vegetable, 1/2 Fruit, 3 Lean Meat, 1 Fat

Citrus Turkey Spinach Salad

START TO FINISH 25 minutes
MAKES 4 servings

NUTRITION FACTS per serving

CALORIES 251
TOTAL FAT 10 g (2 g sat. fat)
CHOLESTEROL 43 mg
SODIUM 233 mg
CARBOHYDRATE 22 g
FIBER 4 g
PROTEIN 20 g
EXCHANGES 1½ Vegetable, 1 Fruit, 2 Lean Meat, 2 Fat

- 8 cups fresh baby spinach or torn fresh spinach
- 1½ cups cut-up cooked turkey (about 8 ounces)
- 2 pink grapefruit, peeled and sectioned
- 2 medium oranges, peeled and sectioned
- 1 recipe Orange-Poppy Seed Dressing
- 2 tablespoons sliced almonds, toasted (see note, page 275) (optional)

1. In a large bowl combine spinach, turkey, grapefruit sections, and orange sections.

2. Shake Orange-Poppy Seed Dressing; pour over salad. Toss gently to coat. If desired, sprinkle with almonds.

Orange-Poppy Seed Dressing: In a screw-top jar combine ¼ cup orange juice, 2 tablespoons olive oil, 1 teaspoon honey, ½ teaspoon poppy seeds, ¼ teaspoon salt, and ¼ teaspoon dry mustard. Cover and shake well. Chill until serving time, up to 24 hours.

Turkey and Sugar Snap Pea Salad

START TO FINISH 20 minutes
MAKES 4 servings

- 5 slices turkey bacon
- 2 cups sugar snap peas
- ⅓ cup light mayonnaise or salad dressing
- 1 tablespoon Dijon mustard
- 1 tablespoon cider vinegar
- 1 tablespoon snipped fresh dill
- Black pepper
- 1 small head romaine lettuce, coarsely chopped or torn
- 8 ounces cooked turkey breast, cut into chunks

1 Line a 9-inch microwave-safe pie plate with paper towels. Arrange bacon slices in a single layer on paper towels. Cover with additional paper towels. Cook on high for 4 to 5 minutes or until bacon is crisp. Carefully remove the pie plate from the microwave. Set cooked bacon slices aside to cool. Crumble 1 bacon slice; set aside. Break remaining bacon slice into 1-inch pieces.

2 Meanwhile, cook sugar snap peas, covered, in a small amount of boiling salted water for 2 to 4 minutes or until crisp-tender; drain.

3 In a small bowl stir together mayonnaise, mustard, vinegar, and dill; season with pepper. Stir in crumbled bacon. Divide romaine among serving bowls. Top with sugar snap peas, turkey, and bacon pieces. Serve with dressing.

NUTRITION FACTS per serving

CALORIES 212
TOTAL FAT 10 g (2 g sat. fat)
CHOLESTEROL 73 mg
SODIUM 484 mg
CARBOHYDRATE 6 g
FIBER 2 g
PROTEIN 21 g
EXCHANGES 1½ Vegetable, 2½ Lean Meat, 1½ Fat

Salmon Salad with Orange-Balsamic Vinaigrette

PREP 20 minutes **GRILL** 8 minutes
MAKES 4 servings

NUTRITION FACTS per serving

CALORIES 323
TOTAL FAT 19 g (3 g sat. fat)
CHOLESTEROL 66 mg
SODIUM 296 mg
CARBOHYDRATE 13 g
FIBER 3 g
PROTEIN 24 g
EXCHANGES 1 Vegetable, ½ Fruit, 3 Lean Meat, 3 Fat

- 4 4- to 5-ounce fresh or frozen skinless salmon fillets
- ¼ teaspoon salt
- ¼ teaspoon black pepper
- Nonstick cooking spray
- 2 tablespoons snipped fresh mint
- 2 tablespoons balsamic vinegar
- 2 tablespoons olive oil
- ¼ teaspoon finely shredded orange peel
- 2 tablespoons orange juice
- ⅛ teaspoon salt
- 5 cups packaged European-style torn mixed salad greens
- 2 oranges, thinly sliced
- ¼ of a medium red onion, thinly sliced
- 2 tablespoons sliced almonds, toasted (see note, page 275) (optional)

1 Thaw salmon, if frozen. Rinse fish; pat dry with paper towels. Sprinkle salmon with the ¼ teaspoon salt and the pepper. Coat both sides of salmon fillets with cooking spray. For a charcoal grill, place salmon on the rack of an uncovered grill directly over medium coals. Grill for 8 to 12 minutes or until salmon flakes easily when tested with a fork, turning once halfway through grilling. (For a gas grill, preheat grill. Reduce heat to medium. Place fish on grill rack over heat. Cover and grill as above.)

2 Meanwhile, for vinaigrette, in a screw-top jar combine mint, vinegar, oil, orange peel, orange juice, and the ⅛ teaspoon salt. Cover and shake well.

3 Divide salad greens among 4 serving plates. Top with orange slices and red onion. Top each with a salmon fillet. Drizzle with vinaigrette. If desired, sprinkle with almonds.

Salmon Penne Salad with Raspberry Vinaigrette

PREP 30 minutes
BROIL 4 to 6 minutes per ½-inch thickness
MAKES 4 servings

- 1 8- to 10-ounce fresh or frozen skinless, boneless salmon fillet or other fish fillet
- 1 recipe Raspberry Vinaigrette
- 6 ounces dried penne pasta (about 2 cups)
- 1 cup bias-sliced fresh asparagus spears
- 1 cup fresh red raspberries or sliced fresh strawberries
- Lettuce leaves (optional)
- ¼ cup sliced green onions (2)

1 Thaw fish, if frozen. Rinse fish; pat dry with paper towels. Measure the thickness of the fish. Remove 2 teaspoons of the Raspberry Vinaigrette; brush onto fish. Cover and chill the remaining vinaigrette until ready to use.

2 Preheat broiler. Place fish on the greased unheated rack of a broiler pan; tuck under any thin edges. Broil 4 inches from heat until fish flakes easily when tested with a fork, allowing 4 to 6 minutes per ½-inch thickness and turning once if fish is 1 inch or more thick.

3 Meanwhile, cook pasta according to package directions, adding asparagus the last 2 minutes. Drain; rinse with cold water. Drain again. Return pasta to pan. Add reserved chilled vinaigrette; toss gently to coat.

4 Flake salmon. Add salmon to pasta; toss gently. Cover and chill until serving time.

5 To serve, add berries to pasta mixture; toss gently to mix. If desired, serve on lettuce-lined plates. Sprinkle with green onions.

Raspberry Vinaigrette: In a small bowl whisk together ¼ cup raspberry vinegar; 2 tablespoons olive oil; 1 tablespoon honey mustard; 2 teaspoons sugar; 1 clove garlic, minced; and ¼ teaspoon black pepper. Cover and chill until serving time.

Make-Ahead Directions: Prepare Raspberry Vinaigrette; cover and chill up to 24 hours. Make salmon-pasta mixture as directed through Step 4; cover and chill up to 4 hours. Serve as directed in Step 5.

NUTRITION FACTS per serving

CALORIES 368
TOTAL FAT 14 g (2 g sat. fat)
CHOLESTEROL 33 mg
SODIUM 42 mg
CARBOHYDRATE 41 g
FIBER 4 g
PROTEIN 18 g
EXCHANGES 1 Vegetable, 2½ Starch, 1½ Lean Meat, 1½ Fat

Thai Tuna Toss

START TO FINISH 25 minutes
MAKES 4 servings

NUTRITION FACTS per serving

CALORIES 268
TOTAL FAT 9 g (2 g sat. fat)
CHOLESTEROL 43 mg
SODIUM 205 mg
CARBOHYDRATE 14 g
FIBER 3 g
PROTEIN 30 g
EXCHANGES 2 Vegetable, 4 Lean Meat, 1 Fat

- 6 cups shredded napa or Chinese cabbage
- 12 ounces cooked tuna,* broken into chunks, or two 6-ounce cans very low-sodium chunk white tuna, drained
- 1 medium red or yellow sweet pepper, cut into thin strips
- 1 cup fresh snow pea pods, trimmed and halved crosswise
- ¼ cup sliced green onions (2)
- ½ cup rice vinegar
- 1 tablespoon sugar
- 1 tablespoon reduced-sodium soy sauce
- 1 teaspoon toasted sesame oil
- ¼ teaspoon ground ginger
- ⅛ to ¼ teaspoon crushed red pepper
- 2 tablespoons chopped cashews

1 In a very large bowl combine cabbage, tuna, sweet pepper, pea pods, and green onions. Gently toss to mix.

2 For dressing, in a screw-top jar combine rice vinegar, sugar, soy sauce, sesame oil, ginger, and crushed red pepper. Cover and shake well.

3 Pour dressing over the cabbage mixture; toss to coat. Serve immediately or cover and chill up to 12 hours. Sprinkle salads with cashews before serving.

***Note:** For cooked tuna, purchase 1 pound frozen tuna steaks, cut 1 inch thick. Thaw fish. Rinse fish; pat dry with paper towels. Place fish on the unheated greased rack of a broiler pan. Broil 4 inches from heat for 8 to 12 minutes or until fish flakes easily when tested with a fork, turning once halfway through cooking. Use right away or freeze for later use. Makes about 12 ounces cooked fish.

Shrimp and Watermelon Salad

START TO FINISH 20 minutes
MAKES 4 servings

NUTRITION FACTS per serving

CALORIES 241
TOTAL FAT 9 g (1 g sat. fat)
CHOLESTEROL 172 mg
SODIUM 363 mg
CARBOHYDRATE 16 g
FIBER 2 g
PROTEIN 25 g
EXCHANGES 1 Vegetable, ½ Fruit, 3 Lean Meat, 1 Fat

- 1 pound fresh or frozen peeled, deveined medium shrimp
- 2 tablespoons olive oil
- 2 teaspoons snipped fresh thyme
- 4 cups sliced bok choy or napa cabbage
- 1 cup grape tomatoes, halved
- Salt and black pepper
- 2 1-inch slices seedless watermelon, halved
- Small limes, halved
- ¼ cup crumbled reduced-fat feta cheese (optional)
- Fresh thyme sprigs (optional)

1 Thaw shrimp, if frozen. Rinse shrimp; pat dry with paper towels. In a large skillet heat 1 tablespoon oil over medium-high heat. Add shrimp; cook and stir for 3 to 4 minutes or until shrimp are opaque. Transfer shrimp to a bowl; stir in thyme. Add remaining olive oil, bok choy, and tomatoes to skillet; cook and stir for 1 minute. Return shrimp to skillet; cook and stir for 1 minute more. Season with salt and pepper.

2 Serve shrimp and vegetables with watermelon. Squeeze lime juice on salads. If desired, sprinkle with feta and thyme sprigs.

Spicy Shrimp Tabbouleh

PREP 30 minutes **CHILL** 4 to 24 hours
MAKES 4 servings

NUTRITION FACTS per serving

CALORIES 201
TOTAL FAT 1 g (0 g sat. fat)
CHOLESTEROL 111 mg
SODIUM 495 mg
CARBOHYDRATE 32 g
FIBER 6 g
PROTEIN 16 g
EXCHANGES ½ Vegetable, 2 Starch, 1½ Lean Meat

- 1⅓ cups water
- ⅔ cup bulgur
- ½ cup bottled fat-free ranch salad dressing
- ½ teaspoon finely shredded lime peel
- 2 tablespoons lime juice
- ¼ teaspoon crushed red pepper
- 1 cup fresh pea pods, halved crosswise
- ½ cup chopped radishes or daikon
- ½ cup snipped fresh cilantro
- ¼ cup bias-sliced green onions (2)
- 8 ounces peeled and deveined cooked shrimp, halved lengthwise

1 In a small saucepan combine the water and bulgur. Bring to boiling; reduce heat. Simmer, covered, about 15 minutes or until most of the water is absorbed and bulgur is tender.

2 Meanwhile, for dressing, in a small bowl combine ranch dressing, lime peel, lime juice, and crushed red pepper.

3 Stir pea pods into bulgur; transfer to a large bowl. Stir in radishes, cilantro, green onions, and the dressing. Cover and refrigerate for 4 to 24 hours. To serve, stir in shrimp.

Ginger Shrimp Pasta Salad

PREP 30 minutes **CHILL** 2 to 24 hours
MAKES 8 servings

NUTRITION FACTS per serving

CALORIES 267
TOTAL FAT 10 g (1 g sat. fat)
CHOLESTEROL 97 mg
SODIUM 122 mg
CARBOHYDRATE 26 g
FIBER 2 g
PROTEIN 17 g
EXCHANGES 1 Vegetable, 1½ Starch, 1½ Lean Meat, 1½ Fat

- 1½ pounds fresh or frozen medium shrimp
- 1 tablespoon olive oil
- 2 cloves garlic, minced
- 1 tablespoon grated fresh ginger
- 8 ounces dried penne pasta
- ¼ cup sherry vinegar or white wine vinegar
- ¼ cup olive oil
- 1½ cups halved yellow or red pear tomatoes or grape tomatoes
- 1 cup chopped red or yellow sweet pepper (1 large)
- ½ cup finely chopped celery (1 stalk)
- ¼ cup finely chopped red onion
- ¼ cup snipped fresh basil
- 1 tablespoon capers, drained
- Black pepper

1 Thaw shrimp, if frozen. Peel and devein shrimp, leaving tails intact. Rinse shrimp; pat dry with paper towels. In a large skillet heat the 1 tablespoon oil over medium heat. Add garlic and ginger; cook and stir for 15 seconds. Add shrimp; cook about 3 minutes or until shrimp are opaque, stirring frequently. Set aside.

2 Meanwhile, cook pasta according to package directions. Drain. Rinse pasta with cold water; drain again.

3 In a very large bowl whisk together vinegar and the ¼ cup oil. Add cooked pasta and shrimp; toss to coat. Stir in tomatoes, sweet pepper, celery, red onion, basil, and capers. Season with black pepper. Cover and chill for 2 to 24 hours.

Crab Cakes with Spring Green Salad

PREP 35 minutes **CHILL** 30 minutes
OVEN 300°F **MAKES** 6 servings

NUTRITION FACTS per serving

CALORIES 181
TOTAL FAT 9 g (1 g sat. fat)
CHOLESTEROL 78 mg
SODIUM 426 mg
CARBOHYDRATE 8 g
FIBER 1 g
PROTEIN 18 g
EXCHANGES 1½ Vegetable, 2 Lean Meat, 1½ Fat

- 1 egg white
- 3 tablespoons light mayonnaise
- 1 tablespoon Dijon mustard
- Few drops bottled hot pepper sauce
- 3 tablespoons finely chopped red or green sweet pepper
- 2 tablespoons snipped fresh parsley
- 1 tablespoon sliced green onion
- 2 teaspoons snipped fresh dill
- 1 pound cooked fresh lump crabmeat or three 6- to 6.5-ounce cans lump crabmeat, drained, flaked, and cartilage removed
- 1¼ cups soft whole wheat or white bread crumbs
- 8 ounces mixed baby greens (8 cups)
- 1 head Belgian endive, sliced
- ½ cup chopped, seeded tomato
- Nonstick cooking spray
- 1 recipe Lime Dressing

1 In a large bowl whisk together egg white, mayonnaise, mustard, and hot pepper sauce. Stir in sweet pepper, parsley, onion, and dill. Add crab and ½ cup of the bread crumbs; stir until well mixed. Using wet hands, shape mixture into six ½-inch-thick patties. Place in a 15×10×1-inch baking pan. Cover; chill for 30 minutes.

2 In a very large bowl combine greens, endive, and tomato. Cover; chill until ready to serve.

3 Place remaining ¾ cup crumbs in a shallow dish. Dip crab cakes in bread crumbs to coat both sides. Coat an unheated large nonstick skillet with cooking spray. Heat over medium heat. Cook crab cakes, 3 at a time, for 8 to 10 minutes or until golden brown (160°F), turning once. Transfer to a baking sheet; keep warm in a 300°F oven. To serve, toss greens mixture with Lime Dressing. Serve warm crab cakes on greens mixture.

Lime Dressing: In a small bowl whisk together 2 tablespoons olive oil; 2 tablespoons lime juice; 1 clove garlic, minced; ⅛ teaspoon salt; and ⅛ teaspoon black pepper.

Scallop Stir-fry Salad

START TO FINISH 30 minutes
MAKES 4 servings

NUTRITION FACTS per serving

CALORIES 203
TOTAL FAT 9 g (1 g sat. fat)
CHOLESTEROL 28 mg
SODIUM 633 mg
CARBOHYDRATE 12 g
FIBER 4 g
PROTEIN 18 g
EXCHANGES 2 Vegetable, 2 Lean Meat, 2 Fat

- 12 ounces fresh or frozen bay scallops
- 2 tablespoons orange juice
- 2 tablespoons reduced-sodium soy sauce
- 1 tablespoon rice vinegar or white wine vinegar
- 1 teaspoon toasted sesame oil
- 2 tablespoons vegetable oil
- 1 cup fresh pea pods, strings and tips removed and, if desired, halved
- 3/4 cup coarsely chopped red sweet pepper (1 medium)
- 1/2 cup sliced green onions (4)
- 1 12-ounce jar baby corn, rinsed and drained
- 2 cups shredded napa cabbage
- 2 cups shredded fresh spinach or romaine lettuce

1 Thaw scallops, if frozen. Rinse scallops; pat dry with paper towels. In a small bowl stir together orange juice, soy sauce, vinegar, and sesame oil. Set aside.

2 In a medium skillet heat 1 tablespoon of the oil over medium-high heat. Add scallops; stir-fry about 2 minutes or until scallops are opaque. Remove scallops from skillet.

3 Add remaining 1 tablespoon oil to skillet. Add pea pods, sweet pepper, and onions; stir-fry for 2 to 3 minutes or until crisp-tender. Add cooked scallops, the baby corn, and orange juice mixture to skillet; stir-fry about 1 minute or until heated through. Remove from heat.

4 In a large salad bowl combine napa cabbage and spinach. Top with scallop mixture; toss gently to combine.

Layered Southwestern Salad with Tortilla Strips

PREP 15 minutes **BAKE** 15 minutes
OVEN 350°F **MAKES** 6 servings

NUTRITION FACTS per serving

CALORIES 227
TOTAL FAT 11 g (3 g sat. fat)
CHOLESTEROL 12 mg
SODIUM 386 mg
CARBOHYDRATE 29 g
FIBER 9 g
PROTEIN 11 g
EXCHANGES 1½ Vegetable, 1 Starch, ½ Lean Meat, 2 Fat

2 6-inch corn tortillas
Nonstick cooking spray
½ cup light sour cream
¼ cup snipped fresh cilantro
2 tablespoons fat-free milk
1 teaspoon olive oil
1 large clove garlic, minced
½ teaspoon chili powder
½ teaspoon finely shredded lime peel
¼ teaspoon salt
¼ teaspoon black pepper
6 cups torn romaine lettuce
4 plum tomatoes, chopped (2 cups)
1 15-ounce can black beans, rinsed and drained
1 cup fresh corn kernels*
½ cup shredded reduced-fat cheddar cheese (2 ounces)
1 avocado, halved, seeded, peeled, and chopped
Snipped fresh cilantro (optional)

1 Preheat oven to 350°F. Cut tortillas into ½-inch-wide strips; place in a 15×10×1-inch baking pan. Coat tortillas lightly with cooking spray. Bake for 15 to 18 minutes or just until crisp, stirring once. Cool on a wire rack.

2 For dressing, in a small bowl stir together sour cream, ¼ cup cilantro, milk, oil, garlic, chili power, lime peel, salt, and pepper.

3 Place lettuce in a large glass serving bowl. Top with tomatoes, beans, corn, cheese, and avocado. Add dressing and sprinkle with tortilla strips. If desired, garnish with additional cilantro.

***Note:** It isn't necessary to cook the corn. However, for a roasted flavor and softer texture, try baking it with the tortilla strips. Place the strips at 1 end of the baking pan and the corn at the other end.

Chapter 6

Soups & Stews

On the opener: Beef Soup with Root Vegetables *(see recipe, page 113)*

BEEF

CHICKEN & TURKEY

FISH & SEAFOOD

PORK & LAMB

Beef Soup with Root Vegetables

PREP 30 minutes **COOK** 1 hour 30 minutes
MAKES 8 servings

NUTRITION FACTS per serving

CALORIES 167
TOTAL FAT 2 g (1 g sat. fat)
CHOLESTEROL 37 mg
SODIUM 453 mg
CARBOHYDRATE 14 g
FIBER 2 g
PROTEIN 23 g
EXCHANGES ½ Vegetable, 1 Starch, 2½ Very Lean Meat

- 1½ pounds boneless beef round steak
- Nonstick cooking spray
- 3 14.5-ounce cans reduced-sodium beef broth
- 1 cup water
- 1 cup sliced celery (2 stalks)
- 1 cup coarsely chopped onion (1 onion)
- ½ cup sliced carrot (1 medium)
- 2 tablespoons snipped fresh thyme or 2 teaspoons dried thyme, crushed
- 2 teaspoons Worcestershire sauce
- 2 cloves garlic, minced
- ¼ teaspoon salt
- ¼ teaspoon black pepper
- 1 bay leaf
- 2 medium potatoes, peeled and cut into ¾-inch cubes
- 2 medium turnips, peeled and cut into ¾-inch cubes
- 1 large sweet potato, peeled and cut into ¾-inch cubes

1 Trim fat from steak. Cut steak into ¾-inch cubes. Coat an unheated 4-quart Dutch oven with cooking spray. Heat over medium-high heat. Cook meat, half at a time, in hot pan until browned.

2 Add beef broth, the water, celery, onion, carrot, dried thyme (if using), Worcestershire sauce, garlic, salt, pepper, and bay leaf.

3 Bring to boiling; reduce heat. Simmer, covered, about 1¼ hours or until meat is nearly tender. Discard bay leaf. Stir in potatoes, turnips, and sweet potato. Return to boiling; reduce heat. Simmer, covered, about 15 minutes more or until meat and vegetables are tender. Stir in fresh thyme (if using).

Three-Pepper Beef Stew

PREP 35 minutes **COOK** 1 hour 30 minutes
MAKES 6 servings

NUTRITION FACTS per serving

CALORIES 401
TOTAL FAT 10 g (3 g sat. fat)
CHOLESTEROL 82 mg
SODIUM 358 mg
CARBOHYDRATE 25 g
FIBER 4 g
PROTEIN 36 g
EXCHANGES 1½ Vegetable, 1 Starch, 4½ Lean Meat

- 1 tablespoon canola oil
- 4 medium carrots, cut into 1-inch pieces
- 2 stalks celery, cut into 1-inch pieces
- 1 cup chopped onion (1 large)
- 6 cloves garlic, minced, or 1 tablespoon minced garlic
- 2 pounds beef chuck, trimmed of fat and cut into 1-inch cubes
- 1¾ cups dry red wine or one 14.5-ounce can lower-sodium beef broth
- 1 14.5-ounce can lower-sodium beef broth
- 2 tablespoons tomato paste
- 1 tablespoon Worcestershire sauce
- 2 to 3 teaspoons bottled cayenne pepper sauce
- ¼ to ½ teaspoon crushed red pepper
- 2 large potatoes, unpeeled, cut into 1-inch pieces
- 2 medium red sweet peppers, cut into 1-inch pieces
- 2 tablespoons cold water
- 1 tablespoon cornstarch

1 In a 4- to 6-quart Dutch oven heat oil over medium heat. Add carrots, celery, onion, and garlic; cook about 5 minutes or until onion is tender, stirring occasionally. Add beef; cook about 15 minutes or until browned, stirring occasionally. Drain off fat.

2 Stir in wine, beef broth, tomato paste, Worcestershire sauce, pepper sauce, and crushed red pepper. Bring to boiling; reduce heat. Simmer, covered, for 1 hour, stirring occasionally.

3 Add potatoes and sweet peppers. Return stew to boiling; reduce heat. Simmer, covered, for 15 to 20 minutes or until meat and potatoes are tender.

4 In a small bowl stir together the cold water and cornstarch. Stir into beef mixture. Cook and stir until thickened and bubbly. Cook and stir for 2 minutes more.

Mustard-Herb Beef Stew

PREP 30 minutes **COOK** 1 hour
MAKES 8 (about 1¼-cup) servings

NUTRITION FACTS per serving

CALORIES 338
TOTAL FAT 8 g (2 g sat. fat)
CHOLESTEROL 37 mg
SODIUM 538 mg
CARBOHYDRATE 36 g
FIBER 4 g
PROTEIN 25 g
EXCHANGES 1 Vegetable, 2 Starch, 2½ Lean Meat, 1 Fat

- ⅓ cup all-purpose flour
- 1 tablespoon snipped fresh Italian (flat-leaf) parsley
- 1 teaspoon snipped fresh thyme or ½ teaspoon dried thyme, crushed
- 1 teaspoon black pepper
- ¼ teaspoon salt
- 1½ pound boneless beef chuck, cut into 1- to 1½-inch pieces
- 2 tablespoons olive oil
- 1 8- to 10-ounce package cipolini onions, peeled, or 1 medium onion, peeled and cut into wedges
- 4 carrots, peeled and cut into 1-inch pieces
- 1 8-ounce package cremini mushrooms, halved if large
- 8 small new Yukon gold potatoes, halved
- 3 tablespoons tomato paste
- 2 tablespoons spicy brown mustard
- 1 14.5-ounce can lower-sodium beef broth
- 1 12-ounce bottle dark porter beer or nonalcoholic beer
- 1 bay leaf
- 8 crusty bread slices

1 In a large bowl or resealable plastic bag combine flour, parsley, thyme, pepper, and salt. Add beef, a few pieces at a time; stir or shake to coat. Reserve leftover flour mixture.

2 In a 6-quart Dutch oven heat oil over medium-high heat. Brown beef in hot oil. Stir in onions, carrots, mushrooms, and potatoes. Cook and stir for 3 minutes. Stir in tomato paste, mustard, and the remaining flour mixture. Add beef broth, beer, and bay leaf. Bring to boiling; reduce heat. Simmer, covered, for 1 to 1¼ hours or until beef is tender. Discard bay leaf. Serve with crusty bread.

Spiced Pork Stew

PREP 40 minutes **BAKE** 1 hour 20 minutes
OVEN 350°F **MAKES** 8 servings

NUTRITION FACTS per serving

CALORIES 245
TOTAL FAT 9 g (3 g sat. fat)
CHOLESTEROL 51 mg
SODIUM 530 mg
CARBOHYDRATE 22 g
FIBER 3 g
PROTEIN 17 g
EXCHANGES 1½ Vegetable, 1 Starch, 1½ Medium-Fat Meat

- 3 tablespoons all-purpose flour
- 1 teaspoon ground cumin
- 2 pounds boneless pork shoulder, trimmed of fat and cut into ¾-inch pieces
- ½ cup chopped onion (1 medium)
- 2 tablespoons vegetable oil
- 2 14.5-ounce cans diced tomatoes, undrained
- ⅓ cup water
- 1 teaspoon salt
- 1 teaspoon ground ginger
- 1 teaspoon ground cinnamon
- ½ teaspoon sugar
- ½ teaspoon black pepper
- 2 cups frozen cut green beans
- 2 cups chopped red potatoes (2 medium)
- 1 cup chopped, peeled sweet potato (1 medium)
- 1 cup sliced carrots (2 medium)
- 2 tablespoons snipped fresh cilantro or parsley
- ½ cup plain low-fat yogurt (optional)

1 Preheat oven to 350°F. In a resealable plastic bag combine flour and cumin. Add pork pieces to plastic bag; shake to coat pork. In an ovenproof 4- to 5-quart Dutch oven cook meat and onion, half at a time, in hot oil over medium-high heat until meat is browned. Drain off fat. Return all pork and onion to the Dutch oven.

2 Stir undrained tomatoes, the water, salt, ginger, cinnamon, sugar, and pepper into pork mixture in Dutch oven. Stir in green beans, red potatoes, sweet potato, and carrots. Bring stew just to boiling.

3 Cover and bake stew about 1 hour and 20 minutes or until meat and vegetables are tender. Sprinkle servings with cilantro. If desired, serve with yogurt.

Spicy Pork and Vegetable Soup

PREP 30 minutes
COOK 10 to 11 hours (low) or 5 to 5½ hours (high)
MAKES 6 servings

- 1 pound lean pork or beef stew meat
- 1 tablespoon canola oil
- ½ cup chopped onion (1 medium)
- 1 teaspoon paprika
- 2 cloves garlic, minced
- 3 cups lower-sodium beef broth
- 8 ounces winter squash, peeled and cut into ½-inch pieces
- 3 medium parsnips or carrots, cut into ¼-inch slices (1½ cups)
- 1 medium sweet potato, peeled and cut into ½-inch pieces
- 1 8.75-ounce can whole kernel corn, undrained
- ¼ teaspoon salt
- ¼ teaspoon cayenne pepper
- 2 cups torn fresh spinach

1 Cut meat into ½-inch pieces. In a large skillet heat oil over medium heat. Cook half the meat in the hot oil until browned. Transfer meat to a 3½- or 4-quart slow cooker. Add the remaining meat, the onion, paprika, and garlic to the skillet. Cook until meat is browned and onion is tender. Drain off fat. Transfer meat mixture to cooker.

2 Stir beef broth, squash, parsnips, sweet potato, corn, salt, and cayenne pepper into meat mixture in cooker. Cover and cook on low-heat setting for 10 to 11 hours or on high-heat setting for 5 to 5½ hours. Just before serving, stir in spinach.

NUTRITION FACTS per serving

CALORIES 227
TOTAL FAT 8 g (2 g sat. fat)
CHOLESTEROL 41 mg
SODIUM 488 mg
CARBOHYDRATE 19 g
FIBER 4 g
PROTEIN 20 g
EXCHANGES ½ Vegetable, 1 Starch, 2½ Lean Meat, ½ Fat

Curried-Cider Pork Stew

PREP 35 minutes **COOK** 1 hour
MAKES 8 servings

NUTRITION FACTS per serving

CALORIES 295
TOTAL FAT 10 g (3 g sat. fat)
CHOLESTEROL 76 mg
SODIUM 311 mg
CARBOHYDRATE 27 g
FIBER 5 g
PROTEIN 24 g
EXCHANGES ½ Vegetable, 1 Fruit, ½ Starch, 3 Lean Meat, 1 Fat

- 2 pounds boneless pork shoulder
- 4 medium red and/or green crisp-tart cooking apples
- 1 tablespoon canola oil
- 1 large onion, cut into thin wedges
- 2 teaspoons curry powder
- 1 14.5-ounce can reduced-sodium chicken broth
- ⅔ cup apple cider or apple juice
- ¼ teaspoon salt
- ¼ teaspoon black pepper
- 12 ounces baby carrots with tops, trimmed, or packaged peeled baby carrots (2 cups)
- 1 cup sliced celery (2 stalks)
- 1 1½-pound butternut squash, peeled, seeded, and cubed (2 cups)
- Light sour cream, shredded orange peel, snipped fresh oregano, and/or freshly ground black pepper (optional)

1 Trim fat from pork; cut into 1-inch cubes. Peel, core, and chop 2 of the apples; set aside. In a 4-quart Dutch oven heat oil over medium heat. Brown pork, half at a time, in hot oil. Return all pork to pan; add chopped apples, the onion, and curry powder. Cook and stir for 2 minutes. Add chicken broth, cider, salt, and pepper. Bring to boiling; reduce heat. Simmer, covered, for 30 minutes, stirring occasionally.

2 Add carrots and celery to pork mixture. Return to boiling; reduce heat. Simmer, covered, for 20 minutes, stirring occasionally. Meanwhile, cut the remaining 2 apples into ¼-inch wedges. Add apple wedges and squash to Dutch oven. Cook, covered, for 10 to 12 minutes more or until pork and vegetables are tender. If desired, top with sour cream, orange peel, oregano, and/or pepper.

Caraway Chicken and Vegetable Stew

START TO FINISH 40 minutes
MAKES 6 (1¼-cup) servings

NUTRITION FACTS per serving

CALORIES 163
TOTAL FAT 5 g (1 g sat. fat)
CHOLESTEROL 63 mg
SODIUM 410 mg
CARBOHYDRATE 12 g
FIBER 3 g
PROTEIN 19 g
EXCHANGES 1½ Vegetable, 2 Lean Meat, 1 Fat

- 2 teaspoons olive oil
- 1 pound skinless, boneless chicken thighs or breast halves, trimmed of fat and cut into 1½-inch pieces
- 2 14.5-ounce cans reduced-sodium chicken broth
- 8 ounces fresh green beans, cut into 2-inch-long pieces
- 2 medium carrots, bias-cut into ½-inch slices
- 2 stalks celery, bias-cut into ½-inch slices
- 2 cups sliced fresh shiitake,* cremini, oyster,* and/or button mushrooms
- 1 cup frozen pearl onions
- 1¼ teaspoons caraway seeds, crushed
- ¼ teaspoon black pepper
- ¼ cup cold water
- 2 tablespoons cornstarch

1 In a 4-quart Dutch oven heat oil over medium-high heat. Add chicken; cook for 3 to 5 minutes or until browned, stirring occasionally. Add chicken broth, beans, carrots, celery, mushrooms, onions, caraway seeds, and pepper. Bring to boiling; reduce heat. Simmer, covered, about 10 minutes or until vegetables are tender and chicken is no longer pink.

2 In a small bowl combine the water and cornstarch; whisk until smooth. Add to stew. Cook and stir until thickened and bubbly. Cook and stir for 2 minutes more.

***Note:** Remove stems from shiitake and oyster mushrooms before slicing.

Chicken and Vegetable Soup

PREP 35 minutes **COOK** 25 minutes
MAKES 8 servings

NUTRITION FACTS per serving

CALORIES 249
TOTAL FAT 5 g (1 g sat. fat)
CHOLESTEROL 66 mg
SODIUM 705 mg
CARBOHYDRATE 20 g
FIBER 3 g
PROTEIN 29 g
EXCHANGES ½ Vegetable, 1 Starch, 3½ Lean Meat, 1 Fat

- 2 pounds skinless, boneless chicken breast halves, cut into bite-size pieces
- 1 teaspoon poultry seasoning
- 2 tablespoons olive oil
- 1½ cups chopped fresh mushrooms
- 1 cup chopped carrots (2 medium)
- ½ cup chopped onion (1 medium)
- ½ cup chopped green sweet pepper
- 4 cloves garlic, minced
- 2 tablespoons snipped fresh basil or 2 teaspoons dried basil, crushed
- 1 tablespoon snipped fresh parsley or 1 teaspoon dried parsley, crushed
- ¼ teaspoon black pepper
- ⅛ teaspoon salt
- 6 cups water
- 2 tablespoons chicken bouillon granules
- 1 pound potatoes, cut into 1-inch pieces (about 2¾ cups)
- ½ cup quick-cooking barley

1 In a medium bowl toss chicken breast pieces with the poultry seasoning; set aside.

2 In a 5- to 6-quart Dutch oven heat 1 tablespoon of the oil over medium heat. Add mushrooms, carrots, onion, sweet pepper, garlic, dried basil and parsley (if using), black pepper, and salt; cook for 10 minutes, stirring occasionally. Remove vegetables from Dutch oven; set aside.

3 Add the remaining 1 tablespoon oil to the Dutch oven; heat over medium heat. Add chicken pieces; cook about 5 minutes or until browned, stirring occasionally. Return vegetables to Dutch oven. Stir in the water and chicken bouillon granules. Bring to boiling; stir in potatoes and barley. Return to boiling; reduce heat. Simmer, covered, about 15 minutes or until potatoes are tender. Stir in fresh basil and parsley (if using).

Chicken, Barley, and Leek Stew

PREP 25 minutes
COOK 4 to 5 hours (low) or 2 to 2½ hours (high)
MAKES 6 servings

NUTRITION FACTS per serving

CALORIES 248
TOTAL FAT 6 g (1 g sat. fat)
CHOLESTEROL 63 mg
SODIUM 558 mg
CARBOHYDRATE 27 g
FIBER 6 g
PROTEIN 22 g
EXCHANGES ½ Vegetable, 1½ Starch, 2½ Lean Meat

- 1 tablespoon olive oil
- 1 pound skinless, boneless chicken thighs, cut into 1-inch pieces
- 3 14.5-ounce cans reduced-sodium chicken broth
- 1 cup regular barley (not quick-cooking)
- ¾ cup water
- 3 medium leeks, halved lengthwise and sliced
- 1 cup thinly sliced carrots (2 medium)
- 1½ teaspoons dried basil or Italian seasoning, crushed
- ¼ teaspoon cracked black pepper

1 In a large skillet heat oil over medium heat. Brown chicken on all sides in hot oil. In a 4- to 5-quart slow cooker combine the chicken, chicken broth, barley, the water, leeks, carrots, basil, and pepper.

2 Cover and cook on low-heat setting for 4 to 5 hours or on high-heat setting for 2 to 2½ hours or until barley is tender.

Yucatan-Style Turkey and Vegetable Soup

START TO FINISH 40 minutes
MAKES 6 servings

NUTRITION FACTS per serving

CALORIES 229
TOTAL FAT 8 g (2 g sat. fat)
CHOLESTEROL 65 mg
SODIUM 609 mg
CARBOHYDRATE 12 g
FIBER 4 g
PROTEIN 27 g
EXCHANGES 1½ Vegetable, 3½ Very Lean Meat, 1½ Fat

- 1 medium onion, thinly sliced
- 3 or 4 cloves garlic
- 1 tablespoon vegetable oil
- 2 canned chipotle chile peppers in adobo sauce, drained and chopped*
- 1 cup chopped carrots (2 medium)
- 5 cups reduced-sodium chicken broth or turkey stock
- 2 cups coarsely chopped tomatoes
- ⅛ teaspoon salt
- 3 cups chopped cooked turkey (about 1 pound)
- 2 cups chopped zucchini (2 small)
- 2 tablespoons snipped fresh cilantro
- ⅓ cup crumbled queso fresco or feta cheese
- 1 avocado, halved, seeded, peeled, and chopped
- Thin strips fresh lime peel (optional)
- 1 lime, cut into wedges (optional)

1 In a nonstick medium skillet combine onion slices and unpeeled garlic cloves; cook and stir for 3 to 5 minutes or until edges are brown. Chop onion; peel and slice garlic cloves.

2 In a 4-quart Dutch oven heat oil over medium-high heat. Add chopped onion, sliced garlic, and chipotle peppers. Cook and stir for 3 minutes. Add carrots. Cook and stir for 3 minutes more. Add broth, tomatoes, and salt. Bring to boiling; reduce heat. Simmer, covered, for 10 minutes. Add turkey, zucchini, and cilantro; cook, covered, for 5 minutes more.

3 Top servings with queso fresco, avocado, and, if desired, lime peel strips. If desired, serve with lime wedges.

***Note:** Because chile peppers contain volatile oils that can burn your skin and eyes, avoid direct contact with them as much as possible. When working with chile peppers, wear plastic or rubber gloves. If your bare hands do touch the peppers, wash your hands and fingernails well with soap and warm water.

Turkey and Sweet Potato Chowder

START TO FINISH 40 minutes
MAKES 5 servings

- 1 14.5-ounce can reduced-sodium chicken broth
- 1 large potato, peeled, if desired, and chopped (about 1½ cups)
- 2 small ears frozen corn on the cob, thawed, or 1 cup frozen whole kernel corn
- 1 medium sweet potato, peeled and cut into ¾-inch cubes (about 1½ cups)
- 1 teaspoon snipped fresh thyme or ¼ teaspoon dried thyme, crushed
- ⅛ to ¼ teaspoon black pepper
- 12 ounces cooked turkey breast, cut into ½-inch cubes (about 2¼ cups)
- 1½ cups fat-free milk

1 In a 3-quart saucepan combine chicken broth and chopped potato. Bring to boiling; reduce heat. Simmer, uncovered, about 12 minutes or until potato is tender, stirring occasionally. Remove from heat. Do not drain. Using a potato masher, mash potato until mixture is thickened and nearly smooth.

2 If using corn on the cob, carefully cut crosswise into ½-inch slices.

3 Stir corn pieces or frozen corn kernels, sweet potato, dried thyme (if using), and pepper into potato mixture in saucepan. Bring to boiling; reduce heat. Cook, covered, for 12 to 15 minutes or until the sweet potato is tender. Stir in turkey and milk; heat through.

4 Ladle chowder into bowls. Sprinkle with fresh thyme (if using).

NUTRITION FACTS per serving

CALORIES 229
TOTAL FAT 1 g (0 g sat. fat)
CHOLESTEROL 58 mg
SODIUM 279 mg
CARBOHYDRATE 29 g
FIBER 2 g
PROTEIN 27 g
EXCHANGES 2 Starch, 2½ Lean Meat

Turkey and Bean Chili

PREP 20 minutes **COOK** 20 minutes
MAKES 8 servings

NUTRITION FACTS per serving

CALORIES 232
TOTAL FAT 3 g (1 g sat. fat)
CHOLESTEROL 23 mg
SODIUM 502 mg
CARBOHYDRATE 34 g
FIBER 12 g
PROTEIN 23 g
EXCHANGES 3½ Vegetable, 1 Starch, 2 Lean Meat

- 1 pound uncooked ground turkey breast
- 1 cup thinly sliced celery (2 medium)
- 1 cup thinly sliced carrots (2 medium)
- ½ cup finely chopped onion (½ cup)
- 3 cloves garlic, minced
- 2 tablespoons chili powder
- 1 tablespoon olive oil
- 2 teaspoons ground cumin
- ½ teaspoon salt
- ½ teaspoon black pepper
- 5 14.5-ounce cans no-salt-added diced tomatoes, undrained
- 2 15-ounce cans dark red kidney beans, rinsed and drained
- 1 4-ounce can diced green chile peppers (optional)
- ½ cup reduced-fat shredded cheddar cheese (optional)

1 In a 6- to 8-quart Dutch oven crumble ground turkey. Add celery, carrots, onion, garlic, chili powder, olive oil, cumin, salt, and black pepper. Cook and stir over medium heat until turkey is no longer pink and vegetables are tender.

2 Stir in undrained tomatoes, beans, and, if desired, chile peppers. Bring to boiling; reduce heat. Simmer, covered, for 20 minutes, stirring occasionally. If desired, sprinkle servings with cheese.

Shrimp and Crab Gumbo

PREP 35 minutes **COOK** 28 minutes
MAKES 8 servings

NUTRITION FACTS per serving

CALORIES 263
TOTAL FAT 5 g (1 g sat. fat)
CHOLESTEROL 102 mg
SODIUM 510 mg
CARBOHYDRATE 31 g
FIBER 4 g
PROTEIN 22 g
EXCHANGES 1½ Vegetable, 1½ Starch, 2 Lean Meat, 1 Fat

- 1 pound fresh or frozen large shrimp in shells
- ⅓ cup all-purpose flour
- 2 tablespoons vegetable oil
- 2 cups chopped onion (2 large)
- 2 cups thinly sliced celery (4 stalks)
- 1½ cups chopped green and/or red sweet peppers (2 medium)
- 4 cloves garlic, minced
- 2 14.5-ounce cans reduced-sodium beef broth
- 1 cup water
- 1 recipe Cajun Spice Mix
- 1 16-ounce package frozen cut okra
- 2 6-ounce cans crabmeat, drained, flaked, and cartilage removed
- 3 cups hot cooked long grain rice or brown rice

1 Thaw shrimp, if frozen. Peel and devein shrimp, leaving tails intact if desired. Rinse shrimp; pat dry with paper towels. In a medium skillet cook flour over medium heat about 6 minutes or until flour is browned, stirring frequently. Place in a small bowl; cool.

2 In a 4-quart Dutch oven heat oil over medium-high heat. Add onion, celery, sweet peppers, and garlic; cook and stir about 5 minutes or until vegetables are tender.

3 Slowly whisk 1 can of the broth into browned flour. Add broth-flour mixture, remaining 1 can broth, the water, and Cajun Spice Mix to mixture in Dutch oven. Stir in okra. Bring to boiling; reduce heat. Simmer, covered, for 15 minutes.

4 Add shrimp; cook for 2 to 3 minutes or until shrimp are opaque. Gently stir in crabmeat. Serve gumbo with rice. If desired, garnish with *green onions* and pass *bottled hot pepper sauce.*

Cajun Spice Mix: In a small bowl combine ½ teaspoon dried thyme, crushed; ¼ teaspoon ground white pepper; ¼ teaspoon salt; ¼ teaspoon ground black pepper; and ¼ teaspoon crushed red pepper.

Shrimp Chowder

PREP 15 minutes **COOK** 30 minutes
MAKES 6 servings

NUTRITION FACTS per serving

CALORIES 256
TOTAL FAT 7 g (2 g sat. fat)
CHOLESTEROL 87 mg
SODIUM 599 mg
CARBOHYDRATE 29 g
FIBER 4 g
PROTEIN 21 g
EXCHANGES ½ Vegetable, 1½ Starch, 2½ Lean Meat

- 8 ounces fresh or frozen flounder fillets (about 2 medium fillets)
- 8 ounces fresh or frozen peeled and deveined medium shrimp
- 1 tablespoon canola oil
- 1 cup chopped onion (1 large)
- 2 cloves garlic, minced
- 1 14.5-ounce can diced tomatoes, undrained
- 1 14.5-ounce can vegetable or reduced-sodium chicken broth
- 1 cup water
- 2¼ cups cubed potatoes (about 12 ounces)
- 1½ teaspoons Creole seasoning
- ⅛ to ¼ teaspoon crushed red pepper
- Dash bottled hot pepper sauce
- 3 ounces reduced-fat cream cheese (Neufchâtel), softened
- 1 cup fat-free milk
- 1½ cups frozen whole kernel corn

1. Thaw flounder and shrimp, if frozen. Rinse flounder; pat dry with paper towels. Cut flounder into bite-size pieces; set aside. In a 4- to 5-quart Dutch oven heat oil over medium heat. Add onion and garlic; cook for 12 to 15 minutes or until onion is tender and lightly browned. Reduce heat as needed to prevent onions from overbrowning.

2. Stir in undrained tomatoes, broth, the water, potatoes, Creole seasoning, crushed red pepper, and hot pepper sauce. Bring to boiling; reduce heat. Simmer, covered, for 15 to 20 minutes or just until potatoes are tender.

3. Meanwhile, in medium mixing bowl beat cream cheese with an electric mixer on medium to high until smooth. Gradually beat in milk on low until mixture is very smooth.

4. Add cream cheese mixture, flounder, shrimp, and corn to chowder. Return to boiling; reduce heat. Simmer, uncovered, for 3 to 5 minutes or until shrimp are opaque.

Chapter 7

Beef & Lamb

On the opener: Cowboy Beef *(see recipe, page 140)*

BEEF FLANK STEAK

BEEF STEAKS

GROUND BEEF

LAMB

Grilled Marinated Flank Steak

PREP 30 minutes **MARINATE** 30 minutes
GRILL 17 minutes **MAKES** 4 servings

NUTRITION FACTS per serving

CALORIES 290
TOTAL FAT 9 g (3 g sat. fat)
CHOLESTEROL 28 mg
SODIUM 509 mg
CARBOHYDRATE 22 g
FIBER 11 g
PROTEIN 27 g
EXCHANGES 1½ Starch, 3 Lean Meat, 1 Fat

- 12 ounces beef flank steak, trimmed
- 3 tablespoons red wine vinegar
- 1 large clove garlic, minced
- 1 tablespoon Dijon mustard
- 1 tablespoon snipped fresh cilantro
- ⅛ teaspoon crushed red pepper
- 4 8-inch whole wheat tortillas
- Shredded lettuce
- ½ cup Sweet-Pepper Salsa, Artichoke-Bean Spread, and/or Quick Steak Sauce

1 Score steak on both sides. Place meat in a resealable plastic bag set in shallow dish. For marinade, stir together vinegar, garlic, mustard, cilantro, and red pepper. Pour over meat in bag; seal bag. Marinate in the refrigerator for 30 minutes. Drain meat, discarding marinade. For a charcoal grill, grill meat, uncovered, for 17 to 21 minutes for medium doneness (160°F). (For gas grill; preheat grill. Reduce heat to medium. Place meat on grill rack. Cover; grill as above.) Thinly slice meat against grain. Serve in tortillas with lettuce, Sweet Pepper Salsa, Artichoke-Bean Spread, and/or Quick Steak Sauce.

Sweet-Pepper Salsa: Toss together 2 sweet peppers, finely chopped; 1 fresh serrano pepper, seeded and chopped (see note, page 142); ½ cup chopped, peeled jicama; ¼ cup chopped red onion; 2 tablespoons snipped fresh cilantro; 1 tablespoon red wine vinegar; and ¼ teaspoon salt. Cover and chill. Makes 2½ cups.

Artichoke-Bean Spread: Drain one 6-ounce jar marinated artichoke hearts; reserve marinade. Chop artichokes. In a food processor process reserved marinade; one 15-ounce can garbanzo beans, rinsed and drained; 2 tablespoons sliced green onion; and 1 tablespoon finely shredded lemon peel until smooth. Stir in artichokes. Stir in ⅛ teaspoon each salt and black pepper. Cover and chill. Makes 2 cups.

Quick Steak Sauce: In a blender combine ¼ cup chopped onion, ¼ cup raisins, 2 tablespoons tomato paste, 1 tablespoon molasses, 1 tablespoon packed brown sugar, 1 tablespoon reduced-sodium soy sauce, and ¼ teaspoon black pepper. Cover; blend until nearly smooth. Cover and chill. Makes ¾ cup.

Cilantro-Lime Flank Steak

PREP 15 minutes **MARINATE** 1 to 2 hours
GRILL 17 minutes **MAKES** 4 servings

NUTRITION FACTS per serving

CALORIES 203
TOTAL FAT 9 g (3 g sat. fat)
CHOLESTEROL 47 mg
SODIUM 250 mg
CARBOHYDRATE 5 g
FIBER 1 g
PROTEIN 26 g
EXCHANGES 4 Lean Meat

1 pound beef flank steak, trimmed
¼ cup lime juice
6 cloves garlic, minced
2 tablespoons snipped fresh cilantro
2 teaspoons snipped fresh oregano
¼ teaspoon ground chipotle chile powder or chili powder
1 cup Avocado-Poblano Pico de Gallo

1 Score both sides of steak in a diamond pattern by making shallow diagonal cuts at 1-inch intervals. Place steak in a resealable plastic bag set in a shallow dish. For marinade, stir together ¼ cup *water,* lime juice, garlic, cilantro, oregano, and chipotle chile powder. Pour over steak in bag. Seal bag; turn to coat steak. Marinate in the refrigerator for 1 to 2 hours, turning bag occasionally.

2 Drain steak, reserving marinade. Sprinkle steak with ¼ teaspoon *salt* and ⅛ teaspoon *black pepper.* For a charcoal grill, place steak on the rack of an uncovered grill directly over medium coals. Grill for 17 to 21 minutes or until medium doneness (160°F), turning once and brushing with the reserved marinade halfway through grilling. Discard any remaining marinade. (For a gas grill, preheat grill. Reduce heat to medium. Place steak on grill rack over heat. Cover and grill as above.) To serve, thinly slice beef across the grain. Serve meat with Avocado-Poblano Pico de Gallo. If desired, garnish with *lime wedges* and *cilantro.*

Avocado-Poblano Pico de Gallo: Place 1 fresh poblano chile pepper and 1 yellow or red sweet pepper on foil-lined baking sheet. Broil 4 inches from heat for 7 to 10 minutes or until skins are blackened, turning occasionally. Enclose peppers in the foil. Let stand 15 minutes or until cool enough to handle. Using a paring knife, pull off and discard skins (see note, page 142). Discard stems, seeds, and membranes; chop the peppers. Combine chopped peppers, ½ cup chopped tomato, ⅓ cup chopped red onion, 2 tablespoons snipped fresh cilantro, ½ teaspoon finely shredded lime peel, 1 tablespoon lime juice, and ¼ teaspoon salt. Toss to combine. Stir in 1 small avocado, halved, seeded, peeled, and chopped. Makes 3¼ cups.

Flank Steak with Corn Salsa

PREP 15 minutes **MARINATE** 6 to 24 hours
GRILL 17 minutes **MAKES** 6 servings

- 1 8.75-ounce can whole kernel corn, drained
- ¾ cup bottled salsa verde
- ½ cup chopped tomato (1 medium)
- 1 1¼- to 1½-pound beef flank steak
- ¾ cup bottled reduced-calorie Italian vinaigrette salad dressing
- 2 tablespoons cracked black pepper
- 1 tablespoon Worcestershire sauce
- 1 teaspoon ground cumin

1. For corn salsa, in a medium bowl combine corn, salsa verde, and tomato. Cover and chill for 6 to 24 hours.

2. Meanwhile, trim fat from steak. Score both sides of steak in a diamond pattern by making shallow diagonal cuts at 1-inch intervals. Place steak in a resealable plastic bag set in a shallow dish.

3. For marinade, in a small bowl combine salad dressing, pepper, Worcestershire sauce, and cumin; pour over steak. Seal bag; turn to coat steak. Marinate in the refrigerator for 6 to 24 hours, turning bag occasionally. Drain steak, discarding marinade.

4. For a charcoal grill, place steak on the rack of an uncovered grill directly over medium coals. Grill for 17 to 21 minutes or until steak is medium doneness (160°F), turning once halfway through grilling. (For a gas grill, preheat grill. Reduce heat to medium. Place steak on the grill rack over heat. Cover and grill as above.)

5. To serve, thinly slice steak diagonally across the grain. Serve steak with corn salsa.

NUTRITION FACTS per serving

CALORIES 193
TOTAL FAT 8 g (3 g sat. fat)
CHOLESTEROL 39 mg
SODIUM 352 mg
CARBOHYDRATE 9 g
FIBER 1 g
PROTEIN 22 g
EXCHANGES ½ Vegetable, ½ Starch, 2½ Lean Meat

Bistro Beef Steak with Wild Mushroom Ragoût

START TO FINISH 30 minutes
MAKES 6 servings

NUTRITION FACTS per serving

CALORIES 206
TOTAL FAT 8 g (2 g sat. fat)
CHOLESTEROL 66 mg
SODIUM 291 mg
CARBOHYDRATE 4 g
FIBER 1 g
PROTEIN 27 g
EXCHANGES ½ Vegetable, 3 Lean Meat, ½ Fat

- 3 cloves garlic, minced
- 2 teaspoons herbes de Provence
- ½ teaspoon black pepper
- ¼ teaspoon salt
- 3 8-ounce boneless beef top loin steaks, cut ¾ inch thick
- 1 tablespoon olive oil
- ⅓ cup finely chopped shallots
- 2 cloves garlic, minced
- 8 ounces assorted wild mushrooms (oyster, cremini, and/or shiitake), sliced, stems removed
- ¼ cup dry sherry (optional)
- 1 14.5-ounce can lower-sodium beef broth
- 1 tablespoon cornstarch

1 Preheat broiler. In a small bowl combine the 3 minced cloves garlic, 1 teaspoon of the herbes de Provence, the pepper, and salt. Trim fat from beef steaks. Sprinkle herb mixture over all sides of steaks; rub in with your fingers. Place steaks on the unheated rack of broiler pan. Broil 3 to 4 inches from the heat for 9 to 11 minutes for medium rare (145°F) or medium (160°F), turning once halfway through broiling.

2 Meanwhile, for mushroom ragoût, in a large nonstick skillet heat oil over medium-high heat. Add shallots and the 2 minced cloves garlic; cook for 1 to 3 minutes or until shallots are tender. Add mushrooms; cook for 6 to 7 minutes or until mushrooms are tender and liquid is evaporated, stirring occasionally. Remove from heat. If desired, stir in sherry. Return to heat. Bring to boiling. Cook, uncovered, for 30 to 60 seconds or until liquid is evaporated.

3 In a medium bowl stir together broth, cornstarch, and the remaining 1 teaspoon herbes de Provence. Stir broth mixture into mushroom mixture in skillet. Cook and stir over medium heat until thickened and bubbly. Cook and stir for 2 minutes more. Cut each steak in half and serve with the mushroom ragout.

Tropical Fiesta Steak

PREP 30 minutes **MARINATE** 12 to 24 hours
GRILL 14 minutes **MAKES** 4 servings

NUTRITION FACTS per serving

CALORIES 211
TOTAL FAT 7 g (2 g sat. fat)
CHOLESTEROL 48 mg
SODIUM 166 mg
CARBOHYDRATE 10 g
FIBER 1 g
PROTEIN 26 g
EXCHANGES ½ Fruit, 3½ Lean Meat

- ⅓ cup mango, pear, or apricot nectar
- ¼ cup snipped fresh mint or basil
- ¼ cup sliced green onions (2)
- 3 tablespoons Pickapeppa sauce or spicy brown mustard
- 1 tablespoon vegetable oil
- 1 tablespoon lemon juice
- ⅛ teaspoon salt
- Several dashes bottled hot pepper sauce
- 1 1-pound boneless beef top sirloin steak, cut 1 inch thick
- ½ cup chopped red sweet pepper
- ½ cup chopped red apple or pear
- ½ cup chopped, peeled mango, unpeeled peach, or unpeeled nectarine
- ¼ cup sliced celery

1 For marinade, in a small bowl stir together nectar, mint, 2 tablespoons of the green onions, the Pickapeppa sauce, oil, lemon juice, salt, and hot pepper sauce. Remove ¼ cup of the marinade; cover and chill.

2 Place steak in a resealable plastic bag set in a shallow bowl. Pour the remaining marinade over steak. Seal bag; turn to coat steak. Marinate in the refrigerator for 12 to 24 hours, turning the bag occasionally.

3 For fruit relish, in a small bowl combine sweet pepper, apple, mango, celery, and the remaining 2 tablespoons green onions. Cover and chill up to 24 hours.

4 Drain steak, discarding marinade. Place steak on rack of an uncovered grill directly over medium coals. Grill until desired doneness, turning once halfway through grilling. Allow 14 to 18 minutes for medium rare (145°F) or 18 to 22 minutes for medium (160°F). (For a gas grill, preheat grill. Reduce heat to medium. Place steak on grill rack over heat. Cover and grill as above.)

5 To serve, thinly slice steak across the grain. Serve steak with fruit relish and drizzle with the reserved ¼ cup marinade. If desired, garnish with *mint sprigs.*

Wine-Balsamic Glazed Steak

START TO FINISH 30 minutes
MAKES 4 servings

NUTRITION FACTS per serving

CALORIES 267
TOTAL FAT 9 g (2 g sat. fat)
CHOLESTEROL 48 mg
SODIUM 336 mg
CARBOHYDRATE 11 g
FIBER 1 g
PROTEIN 28 g
EXCHANGES ½ Vegetable, ½ Other Carbo., 4 Lean Meat

- 2 boneless beef top sirloin steaks, cut ½ to ¾ inch thick (8 to 10 ounces per steak)
- 4 teaspoons olive oil
- 2 cups sliced fresh mushrooms
- 4 cloves garlic, minced
- ¼ teaspoon crushed red pepper
- ½ cup dry red wine or low-calorie cranberry juice*
- ¼ cup balsamic vinegar
- 2 tablespoons reduced-sodium soy sauce
- 2 teaspoons honey

1 Trim fat from steaks; cut each steak into 2 equal portions to make 4 servings. In a very large skillet heat oil over medium-high heat. Add steaks. Reduce heat to medium; cook for 10 to 13 minutes or to desired doneness (145°F for medium rare or 160°F for medium), turning steaks occasionally. If meat browns too quickly, reduce heat to medium-low. Transfer meat to a serving platter; keep warm.

2 Add mushrooms, garlic, and red pepper to skillet; cook and stir for 2 minutes. Remove skillet from heat. Carefully add wine. Return to heat. Boil gently, uncovered, 3 to 5 minutes or until most of the liquid is evaporated. Add vinegar, soy sauce, and honey; return to simmering. Cook and stir about 2 minutes or until slightly thickened. Spoon glaze over steaks.

***Note:** If using the cranberry juice option, omit the honey.

Steak and Vegetables with Chimichurri Sauce

PREP 30 minutes **GRILL** 14 minutes
MAKES 4 servings

NUTRITION FACTS per serving

CALORIES 245
TOTAL FAT 9 g (2 g sat. fat)
CHOLESTEROL 48 mg
SODIUM 387 mg
CARBOHYDRATE 13 g
FIBER 4 g
PROTEIN 28 g
EXCHANGES 2 Vegetable, 3½ Lean Meat, 1 Fat

- 1 pound boneless beef top sirloin steak, cut 1 inch thick
- ½ teaspoon chili powder
- 2 cups grape tomatoes or cherry tomatoes
- 2 medium zucchini and/or yellow summer squash, trimmed and halved lengthwise
- 1 small red onion, cut into ½-inch slices
- Nonstick cooking spray
- 1 recipe Chimichurri Sauce

1 Trim fat from steak. Sprinkle chili powder and ⅛ teaspoon *salt* on the steak. Thread tomatoes onto four 6- to 8-inch skewers.* Lightly coat tomatoes and both sides of the zucchini halves and red onion slices with cooking spray. Sprinkle vegetables with ⅛ teaspoon *salt*.

2 For a charcoal grill, place steak, tomato skewers, and vegetable slices on grill rack directly over medium coals. Grill steak, uncovered, until desired doneness, turning once. Allow 14 to 18 minutes for medium rare (145°F) or 18 to 22 minutes for medium (160°F). Grill zucchini and onion for 10 to 12 minutes or until tender and lightly charred, turning occasionally. Grill tomatoes for 4 to 6 minutes or just until softened and lightly charred, turning once. (For a gas grill, preheat grill. Reduce heat to medium. Place steak, tomato skewers, and vegetable slices on grill rack over heat. Cover and grill as above.)

3 Slice steak and divide among 4 serving plates. Serve with grilled tomatoes, vegetable slices, and Chimichurri Sauce.

Chimichurri Sauce: In a food processor or blender combine 1 cup lightly packed fresh Italian (flat-leaf) parsley; ½ cup lightly packed fresh cilantro; ¼ cup white wine vinegar; 2 tablespoons water; 1 tablespoon olive oil; 6 cloves garlic, minced; ¼ teaspoon salt; ¼ teaspoon black pepper; and, if desired, ¼ teaspoon crushed red pepper. Cover and process or blend with several on/off pulses until chopped but not pureed. Makes about ⅔ cup.

***Note:** Soak wooden or bamboo skewers in water for 30 minutes before using.

Dijon-Pepper Steak

PREP 20 minutes
COOK 7 to 8 hours (low) or 3½ to 4 hours (high)
MAKES 6 servings

NUTRITION FACTS per serving

CALORIES 275
TOTAL FAT 9 g (3 g sat. fat)
CHOLESTEROL 65 mg
SODIUM 410 mg
CARBOHYDRATE 10 g
FIBER 1 g
PROTEIN 34 g
EXCHANGES 1 Vegetable, 4½ Lean Meat

- 2 pounds boneless beef sirloin steak, cut 1 inch thick
- 1 to 1½ teaspoons cracked black pepper
- 1 tablespoon canola oil
- 2 cups packaged whole trimmed baby carrots
- 1 medium onion, sliced
- 1 10.75-ounce can reduced-fat and reduced-sodium condensed cream of celery soup
- 2 tablespoons Dijon mustard
- 3 cups hot cooked multigrain penne pasta (optional)
- Snipped fresh parsley (optional)

1 Trim fat from meat. Cut the meat into 6 serving-size pieces. Sprinkle cracked pepper evenly over meat; press in with your fingers. In a large skillet heat oil over medium-high heat. Brown meat, half at a time, in the hot oil. Drain off fat. Set aside.

2 Place carrots and onion in a 3½- or 4-quart slow cooker. Add meat. In a medium bowl stir together soup and Dijon mustard. Pour over meat and vegetables.

3 Cover and cook on low-heat setting for 7 to 8 hours or on high-heat setting for 3½ to 4 hours. If desired, before serving use a fork to slightly break up steak pieces. If desired, serve over hot cooked pasta and garnish with parsley.

Sweet and Spicy Edamame-Beef Stir-Fry

PREP 20 minutes **COOK** 10 minutes
MAKES 4 servings

NUTRITION FACTS per serving

CALORIES 330
TOTAL FAT 12 g (2 g sat. fat)
CHOLESTEROL 24 mg
SODIUM 272 mg
CARBOHYDRATE 34 g
FIBER 5 g
PROTEIN 22 g
EXCHANGES 1 Vegetable, 2 Starch, 2½ Lean Meat, ½ Fat

- 8 ounces beef sirloin steak
- 4 teaspoons canola oil
- 2 teaspoons finely chopped fresh ginger
- 3 cups packaged cut-up fresh stir-fry vegetables
- 1 cup frozen shelled sweet soybeans (edamame)
- 3 tablespoons hoisin sauce
- 2 tablespoons rice vinegar
- 1 teaspoon red chili paste
- 1 8.8-ounce pouch cooked whole grain brown rice

1 If desired, partially freeze beef for easier slicing. Trim fat from beef. Thinly slice beef across the grain into very thin bite-size strips; set aside.

2 In a nonstick wok or skillet heat 2 teaspoons of the oil over medium-high heat. Cook and stir ginger for 15 seconds. Add vegetables. Cook and stir about 4 minutes or until crisp-tender. Remove vegetables from wok.

3 Add the remaining 2 teaspoons oil to wok. Cook and stir beef and edamame about 2 minutes or until beef is browned. Return vegetables to wok. In a small bowl combine hoisin, vinegar, and chili paste. Add to beef and vegetables; toss to coat. Heat through.

4 Meanwhile, heat rice according to package directions. Serve beef and vegetables over rice.

Ginger Beef Stir-Fry

START TO FINISH 30 minutes
MAKES 4 servings

NUTRITION FACTS per serving

CALORIES 274
TOTAL FAT 7 g (1 g sat. fat)
CHOLESTEROL 32 mg
SODIUM 552 mg
CARBOHYDRATE 34 g
FIBER 5 g
PROTEIN 20 g
EXCHANGES 1½ Vegetable, 1½ Starch, 2 Lean Meat, 1 Fat

- 8 ounces beef top round steak
- ½ cup reduced-sodium beef broth
- 3 tablespoons reduced-sodium soy sauce
- 2½ teaspoons cornstarch
- 2 to 3 teaspoons grated fresh ginger
- Nonstick cooking spray
- 1½ cups sliced fresh mushrooms
- ½ cup thinly bias-sliced carrot (1 medium)
- 3 cups small broccoli florets or 1 pound fresh asparagus spears, trimmed and cut into 2-inch-long pieces
- 1 small red sweet pepper, seeded and cut into ¼-inch-wide strips (1 cup)
- 1 tablespoon vegetable oil
- 2 green onions, bias-sliced into 2-inch lengths (¼ cup)
- 2 cups hot cooked brown rice

1 If desired, partially freeze beef for easier slicing. Trim fat from beef. Thinly slice beef across the grain into bite-size strips; set aside. For sauce, in a small bowl stir together beef broth, soy sauce, cornstarch, and ginger; set aside.

2 Lightly coat an unheated wok or large nonstick skillet with cooking spray. Preheat over medium-high heat. Add mushrooms and carrot; stir-fry for 2 minutes. Add broccoli and sweet pepper; stir-fry about 2 minutes more or until vegetables are crisp-tender. Remove vegetables from wok.

3 Carefully add oil to wok. Add beef; stir-fry for 2 to 3 minutes or until desired doneness. Push beef from center of wok. Stir sauce. Add sauce to center of wok. Cook and stir until thickened and bubbly.

4 Return vegetables to the wok. Add green onions. Stir ingredients together to coat with sauce; heat through. Serve immediately over hot cooked rice.

Spiced Pot Roast with Root Vegetables

PREP 30 minutes
COOK 10 to 12 hours (low) or 5 to 6 hours (high)
MAKES 10 servings

- 1 3-pound boneless beef chuck pot roast
- 3½ teaspoons garam masala
- ½ teaspoon salt
- 1 tablespoon vegetable oil
- 1 cup beef broth
- ¼ cup dry red wine or beef broth
- 30 small carrots with tops (about 12 ounces) or 2 cups packaged peeled baby carrots
- 1 pound round red potatoes, quartered
- 2 medium parsnips, peeled and cut into ½-inch slices
- 1 medium rutabaga, peeled and cut into 1-inch pieces
- 1 red onion, cut into wedges
- 2 tablespoons cornstarch
- 2 tablespoons cold water
- 1 teaspoon garam masala
- 1 cup plain low-fat yogurt
- Salt and black pepper

1 Trim fat from roast. Combine 2½ teaspoons of the garam masala and the ½ teaspoon salt; rub mixture onto the meat. Place meat in a 5- to 6-quart slow cooker. Pour over broth, and wine. Top with carrots, potatoes, parsnips, rutabaga, and onion. Cover and cook on low-heat setting for 10 to 12 hours or on high-heat setting for 5 to 6 hours.

2 Transfer meat and vegetables to a serving platter; keep warm. For sauce, skim and discard fat from cooking liquid. Strain cooking liquid. Measure 1½ cups of the cooking liquid; pour into a medium saucepan. Discard remaining liquid. In a small bowl stir together cornstarch, the cold water, and the remaining 1 teaspoon garam masala. Add cornstarch mixture to liquid in saucepan. Cook and stir over medium heat until thickened and bubbly. Cook and stir for 2 minutes more. Stir in yogurt; heat through but do not boil. Season with salt and pepper. Serve sauce with meat and vegetables.

NUTRITION FACTS per serving

CALORIES 274
TOTAL FAT 7 g (2 g sat. fat)
CHOLESTEROL 82 mg
SODIUM 381 mg
CARBOHYDRATE 18 g
FIBER 3 g
PROTEIN 32 g
EXCHANGES ½ Vegetable, ½ Starch, ½ Other Carbo., 4 Lean Meat, 1 Fat

Cowboy Beef

PREP 10 minutes
COOK 10 to 12 hours (low) or 5 to 6 hours (high)
MAKES 8 servings

NUTRITION FACTS per serving

CALORIES 223
TOTAL FAT 5 g (2 g sat. fat)
CHOLESTEROL 50 mg
SODIUM 473 mg
CARBOHYDRATE 14 g
FIBER 4 g
PROTEIN 29 g
EXCHANGES 1 Starch, 3½ Lean Meat

- 1 2- to 2½-pound boneless beef chuck pot roast
- 1 15-ounce can chili beans in chili gravy, undrained
- 1 11-ounce can whole kernel corn with sweet peppers, drained
- 1 10-ounce can diced tomatoes and green chiles, undrained
- 1 to 2 teaspoons finely chopped canned chipotle peppers in adobo sauce (see note, page 142)

1 Trim fat from meat. If necessary, cut meat to fit into a 3½- or 4-quart slow cooker. Place meat in cooker. In a medium bowl stir together the undrained beans, drained corn, undrained tomatoes and green chiles, and the chipotle peppers. Pour bean mixture over meat in cooker.

2 Cover and cook on low-heat setting for 10 to 12 hours or on high-heat setting for 5 to 6 hours.

3 Transfer meat to a cutting board. Pull meat into pieces and arrange in a shallow serving bowl. Using a slotted spoon, spoon bean mixture into bowl with meat. Drizzle some of the cooking liquid over meat and bean mixture to moisten.

Herb-Garlic Beef Roast

START TO FINISH 20 minutes
MAKES 4 servings

- 1 17-ounce package refrigerated cooked beef roast au jus
- 1 pound small round red potatoes
- 3 medium carrots
- 1 tablespoon canola oil
- Freshly ground black pepper
- 3 tablespoons chopped fresh Italian (flat-leaf) parsley
- 3 to 6 cloves garlic, minced
- 1 tablespoon finely shredded lemon peel

1 In a large skillet reheat beef roast, covered, on medium heat for 10 minutes. Uncover and simmer about 5 minutes more or until juices are slightly reduced.

2 Meanwhile, quarter potatoes. Peel and diagonally slice carrots into ¾-inch pieces. Place vegetables in a microwave-safe dish. Drizzle with oil and sprinkle with pepper; toss to coat. Cover with lid or vented plastic wrap. Microwave on high about 10 minutes or until tender.

3 For herb-garlic mixture, in a small bowl combine parsley, garlic, and lemon peel. To serve, stir vegetables into skillet with beef and juices. Divide among serving dishes. Sprinkle with herb-garlic mixture.

NUTRITION FACTS per serving

CALORIES 311
TOTAL FAT 12 g (5 g sat. fat)
CHOLESTEROL 64 mg
SODIUM 465 mg
CARBOHYDRATE 28 g
FIBER 4 g
PROTEIN 25 g
EXCHANGES ½ Vegetable, 1½ Starch, 3 Lean Meat, 1 Fat

Indian-Style Beef Patties with Cucumber-Yogurt Sauce

PREP 15 minutes **GRILL** 14 minutes
MAKES 4 servings

NUTRITION FACTS per serving

CALORIES 241
TOTAL FAT 12 g (5 g sat. fat)
CHOLESTEROL 75 mg
SODIUM 377 mg
CARBOHYDRATE 8 g
FIBER 1 g
PROTEIN 24 g
EXCHANGES ½ Milk, ½ Vegetable, 2½ Medium-Fat Meat

- 1 cup plain low-fat yogurt
- ⅔ cup chopped, seeded cucumber
- ½ cup finely chopped onion (1 medium)
- 1 jalapeño, seeded and finely chopped*
- 2 tablespoons snipped fresh mint or 1 teaspoon dried mint, crushed
- 1 teaspoon ground cumin
- 2 cloves garlic, minced, or ½ teaspoon garlic powder
- ½ teaspoon salt
- 1 pound lean ground beef
- Indian flatbread (optional)

1. For sauce, in a small bowl stir together yogurt and cucumber. Cover and chill.

2. In a medium bowl combine onion, jalapeño, mint, cumin, garlic, and salt. Add ground meat; mix well. Form meat mixture into four ¾-inch-thick patties.

3. For a charcoal grill, place patties on the rack of an uncovered grill directly over medium coals. Grill for 14 to 18 minutes or until patties are done (160°F),** turning once halfway through grilling. (For a gas grill, preheat grill. Place patties on grill rack over heat. Cover and grill as above.) If desired, serve patties on flatbread. Spoon sauce over patties.

***Note:** Because chile peppers contain volatile oils that can burn your skin and eyes, avoid direct contact with them as much as possible. When working with chile peppers, wear plastic or rubber gloves. If your bare hands do touch the peppers, wash your hands and fingernails well with soap and warm water.

****Note:** The internal color of a burger is not a reliable doneness indicator. A beef or pork patty cooked to 160°F is safe, regardless of color. To measure the doneness of a patty, insert an instant-read thermometer 2 to 3 inches through the side of a patty.

Asian Burgers

PREP 25 minutes **GRILL** 10 minutes
MAKES 6 burgers

NUTRITION FACTS per burger

CALORIES 351
TOTAL FAT 11 g (4 g sat. fat)
CHOLESTEROL 72 mg
SODIUM 416 mg
CARBOHYDRATE 34 g
FIBER 3 g
PROTEIN 28 g
EXCHANGES ½ Fruit, 1½ Starch, 3½ Lean Meat, 1 Fat

- 3 tablespoons bottled hoisin sauce
- 1 tablespoon finely chopped onion
- 1 teaspoon five-spice powder
- ¼ teaspoon crushed red pepper
- 1 pound lean ground beef
- 8 ounces lean ground pork
- 6 ½- to ¾-inch slices peeled and cored fresh or canned pineapple
- 6 ½-inch slices red onion
- 6 whole wheat hamburger buns, split and toasted
- ½ cup fresh snow pea pods, strings and tips removed

1 In a very large bowl combine hoisin sauce, chopped onion, five-spice powder, and crushed red pepper. Add beef and pork; mix well. Shape meat mixture into six ½-inch-thick patties.

2 For a charcoal grill, place patties, pineapple, and red onion slices on the grill rack directly over medium coals. Grill patties, uncovered, for 10 to 13 minutes or until patties are done (160°F),** turning once. Grill pineapple and onion for 4 to 6 minutes or until lightly browned, turning once. (For a gas grill, preheat grill. Reduce heat to medium. Place patties, pineapple, and red onion on grill rack over heat. Cover and grill as above.)

3 Place pineapple slices on bun bottoms. Top with patties, red onion slices, pea pods, and bun tops.

Balsamic-Glazed Lamb Chops

PREP 15 minutes **MARINATE** 4 to 24 hours
COOK 15 minutes **GRILL** 12 minutes
MAKES 4 servings

NUTRITION FACTS per serving

CALORIES 161
TOTAL FAT 6 g (2 g sat. fat)
CHOLESTEROL 48 mg
SODIUM 334 mg
CARBOHYDRATE 10 g
FIBER 0 g
PROTEIN 15 g
EXCHANGES ½ Other Carbo., 2½ Lean Meat

- 8 lamb rib chops, cut 1 inch thick (1½ pounds total)
- ¼ teaspoon salt
- ¼ teaspoon black pepper
- ½ cup orange juice
- ¼ cup balsamic vinegar
- 1 tablespoon honey
- 1 tablespoon reduced-sodium soy sauce

1 Trim fat from chops. Sprinkle chops with salt and pepper. Place chops in a resealable plastic bag set in a shallow dish. For marinade, in a small bowl stir together orange juice, balsamic vinegar, honey, and soy sauce; pour over chops. Seal bag; turn to coat chops. Marinate in the refrigerator for 4 to 24 hours, turning bag occasionally.

2 Drain lamb, reserving marinade. For glaze, pour marinade into a small heavy saucepan. Bring to boiling; reduce heat. Boil gently, uncovered, about 15 minutes or until reduced to about ⅓ cup; set aside.

3 For a charcoal grill, place chops on the rack of an uncovered grill directly over medium coals. Grill to desired doneness, turning and brushing with glaze halfway through grilling. Allow 12 to 14 minutes for medium rare (145°F) or 15 to 17 minutes for medium (160°F). (For a gas grill, preheat grill. Reduce heat to medium. Place chops on grill rack over heat. Cover and grill as above.) Discard any remaining glaze.

Garlic-Chili-Rubbed Lamb

PREP 15 minutes **MARINATE** 4 to 24 hours
GRILL 16 minutes **MAKES** 4 servings

NUTRITION FACTS per serving

CALORIES 199
TOTAL FAT 12 g (4 g sat. fat)
CHOLESTEROL 64 mg
SODIUM 381 mg
CARBOHYDRATE 3 g
FIBER 1 g
PROTEIN 20 g
EXCHANGES 3 Medium-Fat Meat

- 4 large cloves garlic, minced
- ½ teaspoon salt
- 1 tablespoon chili powder
- 1 teaspoon ground cumin
- ½ teaspoon sugar
- ½ teaspoon black pepper
- ½ teaspoon dried thyme, crushed
- ¼ teaspoon ground cinnamon
- ¼ teaspoon ground allspice
- 2 to 3 teaspoons olive oil
- 8 lamb rib or loin chops, cut 1 inch thick
- Grilled tomatoes (optional)

1 On a cutting board, using the flat side of a chef's knife, smear together the garlic and salt to form a paste. Transfer garlic paste to a small bowl. Stir in chili powder, cumin, sugar, pepper, thyme, cinnamon, and allspice. Stir in enough olive oil to make a paste. Rub lamb chops all over with the paste. Cover and chill lamb for 4 to 24 hours to absorb flavors.

2 For a charcoal grill, arrange medium-hot coals around a drip pan. Test for medium heat above the pan. Place chops on grill rack over drip pan. Cover and grill to desired doneness, turning once halfway through grilling. Allow 16 to 18 minutes for medium rare (145°F) or 18 to 20 for medium (160°F). (For a gas grill, preheat grill. Reduce heat to medium. Adjust for indirect cooking. Place chops on grill rack over the burner that is turned off. Grill as above.) If desired, serve with grilled tomatoes.

Cherry-Kissed Tacos with Feta Cheese Salsa

START TO FINISH 25 minutes **MAKES** 12 tacos

NUTRITION FACTS per taco

CALORIES 207
TOTAL FAT 9 g (3 g sat. fat)
CHOLESTEROL 26 mg
SODIUM 274 mg
CARBOHYDRATE 21 g
FIBER 1 g
PROTEIN 8 g
EXCHANGES 1 Starch, ½ Other Carbo., 1 Medium-Fat Meat, ½ Fat

- 1 pound lean ground lamb or pork
- 1 cup finely chopped onion (1 large)
- 1 teaspoon curry powder
- ½ cup mango chutney
- ½ cup dried tart red cherries, chopped
- 1 tablespoon lemon juice
- ¼ teaspoon salt
- ¼ teaspoon black pepper
- 12 taco shells, warmed
- 1 recipe Feta Cheese Salsa

1 In a large skillet cook ground meat and onion over medium-high heat until meat is browned and onion is tender. Drain off fat. Add curry powder; cook and stir for 1 minute.

2 Cut up any large pieces of chutney. Stir chutney, cherries, lemon juice, salt, and pepper into meat mixture. Bring to boiling; reduce heat. Simmer, covered, for 5 minutes.

3 Spoon meat mixture into taco shells. Top with Feta Cheese Salsa.

Feta Cheese Salsa: In a medium bowl combine 1 medium tomato, seeded and finely chopped; ⅓ cup finely chopped cucumber; ¼ cup crumbled reduced-fat feta cheese; ¼ cup finely chopped red onion; ¼ cup finely chopped green sweet pepper; 1 tablespoon olive oil; 1 tablespoon lemon juice; ⅛ teaspoon salt; and ⅛ teaspoon black pepper. Stir until combined. Serve with a slotted spoon. Makes about 1½ cups.

Chapter 8

Pork

On the opener: Pork Chops Primavera *(see recipe, page 158)*

CHOPS

ROAST

TENDERLOIN

Herb-Scented Tuscan Pork Loin

PREP 20 minutes **CHILL** 8 to 24 hours
ROAST 2 hours **STAND** 15 minutes
OVEN 325°F **MAKES** 12 to 15 servings

- 3 tablespoons snipped fresh rosemary
- 8 cloves garlic, minced
- 4 teaspoons finely shredded lemon peel
- 1 teaspoon kosher salt
- 1 4½- to 5-pound boneless pork top loin roast (double loin, tied)
- 4 ounces thinly sliced pancetta

1 In a small bowl combine rosemary, garlic, lemon peel, and salt. Set aside.

2 Untie meat; trim fat from meat. Spread rosemary mixture on top of 1 loin. Place pancetta on top of second loin. Reassemble meat, placing the pancetta-topped loin on top and the rosemary mixture in the center. Retie with 100%-cotton kitchen string. Wrap meat tightly in plastic wrap and chill for 8 to 24 hours.

3 Preheat oven to 325°F. Place meat on a rack in a shallow roasting pan. Insert an oven-going meat thermometer into center of meat. Roast for 2 to 2½ hours or until meat thermometer registers 150°F. Cover meat with foil and let stand for 15 minutes. The temperature of the meat after standing should be 160°F.

NUTRITION FACTS per serving

CALORIES 286
TOTAL FAT 12 g (4 g sat. fat)
CHOLESTEROL 99 mg
SODIUM 396 mg
CARBOHYDRATE 1 g
FIBER 0 g
PROTEIN 39 g
EXCHANGES 5½ Lean Meat, 1 Fat

Roasted Pork with Apples

PREP 15 minutes **ROAST** 20 minutes
STAND 10 minutes **OVEN** 425°F
MAKES 4 servings

NUTRITION FACTS per serving

CALORIES 239
TOTAL FAT 6 g (1 g sat. fat)
CHOLESTEROL 74 mg
SODIUM 209 mg
CARBOHYDRATE 22 g
FIBER 3 g
PROTEIN 24 g
EXCHANGES 1½ Fruit, 3½ Lean Meat

- 1 teaspoon snipped fresh sage or ½ teaspoon dried sage, crushed
- ¼ teaspoon salt
- ¼ teaspoon coarsely ground black pepper
- 1 1-pound pork tenderloin
- 1 tablespoon canola oil
- 1 medium red onion, cut into thin wedges
- 3 medium cooking apples (such as Granny Smith or Jonathan) (1 pound), cored and cut into ½-inch-thick wedges
- ⅔ cup apple juice or apple cider
- Fresh sage leaves (optional)

1 Preheat oven to 425°F. In a small bowl combine the snipped sage, salt, and pepper; rub on all sides of tenderloin. In a large skillet heat oil over medium heat. Brown tenderloin in hot oil, turning to brown all sides.

2 Transfer pork to a shallow roasting pan. Add onion to pan around pork. Roast, uncovered, for 10 minutes. Stir in apples; roast for 10 to 15 minutes more or until an instant-read thermometer inserted into the thickest part of the tenderloin registers 155°F.

3 Transfer pork and apple mixture to a serving platter; cover with foil. Let stand for 10 minutes. The temperature of the meat after standing should be 160°F.

4 Meanwhile, in a small saucepan bring apple juice to boiling; simmer gently, uncovered, for 8 to 10 minutes or until reduced to ¼ to ⅓ cup. Drizzle over meat and apple mixture. If desired, garnish with additional sage.

Cider-Braised Pork Roast and Apples

PREP 30 minutes
COOK 8 to 10 hours (low) or 4 to 5 hours (high)
MAKES 6 servings plus leftovers

- 1 3-pound boneless pork top loin roast
- ½ teaspoon salt
- ½ teaspoon dried thyme, crushed
- ½ teaspoon dried sage, crushed
- ¼ teaspoon black pepper
- 2 tablespoons vegetable oil
- 4 red, yellow, and/or green apples, cored and each cut into 6 wedges
- ⅓ cup chopped shallots
- 6 cloves garlic, minced, or 1 tablespoon bottled minced garlic
- 3 tablespoons quick-cooking tapioca
- ¾ cup reduced-sodium chicken broth
- ¾ cup apple cider or juice

1 Trim fat from meat. In a small bowl stir together salt, thyme, sage, and pepper. Sprinkle spice mixture on meat; rub in with your fingers. In a large skillet heat oil over medium heat. Brown meat on all sides in hot oil.

2 In a 6- to 7-quart slow cooker combine apples, shallots, and garlic; sprinkle with tapioca. Place meat on apple mixture. Pour chicken broth and apple cider over meat.

3 Cover and cook on low-heat setting for 8 to 10 hours or high-heat setting for 4 to 5 hours.

4 Slice pork. Spoon some of the cooking liquid over pork and apples to serve.

Note: To store leftover meat, place meat in an airtight container. Chill, covered, for up to 3 days or freeze up to 3 months. Thaw in refrigerator overnight before reheating and serving.

NUTRITION FACTS per serving

CALORIES 285
TOTAL FAT 8 g (2 g sat. fat)
CHOLESTEROL 70 mg
SODIUM 258 mg
CARBOHYDRATE 23 g
FIBER 2 g
PROTEIN 29 g
EXCHANGES 1½ Fruit, 4 Lean Meat, ½ Fat

Pork Medallions with Lemon-Pecan Spinach

START TO FINISH 20 minutes
MAKES 4 servings

NUTRITION FACTS per serving

CALORIES 213
TOTAL FAT 10 g (2 g sat. fat)
CHOLESTEROL 73 mg
SODIUM 318 mg
CARBOHYDRATE 5 g
FIBER 3 g
PROTEIN 27 g
EXCHANGES 1 Vegetable, 3½ Lean Meat, ½ Fat

- 1 pound pork tenderloin, cut crosswise into 8 slices
- ¼ teaspoon salt
- ¼ teaspoon coarsely ground black pepper
- 1 tablespoon canola oil
- 2 tablespoons lemon juice
- ⅛ teaspoon bottled hot pepper sauce
- 1 10-ounce package frozen chopped spinach, thawed and well drained
- ¼ cup sliced green onions (2)
- 2 tablespoons chopped pecans
- 1 tablespoon snipped fresh parsley
- ⅛ teaspoon salt
- Lemon slices, halved (optional)

1 If necessary, press each pork tenderloin slice to 1-inch thickness. Sprinkle pork lightly with the ¼ teaspoon salt and the pepper. In a large skillet heat oil over medium-high heat. Add pork slices; cook for 6 to 8 minutes or until slightly pink in the center (160°F), turning once halfway through cooking. Remove pork slices from skillet, reserving drippings in the skillet. Cover pork and keep warm.

2 Stir lemon juice and hot pepper sauce into reserved drippings in skillet. Stir in spinach, green onions, pecans, parsley, and the ⅛ teaspoon salt; cook over low heat until spinach mixture is heated through. Place spinach mixture on a serving platter; arrange pork slices on top. If desired, garnish with lemon slices.

Thai Pork Stir-Fry

START TO FINISH 30 minutes
MAKES 6 servings

- 2 tablespoons olive oil
- 1 tablespoon reduced-sodium soy sauce
- ½ teaspoon garlic powder
- ½ teaspoon finely chopped fresh ginger or ¼ teaspoon ground ginger
- ½ teaspoon black pepper
- ½ teaspoon ground cardamom
- ½ teaspoon chili powder
- 1½ pounds pork loin, cut into bite-size strips
- 2 cups broccoli florets
- 1 cup cauliflower florets
- 1 cup thinly sliced carrots (2 medium)
- 2 tablespoons white vinegar
- 1 tablespoon curry powder
- 2 cups hot cooked brown rice

1 In a very large skillet combine oil, soy sauce, garlic powder, ginger, pepper, cardamom, and chili powder. Add half the pork; stir-fry pork over medium-high heat for 3 minutes. Using a slotted spoon, remove pork from skillet. Stir-fry with the remaining pork. Return all of the pork to the skillet.

2 Add broccoli, cauliflower, carrots, vinegar, and curry powder to pork mixture in skillet. Bring to boiling; reduce heat. Simmer, covered, for 3 to 5 minutes or until vegetables are crisp-tender, stirring occasionally. Serve pork and vegetables over brown rice.

NUTRITION FACTS per serving

CALORIES 301
TOTAL FAT 11 g (3 g sat. fat)
CHOLESTEROL 71 mg
SODIUM 206 mg
CARBOHYDRATE 21 g
FIBER 3 g
PROTEIN 28 g
EXCHANGES 1 Vegetable, 1 Starch, 3 Lean Meat, 1 Fat

Curried Pork and Rice

PREP 20 minutes **BAKE** 45 minutes
STAND 5 minutes **OVEN** 350°F
MAKES 4 servings

NUTRITION FACTS per serving

CALORIES 275
TOTAL FAT 7 g (2 g sat. fat)
CHOLESTEROL 56 mg
SODIUM 289 mg
CARBOHYDRATE 27 g
FIBER 3 g
PROTEIN 25 g
EXCHANGES ½ Milk, 1½ Starch, 2½ Lean Meat

- 1 teaspoon canola oil
- 12 ounces boneless pork loin, cut into thin bite-size strips
- 2 cups fat-free milk
- 2 tablespoons all-purpose flour
- 1½ teaspoons curry powder
- ¼ teaspoon salt
- ¾ cup instant brown rice
- 1 medium green apple (such as Granny Smith), cored and chopped
- ½ cup coarsely shredded carrot (1 medium)
- 3 green onions, bias-sliced
- 2 tablespoons chopped peanuts
- 2 tablespoons snipped fresh cilantro

1. Preheat oven to 350°F. In a large nonstick skillet heat oil over medium heat. Add pork; cook for 3 to 5 minutes or until no longer pink. Drain off fat. Set aside.

2. In a screw-top jar combine ½ cup of the milk, the flour, curry powder, and salt; cover and shake until well mixed. Transfer to a medium saucepan; add remaining milk. Cook and stir over medium heat until thickened and bubbly. Stir in pork, uncooked rice, apple, carrot, and green onions. Transfer to a 1½-quart casserole. Place casserole on a baking sheet.

3. Bake, covered, about 45 minutes or until rice is tender and most of the liquid is absorbed. Let stand, covered, on a wire rack for 5 minutes. Sprinkle with peanuts and cilantro before serving.

Pork Chops with Red Cabbage and Pears

START TO FINISH 30 minutes
MAKES 6 servings

NUTRITION FACTS per serving

CALORIES 239
TOTAL FAT 4 g (1 g sat. fat)
CHOLESTEROL 70 mg
SODIUM 323 mg
CARBOHYDRATE 20 g
FIBER 4 g
PROTEIN 30 g
EXCHANGES 1 Vegetable, ½ Fruit, ½ Other Carbo., 4 Lean Meat

- ¼ cup cider vinegar
- 2 tablespoons packed brown sugar
- ½ teaspoon dried sage, crushed
- 6 small pork loin chops, cut ½ inch thick (about 2 pounds total)
- ½ teaspoon dried thyme, crushed
- ¼ teaspoon salt
- ⅛ teaspoon black pepper
- 2 teaspoons canola oil
- 6 cups coarsely shredded red cabbage
- 1 cup sliced onion
- 2 medium pears, cored and sliced
- Snipped fresh sage and/or thyme (optional)

1. In a small bowl combine cider vinegar, brown sugar, and ¼ teaspoon of the sage. Reserve 1 tablespoon of the mixture; set aside both portions of vinegar mixture.

2. Trim fat from pork chops. Sprinkle pork with dried thyme, salt, the remaining ¼ teaspoon sage, and the pepper. In a very large skillet heat oil over medium-high heat. Add pork chops. Cook for 6 to 8 minutes or until juices run clear (160°F), turning once halfway through cooking and brushing with the 1 tablespoon vinegar mixture for the last 1 minute of cooking time. Remove pork chops from skillet; cover and keep warm.

3. Add red cabbage and onion to skillet. Cook and stir over medium-high heat for 6 minutes. Add the remaining vinegar mixture and the pears to skillet. Bring to boiling; reduce heat. Simmer, covered, for 5 minutes. Top with pork chops; heat through. If desired, sprinkle chops with additional fresh sage and/or thyme.

Pork Chops Pizziola

PREP 20 minutes **COOK** 36 minutes
MAKES 4 servings

NUTRITION FACTS per serving

CALORIES 210
TOTAL FAT 10 g (3 g sat. fat)
CHOLESTEROL 58 mg
SODIUM 130 mg
CARBOHYDRATE 7 g
FIBER 2 g
PROTEIN 19 g
EXCHANGES 1 Vegetable, 2½ Lean Meat, 1 Fat

- 4 pork loin rib chops, cut ½ inch thick (about 1½ pounds total)
- 1 tablespoon canola oil
- 2 cloves garlic, minced
- 1 tablespoon snipped fresh oregano or 1 teaspoon dried oregano, crushed
- 1 14.5-ounce can no-salt-added diced tomatoes, undrained
- ¼ cup dry red wine or low-sodium tomato juice
- 1 tablespoon tomato paste

1 Trim fat from pork chops. In a large skillet heat oil over medium-high heat. Cook the chops in hot oil for 4 to 6 minutes or until evenly browned, turning once. Remove chops from skillet; set aside.

2 For sauce, add garlic and dried oregano (if using) to skillet; cook and stir for 15 seconds. Add undrained tomatoes, red wine, and tomato paste; stir to combine. Bring to boiling; reduce heat.

3 Return pork chops to skillet. Simmer, covered, for 30 minutes. Transfer chops to a serving dish. Skim any fat from sauce. Stir fresh oregano (if using) into sauce. If desired, cook sauce, uncovered, for 1 to 2 minutes more or until desired consistency, stirring occasionally. Serve sauce over chops.

Mushroom-Sauced Pork Chops

PREP 20 minutes
COOK 8 to 9 hours (low) or 4 to 4½ hours (high)
MAKES 4 servings

NUTRITION FACTS per serving

CALORIES 314
TOTAL FAT 12 g (4 g sat. fat)
CHOLESTEROL 74 mg
SODIUM 356 mg
CARBOHYDRATE 17 g
FIBER 1 g
PROTEIN 30 g
EXCHANGES ½ Vegetable, 1 Other Carbo., 4 Lean Meat, 2 Fat

- 4 pork loin chops, cut ¾ inch thick (about 2 pounds)
- 1 tablespoon vegetable oil
- 1 small onion, thinly sliced
- 2 tablespoons quick-cooking tapioca
- 1 10.75-ounce can reduced-fat and reduced-sodium condensed cream of mushroom soup
- ½ cup apple juice or apple cider
- 1½ teaspoons Worcestershire sauce
- 2 teaspoons snipped fresh thyme or ¾ teaspoon dried thyme, crushed
- ¼ teaspoon garlic powder
- 1½ cups sliced fresh mushrooms
- Fresh thyme sprigs (optional)

1 Trim fat from chops. In a large skillet heat oil over medium heat. Add chops; cook until browned, turning to brown evenly. Drain off fat. Place onion in a 3½- or 4-quart slow cooker. Add chops. Using a mortar and pestle, crush tapioca. In a medium bowl combine tapioca, mushroom soup, apple juice, Worcestershire sauce, snipped or dried thyme, and garlic powder; stir in mushrooms. Pour over chops in slow cooker.

2 Cover and cook on low-heat setting for 8 to 9 hours or on high-heat setting for 4 to 4½ hours. If desired, garnish with thyme sprigs.

Note: If you prefer to use a 5- to 6-quart slow cooker, use 6 pork loin chops. Leave remaining ingredient amounts the same and prepare as above. Makes 6 servings.

Pork Chops Primavera

START TO FINISH 20 minutes
MAKES 4 servings

NUTRITION FACTS per serving

CALORIES 307
TOTAL FAT 7 g (3 g sat. fat)
CHOLESTEROL 83 mg
SODIUM 309 mg
CARBOHYDRATE 26 g
FIBER 4 g
PROTEIN 33 g
EXCHANGES 1 Vegetable, 1½ Other Carbo., 4 Lean Meat

- 2 slices turkey bacon, cut into 1-inch pieces
- 12 ounces trimmed fresh young green beans
- 2 tablespoons water
- 4 bone-in pork chops, cut ½ inch thick
- 1 tablespoon reduced-sodium soy sauce
- 2 teaspoons canola oil
- 3 tablespoons apple butter
- 3 tablespoons water
- 1 cup red and/or yellow cherry and/or grape tomatoes

1 In a very large nonstick skillet cook bacon according to package directions. Remove from skillet; set aside.

2 Meanwhile, in a 2-quart microwave-safe dish combine green beans and the 2 tablespoons water. Cover and cook on high for 4 minutes; stir once. Drain; set aside.

3 Brush chops with soy sauce. In the same skillet heat oil over medium heat. Add chops to skillet; cook until brown on both sides. Add apple butter and the 3 tablespoons water; reduce heat. Simmer, covered, for 5 minutes. Add green beans, tomatoes, and bacon; cook, uncovered, for 3 to 5 minutes or until heated through.

Pork Diane

START TO FINISH 25 minutes
MAKES 4 servings

- 1 tablespoon water
- 1 tablespoon Worcestershire-style marinade for chicken
- 1 teaspoon lemon juice
- 1 teaspoon Dijon mustard
- 4 boneless pork top loin chops, cut ¾ to 1 inch thick (about 12 ounces total)
- ½ to 1 teaspoon lemon-pepper seasoning
- 1 tablespoon butter or margarine
- 1 tablespoon snipped fresh chives, parsley, or oregano

1 For sauce, in a small bowl stir together the water, Worcestershire-style marinade for chicken, lemon juice, and mustard; set aside.

2 Trim fat from chops. Sprinkle both sides of chops with lemon-pepper seasoning. In a large skillet melt butter over medium heat. Add chops; cook for 8 to 12 minutes or until juices run clear (160°F), turning once halfway through cooking time. Remove from heat. Transfer chops to a serving platter; cover and keep warm.

3 Pour sauce into skillet; stir to scrape up any crusty browned bits from bottom of skillet, add chives. Pour sauce over chops.

NUTRITION FACTS per serving

CALORIES 131
TOTAL FAT 5 g (2 g sat. fat)
CHOLESTEROL 55 mg
SODIUM 377 mg
CARBOHYDRATE 1 g
FIBER 0 g
PROTEIN 19 g
EXCHANGES 3 Lean Meat, ½ Fat

Chops and Pineapple with Chili Slaw

START TO FINISH 20 minutes
MAKES 4 servings

NUTRITION FACTS per serving

CALORIES 357
TOTAL FAT 12 g (3 g sat. fat)
CHOLESTEROL 112 mg
SODIUM 392 mg
CARBOHYDRATE 20 g
FIBER 4 g
PROTEIN 40 g
EXCHANGES 1½ Vegetable, 1 Fruit, 5 Lean Meat, ½ Fat

- 8 boneless top loin pork chops, cut ½ inch thick (about 1½ pounds total)
- Salt
- 1½ teaspoons chili powder
- ½ of a cored fresh pineapple, sliced
- 3 tablespoons cider vinegar
- 2 tablespoons orange juice
- 2 tablespoons olive oil
- 1 tablespoon sugar
- ⅓ of a small green cabbage, cored and sliced (about 5 cups)
- ½ of a red onion, thinly sliced
- 1 small red sweet pepper, cut into thin strips
- Black pepper

1 Sprinkle chops with salt and 1 teaspoon of the chili powder. For a charcoal grill, cook chops and pineapple on an uncovered grill directly over medium coals for 6 to 8 minutes or until juices run clear (160°F), turning once halfway through grilling. (For gas grill, preheat grill; reduce to medium. Place chops and pineapple on grill rack over heat. Cover and grill as above.)

2 Meanwhile, for chili slaw, in a large bowl whisk together vinegar, orange juice, oil, sugar, and the remaining ½ teaspoon chili powder. Add cabbage, onion, and sweet pepper; toss. Season with salt and black pepper. Serve chops with pineapple and slaw.

Mediterranean Pork Chops

PREP 10 minutes **ROAST** 35 minutes
OVEN 425°F/350°F **MAKES** 4 servings

- 4 boneless or bone-in pork loin chops, cut ½ inch thick (1 to 1½ pounds total)
- ¼ teaspoon salt
- ¼ teaspoon freshly ground black pepper
- 1 tablespoon finely snipped fresh rosemary or 1 teaspoon dried rosemary, crushed
- 3 cloves garlic, minced

1. Preheat oven to 425°F. Sprinkle both sides of chops with salt and pepper; set aside.

2. In a small bowl combine rosemary and garlic. Sprinkle rosemary mixture evenly on both sides of chops; rub in with your fingers.

3. Place chops on a rack in a shallow roasting pan. Roast for 10 minutes. Reduce oven temperature to 350°F. Roast about 25 minutes more or until juices run clear (160°F).

NUTRITION FACTS per serving

CALORIES 161
TOTAL FAT 5 g (2 g sat. fat)
CHOLESTEROL 62 mg
SODIUM 192 mg
CARBOHYDRATE 1 g
FIBER 0 g
PROTEIN 25 g
EXCHANGES 3½ Lean Meat, 1 Fat

Orange and Rosemary Pork Chops

PREP 15 minutes **MARINATE** 4 to 24 hours
GRILL 20 minutes **MAKES** 4 servings

NUTRITION FACTS per serving

CALORIES 178
TOTAL FAT 6 g (2 g sat. fat)
CHOLESTEROL 62 mg
SODIUM 86 mg
CARBOHYDRATE 3 g
FIBER 0 g
PROTEIN 25 g
EXCHANGES 3½ Lean Meat, ½ Fat

- 4 boneless pork loin chops, cut 1 inch thick (1 to 1¼ pounds total)
- 2 teaspoons finely shredded orange peel
- ½ cup orange juice
- 2 tablespoons snipped fresh rosemary or 2 teaspoons dried rosemary, crushed
- 2 tablespoons Worcestershire-style marinade for chicken
- 1 tablespoon olive oil
- 1 tablespoon mild-flavor molasses or maple syrup
- ⅛ teaspoon black pepper
- 2 cups orange, apple, or peach wood chips or 6 orange, apple, or peach wood chunks
- Fresh rosemary sprigs (optional)

1 Trim fat from chops. Place chops in a large resealable plastic bag set in a shallow dish. For marinade, in a small bowl combine orange peel, orange juice, the snipped or dried rosemary, Worcestershire-style marinade, olive oil, molasses, and pepper.

2 Pour marinade over chops. Seal bag; turn to coat chops. Marinate in the refrigerator for 4 to 24 hours, turning bag occasionally.

3 At least 1 hour before grilling, soak wood chips or chunks in enough water to cover. Drain before using.

4 Drain chops, reserving marinade. For a charcoal grill, arrange medium-hot coals around a drip pan. Test for medium heat above the pan. Sprinkle the drained wood chips or chunks over the coals. Place chops on the grill rack over drip pan. Cover and grill for 20 to 24 minutes or until juices run clear (160°F), brushing once with marinade halfway through grilling. (For a gas grill, preheat grill. Reduce heat to medium. Adjust for indirect cooking. Add wood chips according to manufacturer's directions. Place chops on grill rack over burner that is turned off. Grill as above.) Discard any remaining marinade. If desired, garnish with rosemary sprigs.

Cranberry Pork Loin Chops

START TO FINISH 30 minutes
MAKES 4 servings

NUTRITION FACTS per serving

CALORIES 285
TOTAL FAT 7 g (2 g sat. fat)
CHOLESTEROL 89 mg
SODIUM 172 mg
CARBOHYDRATE 21 g
FIBER 1 g
PROTEIN 31 g
EXCHANGES 1½ Other Carbo., 4 Lean Meat

- Nonstick cooking spray
- 4 boneless pork loin chops, cut ½ inch thick (about 1¼ pounds total)
- ⅛ teaspoon salt
- ⅛ teaspoon black pepper
- ½ cup canned whole cranberry sauce
- 2 tablespoons frozen orange juice concentrate, thawed
- 1 tablespoon honey
- ¼ teaspoon ground ginger
- ⅛ teaspoon ground nutmeg

1 Lightly coat an unheated large nonstick skillet with cooking spray. Heat over medium-high heat. Sprinkle both sides of the chops with salt and pepper. Add chops to hot skillet; reduce heat to medium. Cook for 8 to 10 minutes or until an instant-read thermometer registers 160°F and juices run clear, turning once. Remove chops from skillet; cover to keep warm.

2 Meanwhile, for sauce, in a small bowl combine cranberry sauce, orange juice concentrate, honey, ginger, and nutmeg. Add cranberry mixture to same skillet. Cook, uncovered, for 1 to 2 minutes or until sauce thickens slightly. Serve sauce over pork.

Adobo Pork Chops

PREP 25 minutes **MARINATE** 2 to 24 hours
GRILL 12 minutes **MAKES** 6 servings

NUTRITION FACTS per serving

CALORIES 189
TOTAL FAT 7 g (2 g sat. fat)
CHOLESTEROL 71 mg
SODIUM 170 mg
CARBOHYDRATE 3 g
FIBER 0 g
PROTEIN 25 g
EXCHANGES 4 Lean Meat, 1 Fat

- 6 boneless pork top loin chops, cut ¾ inch thick (1½ to 1¾ pounds total)
- 2 tablespoons packed brown sugar
- 2 tablespoons olive oil
- 2 tablespoons orange juice
- 2 tablespoons snipped cilantro
- 1 tablespoon red wine vinegar or cider vinegar
- 2 teaspoons hot chili powder
- 1 teaspoon ground cumin
- 1 teaspoon dried oregano, crushed
- ½ teaspoon salt
- ½ teaspoon cayenne pepper (optional)
- ¼ teaspoon ground cinnamon
- 3 cloves garlic, minced

1 Trim fat from pork chops. Place chops in a resealable plastic bag set in a shallow dish. For marinade, in a small bowl combine brown sugar, olive oil, orange juice, cilantro, vinegar, chili powder, cumin, oregano, salt, cayenne pepper (if desired), cinnamon, and garlic. Pour marinade over chops. Seal bag; turn to coat chops. Marinate in the refrigerator for 2 to 24 hours, turning bag occasionally.

2 Drain chops, discarding marinade. For a charcoal grill, place chops on the rack of an uncovered grill directly over medium coals. Grill for 12 to 15 minutes or until chops are done (160°F) and juices run clear, turning once halfway through grilling. (For a gas grill, preheat grill. Reduce heat to medium. Place chops on grill rack over heat. Cover and grill as above.)

Chapter 9

Chicken & Turkey

On the opener: Chicken Breasts with Herbs *(see recipe, page 168)*

CHICKEN BREASTS

TURKEY

Feta-Stuffed Chicken Breasts

START TO FINISH 30 minutes
MAKES 4 servings

NUTRITION FACTS per serving

CALORIES 168
TOTAL FAT 5 g (2 g sat. fat)
CHOLESTEROL 75 mg
SODIUM 221 mg
CARBOHYDRATE 1 g
FIBER 0 g
PROTEIN 29 g
EXCHANGES 4 Lean Meat, ½ Fat

- 1 tablespoon snipped dried tomatoes (not oil-packed)
- 4 skinless, boneless chicken breast halves (1 to 1½ pounds total)
- ¼ cup crumbled feta cheese (1 ounce)
- 2 tablespoons softened fat-free cream cheese (1 ounce)
- 2 teaspoons snipped fresh basil or ½ teaspoon dried basil, crushed
- ⅛ teaspoon black pepper
- 1 teaspoon olive oil or vegetable oil
- Fresh basil sprigs (optional)

1 Place tomatoes in a small bowl. Pour enough boiling water over the tomatoes to cover. Let stand for 10 minutes. Drain and pat dry; set aside.

2 Meanwhile, using a sharp knife, cut a pocket in each chicken breast by cutting horizontally through the thickest portion to, but not through, the opposite side. Set aside.

3 In a small bowl combine feta cheese, cream cheese, the snipped or dried basil, and tomatoes. Spoon about 1 rounded tablespoon cheese mixture into each pocket. If necessary, secure openings with wooden toothpicks. Sprinkle chicken with pepper.

4 In a large nonstick skillet heat oil over medium-high heat. Cook chicken in hot oil for 12 to 14 minutes or until tender and no longer pink (170°F), turning once. (Reduce heat to medium if chicken browns too quickly.) Serve warm. If desired, garnish with basil sprigs.

Chicken Breasts with Herbs

PREP 15 minutes **COOK** 14 minutes
MAKES 4 servings

NUTRITION FACTS per serving

CALORIES 213
TOTAL FAT 7 g (4 g sat. fat)
CHOLESTEROL 97 mg
SODIUM 154 mg
CARBOHYDRATE 1 g
FIBER 0 g
PROTEIN 33 g
EXCHANGES 4½ Lean Meat

- ⅓ cup snipped fresh Italian (flat-leaf) parsley
- 1 tablespoon snipped fresh oregano
- 1 tablespoon finely shredded lemon peel
- 3 cloves garlic, minced
- 4 skinless, boneless chicken breast halves
- Salt and black pepper
- 2 tablespoons butter
- ¼ cup reduced-sodium chicken broth

1 In small bowl stir together parsley, oregano, lemon peel, and garlic. Set aside. Sprinkle chicken with salt and pepper.

2 In a large skillet melt butter over medium-high heat. Add chicken; cook for 6 minutes or until browned, turning once. Transfer chicken to plate. Remove skillet from heat; stir in half the herb mixture. Return skillet to heat. Add chicken broth; bring to boiling, stirring to scrape up browned bits. Return chicken to skillet; reduce heat. Simmer, covered, about 8 minutes or until chicken is no longer pink.

3 Serve chicken with pan sauce; sprinkle with remaining herb mixture.

Jerk Chicken Breast

PREP 20 minutes
CHILL 30 minutes to 24 hours
GRILL 6 minutes **MAKES** 6 servings

NUTRITION FACTS per serving

CALORIES 180
TOTAL FAT 2 g (1 g sat. fat)
CHOLESTEROL 88 mg
SODIUM 283 mg
CARBOHYDRATE 2 g
FIBER 0 g
PROTEIN 35 g
EXCHANGES 5 Very Lean Meat

- 6 skinless, boneless chicken breast halves (about 2 pounds total)
- 4 teaspoons Jamaican jerk seasoning
- 8 cloves garlic, minced
- 2 teaspoons snipped fresh thyme or ½ teaspoon dried thyme, crushed
- 2 teaspoons finely shredded lemon peel
- 2 tablespoons lemon juice
- Olive oil cooking spray or 2 teaspoons olive oil
- Lemon wedges

1 Place a chicken breast half between 2 pieces of plastic wrap. Using the flat side of a meat mallet, pound chicken to ½-inch thickness. Discard plastic wrap. Repeat with remaining chicken breast halves.

2 In a small bowl combine jerk seasoning, garlic, thyme, and lemon peel. Brush chicken breasts with lemon juice. Sprinkle garlic mixture evenly on chicken breasts; rub in with your fingers. Place chicken in a resealable plastic bag; seal bag. Chill for 30 minutes to 24 hours.

3 Lightly coat chicken with cooking spray or brush lightly with olive oil. For a charcoal grill, place chicken on the grill rack of an uncovered grill directly over medium coals. Grill for 6 to 10 minutes or until chicken is tender and no longer pink, turning once halfway through grilling. (For a gas grill, preheat grill. Reduce heat to medium. Place chicken on grill rack over heat. Cover and grill as above.) To serve, slice chicken; pass lemon wedges.

Broiler Method: Preheat broiler. Place chicken on the unheated rack of a broiler pan. Broil 3 to 4 inches from heat for 6 to 10 minutes or until chicken is tender and no longer pink, turning once halfway through broiling.

Pan-Roasted Chicken with Shallots

START TO FINISH 20 minutes
MAKES 4 servings

NUTRITION FACTS per serving

CALORIES 193
TOTAL FAT 5 g (1 g sat. fat)
CHOLESTEROL 66 mg
SODIUM 231 mg
CARBOHYDRATE 9 g
FIBER 1 g
PROTEIN 28 g
EXCHANGES 1 Vegetable, 3½ Lean Meat

- 8 shallots or 1 large onion
- 4 medium skinless, boneless chicken breast halves (1 to 1¼ pounds total)
- ¼ teaspoon salt
- ⅛ teaspoon black pepper
- 1 tablespoon olive oil
- 1 medium zucchini, halved lengthwise and cut into ¼-inch slices
- ¼ cup snipped fresh parsley

1 Peel shallots; halve small shallots and quarter large shallots. If using onion, cut into thin wedges (should have 1 cup shallots or onion wedges); set aside. Sprinkle chicken with salt and pepper. In a large skillet heat oil over medium-high heat. Reduce heat to medium. Add chicken; cook for 2 minutes.

2 Turn chicken. Add shallots to skillet. Cook for 8 to 10 minutes more or until chicken is no longer pink (170°F), stirring shallots frequently and turning chicken, if necessary, to brown evenly. If necessary, add additional oil to prevent sticking. Reduce heat to medium-low if chicken or shallots brown too quickly.

3 Transfer chicken and shallots to a serving platter. Cover to keep warm. Add zucchini to skillet. Cook and stir for 3 to 5 minutes or until crisp-tender. Add to platter with chicken. Sprinkle with parsley.

Parmesan-Stuffed Chicken and Melted Strawberries

PREP 30 minutes **BAKE** 15 minutes
OVEN 400°F **MAKES** 6 servings

NUTRITION FACTS per serving

CALORIES 229
TOTAL FAT 6 g (2 g sat. fat)
CHOLESTEROL 72 mg
SODIUM 355 mg
CARBOHYDRATE 11 g
FIBER 2 g
PROTEIN 30 g
EXCHANGES ½ Fruit, 4 Lean Meat, ½ Fat

- 3 cups fresh strawberries (halve or quarter large berries)
- ¼ cup low-sugar strawberry preserves
- 2 tablespoons white balsamic vinegar or white wine vinegar
- ½ teaspoon sea salt or salt
- ¼ teaspoon black pepper
- 6 skinless, boneless chicken breast halves (1½ to 2 pounds total)
- 2 ounces Parmesan or white cheddar cheese
- 6 large fresh basil leaves
- 1 tablespoon olive oil
- 2 cloves garlic, minced
- Snipped fresh basil

1. Preheat oven to 400°F. In a 3-quart baking dish combine strawberries, preserves, and vinegar. Sprinkle with ¼ teaspoon of the salt and ⅛ teaspoon of the pepper; set aside.

2. Cut a horizontal pocket in each chicken breast half, cutting from 1 side almost to, but not through, the opposite side. Cut cheese into six 3×½-inch pieces. Wrap a basil leaf around each piece of cheese; stuff into chicken breast pocket. Secure pockets closed with wooden toothpicks or skewers. Sprinkle with remaining ¼ teaspoon salt and ⅛ teaspoon pepper.

3. In a very large oven-safe skillet cook garlic in oil over medium heat for 30 seconds. Add chicken; cook about 5 minutes or until golden brown, turning once. Transfer to oven. Bake, uncovered, for 5 minutes. Add baking dish with the strawberry-preserves mixture to oven. Bake for 10 to 13 minutes or until chicken is no longer pink (170°F) and the berries are softened and jam mixture has thickened. Serve chicken with melted strawberries. Sprinkle with basil.

Chicken Breasts with Red Pepper Sauce

START TO FINISH 50 minutes
MAKES 5 servings

NUTRITION FACTS per serving

CALORIES 242
TOTAL FAT 5 g (1 g sat. fat)
CHOLESTEROL 53 mg
SODIUM 323 mg
CARBOHYDRATE 25 g
FIBER 5 g
PROTEIN 26 g
EXCHANGES 1½ Vegetable, 1 Starch, 3 Lean Meat, ½ Fat

2 medium red sweet peppers, quartered, seeded, and stems and ribs removed
1 tablespoon olive oil
½ teaspoon salt
¼ to ½ teaspoon bottled hot pepper sauce
1 teaspoon Cajun seasoning
4 skinless, boneless chicken breast halves (1 to 1¼ pounds total)
4 ounces whole wheat linguine or fettuccine
3 cups fresh green beans (about 10 ounces), trimmed and bias-sliced into 1-inch pieces
Snipped fresh Italian (flat-leaf) parsley

1 For red pepper sauce, place a steamer insert in a large skillet or 4-quart Dutch oven with a tight-fitting lid. Add water to the skillet to just below the steamer insert. Bring water in skillet to boiling. Place pepper quarters in the steamer insert. Cover and steam over medium heat about 18 minutes or until the peppers are tender, adding more water as needed to maintain steam. Transfer pepper halves to a food processor or blender. Add olive oil, salt, and bottled hot pepper sauce. Cover and process or blend until smooth. Set aside.

2 Sprinkle Cajun seasoning on chicken. Place chicken in the steamer insert, overlapping thin portions as needed. Cover and steam for 15 to 20 minutes or until chicken is tender and no longer pink (170°F), adding more water as needed to maintain steam.

3 Meanwhile, in a large saucepan cook linguine according to package directions, adding green beans the last 8 minutes of cooking. Drain and return to saucepan. Cut cooked chicken into bite-size pieces. Add chicken and red pepper sauce to linguine mixture. Toss to coat. Sprinkle with parsley before serving.

Chicken-Pineapple Fajitas

START TO FINISH 20 minutes
OVEN 350°F **MAKES** 4 servings

NUTRITION FACTS per serving

CALORIES 315
TOTAL FAT 8 g (2 g sat. fat)
CHOLESTEROL 49 mg
SODIUM 519 mg
CARBOHYDRATE 30 g
FIBER 13 g
PROTEIN 29 g
EXCHANGES ½ Vegetable, ½ Fruit, 1½ Starch, 3½ Lean Meat

- 4 8-inch whole wheat flour tortillas
- Nonstick cooking spray
- 4 1-inch slices peeled fresh pineapple (about half)
- 12 ounces skinless, boneless chicken breast halves
- 2 small red or orange sweet peppers, seeded and cut into strips
- 2 teaspoons Jamaican jerk seasoning
- ⅛ teaspoon black pepper
- 1 tablespoon canola oil
- Fresh cilantro and lime wedges

1 Preheat oven to 350°F. Wrap tortillas in foil and bake about 10 minutes or until heated through. Meanwhile, coat a very large nonstick skillet with cooking spray; heat over medium-high heat. Add pineapple slices; cook for 4 to 6 minutes or until browned, turning once. Remove from skillet.

2 Cut chicken into strips. In a large bowl toss chicken with sweet peppers, jerk seasoning, and black pepper. In the same skillet heat oil over medium-high heat; add chicken and sweet peppers. Cook and stir for 4 to 6 minutes or until chicken is no longer pink. Core and chop pineapple. Serve chicken with pineapple, tortillas, cilantro, and lime wedges.

Middle Eastern Chicken Kabobs

PREP 25 minutes **MARINATE** 1 to 4 hours
BROIL 8 minutes **MAKES** 6 servings

NUTRITION FACTS per serving

CALORIES 206
TOTAL FAT 2 g (1 g sat. fat)
CHOLESTEROL 44 mg
SODIUM 464 mg
CARBOHYDRATE 25 g
FIBER 4 g
PROTEIN 22 g
EXCHANGES 1 Vegetable, 1 Starch, 2½ Lean Meat

- 1 pound skinless, boneless chicken breast halves, cut into 1-inch pieces
- ¼ cup plain low-fat yogurt
- 1 tablespoon lemon juice
- 1 teaspoon dry mustard
- 1 teaspoon ground cinnamon
- 1 teaspoon curry powder
- ½ teaspoon salt
- ¼ to ½ teaspoon crushed red pepper
- 1 large red sweet pepper, cut into 1-inch pieces
- 1 medium yellow summer squash, halved lengthwise and cut into ½-inch slices
- 3 whole wheat pita bread rounds, warmed and cut into wedges
- 1 recipe Tomato Relish

1 Place chicken in resealable plastic bag set in a shallow dish. For marinade, in a bowl combine yogurt, lemon juice, mustard, cinnamon, curry powder, salt, and crushed red pepper. Pour over chicken. Seal bag; shake to coat. Marinate in refrigerator for 1 to 4 hours.

2 Preheat broiler. On 6 long wooden* or metal skewers, alternately thread chicken, sweet pepper, and squash, leaving a ¼-inch space between pieces.

3 Broil kabobs 4 to 5 inches from heat for 8 to 10 minutes or until chicken is no longer pink, turning once. Serve kabobs with warm pita bread and Tomato Relish.

Tomato Relish: In a medium bowl combine 2 roma tomatoes, coarsely chopped; ½ cup yellow or red grape tomatoes, halved; 1 teaspoon snipped fresh oregano or ¼ teaspoon dried oregano, crushed; 1 teaspoon snipped fresh thyme or ¼ teaspoon dried thyme, crushed; 1 clove garlic, minced; 1 tablespoon white balsamic or balsamic vinegar; 1 teaspoon honey; ⅛ teaspoon salt; and ⅛ teaspoon black pepper. Cover and chill up to 4 hours.

***Note:** If using wooden or bamboo skewers, soak in water for 30 minutes before using.

Creamy Chicken Enchiladas

PREP 40 minutes **BAKE** 40 minutes
STAND 5 minutes **OVEN** 350°F
MAKES 6 servings

NUTRITION FACTS per serving

CALORIES 269
TOTAL FAT 11 g (6 g sat. fat)
CHOLESTEROL 47 mg
SODIUM 618 mg
CARBOHYDRATE 24 g
FIBER 2 g
PROTEIN 20 g
EXCHANGES 1 Vegetable, 1 Starch, 2 Lean Meat, 1 Fat

- 8 ounces skinless, boneless chicken breasts
- 2/3 cup water
- 1/4 teaspoon black pepper
- 1 10-ounce package frozen chopped spinach, thawed and well drained
- 2 tablespoons thinly sliced green onion (1)
- 1 8-ounce tub light cream cheese
- 2 tablespoons all-purpose flour
- 1/4 teaspoon ground cumin
- 1/4 cup fat-free milk
- 1 4-ounce can diced green chiles, drained
- Nonstick cooking spray
- 6 7-inch white or whole wheat flour tortillas
- 1/2 cup bottled salsa
- 1/2 cup shredded reduced-fat cheddar or Monterey Jack cheese (2 ounces)
- Chopped romaine lettuce (optional)

1 Preheat oven to 350°F. In a large skillet combine chicken, the water, and black pepper. Bring to boiling; reduce heat. Simmer, covered, for 12 to 14 minutes or until chicken is no longer pink. Drain well; cool slightly. When cool enough to handle, use 2 forks to shred chicken into bite-size pieces; set aside.

2 For filling, in a large bowl combine chicken, spinach, and green onion. In a small bowl combine cream cheese, flour, and cumin. Stir in milk and chiles. Stir cheese mixture into chicken mixture. Coat a 2-quart rectangular baking dish with cooking spray. Divide the filling among the tortillas. Roll up tortillas. Place tortillas, seam sides down, in the prepared dish.

4 Cover dish with foil. Bake for 20 minutes. Uncover; pour salsa over enchiladas and sprinkle with cheese. Bake, uncovered, about 20 minutes more or until heated through and cheese is melted. Let stand for 5 minutes before serving. If desired, top with romaine lettuce.

Turkey Steaks with Spinach, Pears, and Blue Cheese

START TO FINISH 20 minutes
MAKES 4 servings

NUTRITION FACTS per serving

CALORIES 230
TOTAL FAT 8 g (5 g sat. fat)
CHOLESTEROL 89 mg
SODIUM 357 mg
CARBOHYDRATE 8 g
FIBER 2 g
PROTEIN 31 g
EXCHANGES 1 Vegetable, ½ Fruit, 4 Lean Meat

- 2 turkey breast tenderloins (1 to 1¼ pounds total)
- 1 teaspoon dried sage, crushed
- ¼ teaspoon salt
- ⅛ teaspoon black pepper
- 2 tablespoons butter
- 1 6-ounce package fresh baby spinach
- 1 large pear, cored and thinly sliced
- ¼ cup crumbled reduced-fat blue cheese

1 Horizontally split tenderloins to make four ½-inch-thick steaks. Rub turkey with sage; sprinkle with salt and pepper. In a very large skillet melt 1 tablespoon butter over medium-high heat. Add turkey; cook for 14 to 16 minutes or until no longer pink (170°F), turning once. (Reduce heat to medium if turkey browns too quickly.) Remove from skillet. Add spinach to skillet. Cook and stir just until wilted.

2 Meanwhile, in a small skillet melt the remaining 1 tablespoon butter over medium heat. Add pear slices; cook over medium to medium-high heat, stirring occasionally for 5 minutes or until tender and lightly browned.

3 Serve steaks with spinach and pears. Sprinkle with blue cheese.

Sage and Cream Turkey Fettuccine

START TO FINISH 30 minutes
MAKES 2 servings

- 6 ounces dried spinach and/or plain fettuccine
- ⅔ cup fat-free or light sour cream
- 4 teaspoons all-purpose flour
- ½ cup reduced-sodium chicken broth
- 2 teaspoons snipped fresh sage or 1 teaspoon dried sage, crushed
- ¼ teaspoon black pepper
- Nonstick cooking spray
- 12 ounces turkey breast tenderloin, cut into bite-size strips
- ½ teaspoon salt
- 2 cups sliced fresh mushrooms
- ½ cup sliced green onions (4)
- 2 cloves garlic, minced
- Fresh sage sprigs (optional)

1 Cook pasta according to package directions; drain and set aside.

2 Meanwhile, in a medium bowl stir together sour cream and flour until smooth. Gradually stir in chicken broth until smooth. Stir in snipped or dried sage and pepper; set aside.

3 Coat a large skillet with nonstick cooking spray. Preheat over medium-high heat. Sprinkle turkey with salt. Add turkey, mushrooms, green onions, and garlic to hot skillet. Cook and stir about 3 minutes or until turkey is no longer pink.

4 Stir sour cream mixture into turkey mixture in skillet. Cook and stir until thickened and bubbly. Cook and stir for 1 minute more. Serve turkey mixture over hot cooked pasta. If desired, garnish with sage sprigs.

NUTRITION FACTS per serving

CALORIES 312
TOTAL FAT 2 g (0 g sat. fat)
CHOLESTEROL 60 mg
SODIUM 478 mg
CARBOHYDRATE 43 g
FIBER 2 g
PROTEIN 30 g
EXCHANGES 1 Vegetable, 2½ Starch, 3 Lean Meat

Pineapple-Turkey Kabobs

PREP 15 minutes **MARINATE** 4 to 24 hours
GRILL 12 minutes **MAKES** 4 servings

NUTRITION FACTS per serving

CALORIES 326
TOTAL FAT 5 g (1 g sat. fat)
CHOLESTEROL 53 mg
SODIUM 41 mg
CARBOHYDRATE 39 g
FIBER 3 g
PROTEIN 24 g
EXCHANGES 1 Fruit, 1½ Starch, 3 Lean Meat

- 12 ounces turkey breast tenderloin
- ⅓ cup unsweetened pineapple juice
- 3 tablespoons rum or unsweetened pineapple juice
- 1 tablespoon finely chopped lemongrass or 2 teaspoons finely shredded lemon peel
- 1 tablespoon olive oil
- 1 medium red onion, cut into thin wedges
- 2 plums or 1 nectarine, pitted and cut into thick slices
- 1½ cups fresh or canned pineapple chunks
- 2 cups hot cooked brown rice
- ¼ cup thinly sliced sugar snap peas

1 Cut turkey into 1-inch cubes. Place turkey in a resealable plastic bag set in a shallow dish. For marinade, in a small bowl combine the ⅓ cup pineapple juice, the rum, lemongrass, and olive oil. Pour over turkey; seal bag. Marinate in the refrigerator for 4 to 24 hours, turning bag occasionally.

2 Drain turkey, reserving marinade. In a small saucepan bring marinade to boiling. Boil gently, uncovered, for 1 minute. Remove from heat. On eight 10- to 12-inch skewers alternately thread turkey and onion, leaving about a ¼-inch space between each piece. Alternately thread plums and pineapple onto 4 more skewers.

3 For a charcoal grill, place turkey and fruit kabobs on the rack of an uncovered grill directly over medium coals. Grill until turkey and onion are tender, turkey is no longer pink, and fruit is heated through, turning once and brushing occasionally with marinade during the last half of grilling. (Allow 12 to 14 minutes for turkey and onion and about 5 minutes for fruit.) (For a gas grill, preheat grill. Reduce heat to medium. Place turkey and fruit kabobs on grill rack over heat. Cover and grill as above.)

4 To serve, toss hot cooked rice with snap peas; serve turkey, onion, and fruit with rice.

Turkey Stroganoff

START TO FINISH 30 minutes
MAKES 4 servings

NUTRITION FACTS per serving

CALORIES 372
TOTAL FAT 11 g (5 g sat. fat)
CHOLESTEROL 90 mg
SODIUM 328 mg
CARBOHYDRATE 34 g
FIBER 5 g
PROTEIN 37 g
EXCHANGES 1 Vegetable, 2 Starch, 4 Lean Meat

- 4 ounces dried whole wheat or plain noodles
- 1 8-ounce carton light sour cream
- 2 tablespoons all-purpose flour
- 1 tablespoon olive or canola oil
- 1 pound turkey breast tenderloin, cut into bite-size slices
- 8 ounces sliced fresh mushrooms
- 2 cups fresh broccoli florets
- 1½ cups reduced-sodium chicken broth
- ½ teaspoon onion powder
- ¼ teaspoon black pepper

1 Cook noodles according to package directions. Drain; keep warm. In a small bowl stir together sour cream and flour; set aside.

2 Meanwhile, in a large skillet heat oil over medium-high heat. Add turkey. Cook and stir for 4 to 5 minutes or until browned and no longer pink. Remove from skillet. Add mushrooms to skillet. Cook and stir for 3 minutes. Add broccoli. Cook and stir for 2 minutes more or until mushrooms are browned and tender and broccoli is crisp-tender.

3 Add chicken broth, onion powder, and pepper to skillet. Bring to boiling. Whisk in sour cream mixture. Cook and stir until thickened and bubbly. Cook and stir for 1 minute more. Stir turkey into mixture in skillet; heat through. Serve turkey mixture with noodles.

Turkey Tetrazzini

PREP 30 minutes **BAKE** 10 minutes
OVEN 400°F **MAKES** 6 servings

NUTRITION FACTS per serving

CALORIES 202
TOTAL FAT 2 g (1 g sat. fat)
CHOLESTEROL 24 mg
SODIUM 253 mg
CARBOHYDRATE 32 g
FIBER 2 g
PROTEIN 17 g
EXCHANGES ½ Milk, ½ Vegetable, 1½ Starch, 1 Lean Meat

- 4 ounces dried whole wheat spaghetti
- 2 cups sliced fresh cremini, stemmed shiitake, or button mushrooms
- ¾ cup chopped red and/or green sweet pepper
- ½ cup cold water
- 3 tablespoons all-purpose flour
- 1 12-ounce can evaporated fat-free milk
- ½ teaspoon instant chicken bouillon granules
- ⅛ teaspoon salt
- ⅛ teaspoon black pepper
- Dash ground nutmeg
- 1 cup chopped cooked turkey breast or chicken breast (5 ounces)
- ¼ cup finely shredded Parmesan cheese (1 ounce)
- 2 tablespoons snipped fresh parsley
- Nonstick cooking spray

1 Preheat oven to 400°F. Cook the spaghetti according to package directions, except omit the vegetable oil and only lightly salt the water. Drain well.

2 Meanwhile, in a covered large saucepan cook the mushrooms and sweet pepper in a small amount of boiling water for 3 to 6 minutes or until the vegetables are tender. Drain well; return to saucepan.

3 In a screw-top jar combine the ½ cup cold water and the flour; cover and shake until well mixed. Stir flour mixture into the vegetable mixture in saucepan. Stir in evaporated milk, bouillon granules, salt, black pepper, and nutmeg. Cook and stir until thickened and bubbly. Stir in the cooked spaghetti, turkey, Parmesan cheese, and parsley.

4 Lightly coat a 2-quart square baking dish with cooking spray. Spoon spaghetti mixture into dish. Bake, covered, for 10 to 15 minutes or until heated through.

Saucy Meatballs

START TO FINISH 25 minutes
MAKES 4 servings

NUTRITION FACTS per serving

CALORIES 244
TOTAL FAT 11 g (3 g sat. fat)
CHOLESTEROL 143 mg
SODIUM 604 mg
CARBOHYDRATE 14 g
FIBER 3 g
PROTEIN 24 g
EXCHANGES ½ Vegetable, ½ Starch, 3 Lean Meat, ½ Fat

- ⅓ cup water
- ¼ cup bulgur
- 1 egg
- 1 teaspoon dried Italian seasoning, chili powder, or salt-free Cajun seasoning
- ¼ teaspoon salt
- ⅛ teaspoon black pepper
- 1 pound uncooked ground turkey or lean ground beef
- 1 14.5-ounce can Italian-, Mexican-, or Cajun-style stewed tomatoes, undrained, cut up
- 2 cups hot cooked spaghetti squash (optional)
- 2 tablespoons small fresh basil or cilantro leaves or thinly sliced green onion

1 In a large microwave-safe bowl combine the water and bulgur. Microwave on high for 1 minute; do not drain. Cool slightly.

2 Stir egg, desired seasoning, salt, and pepper into bulgur mixture. Add ground turkey; mix well. Shape into 24 meatballs. Place in a microwave-safe 2-quart square baking dish. Cover with vented plastic wrap. Microwave on high for 4 minutes, rearranging once; drain off liquid.

3 Pour undrained stewed tomatoes over meatballs. Cover with vented plastic wrap. Microwave on high for 1 to 3 minutes more or until meatballs are no longer pink in centers (165°F).* If desired, serve meatballs over spaghetti squash. Sprinkle with basil.

***Note:** Low-wattage microwave ovens may require more time; high-wattage microwave ovens may require less time.

Baked Ratatouille-Sausage Penne

PREP 30 minutes **BAKE** 35 minutes
OVEN 350°F **MAKES** 6 servings

NUTRITION FACTS per serving

CALORIES 251
TOTAL FAT 8 g (2 g sat. fat)
CHOLESTEROL 39 mg
SODIUM 559 mg
CARBOHYDRATE 30 g
FIBER 6 g
PROTEIN 17 g
EXCHANGES 1 Vegetable, 1½ Starch, 1½ Medium-Fat Meat

- 3 uncooked turkey Italian sausage links (12 ounces total)
- 1 teaspoon olive oil
- 4 cloves garlic, minced
- 1 14.5-ounce can no-salt-added diced tomatoes, undrained
- 3 tablespoons snipped fresh parsley
- ¼ teaspoon crushed red pepper (optional)
- 1 pound eggplant, peeled and cut into ½-inch cubes
- 6 ounces dried whole wheat penne pasta (about 2¼ cups)
- ⅓ cup finely shredded Parmesan cheese
- Snipped fresh parsley (optional)

1 Preheat oven to 350°F. Place sausage links in an unheated skillet. Add ½ inch of water to the skillet. Bring to boiling; reduce heat. Simmer, covered, about 15 minutes or until juices run clear; drain off liquid. Cook for 2 to 4 minutes more or until browned, turning occasionally. Remove from heat. When cool enough to handle, cut sausages in half lengthwise; bias-cut into ½-inch slices. Set aside.

2 In a large skillet heat oil over medium heat. Add garlic; cook for 1 minute. Stir in undrained tomatoes, the 3 tablespoons parsley, and, if desired, the crushed red pepper. Bring to boiling. Stir in eggplant. Reduce heat. Simmer, covered, for 15 minutes.

3 Meanwhile, cook pasta according to package directions, cooking for the minimum time listed; drain. Return pasta to hot pan. Stir in eggplant mixture and sausage. Spoon into a 2-quart baking dish.

4 Bake, covered, about 30 minutes or until heated through. Sprinkle with Parmesan cheese. Uncover and bake about 5 minutes more or until cheese is melted. If desired, sprinkle with additional parsley.

Chapter 10

Fish & Seafood

On the opener: Poached Halibut and Peppers *(see recipe, page 193)*

SALMON

SHRIMP & SCALLOPS

STEAKS & FILLETS

Baked Herb Salmon

PREP 10 minutes **BAKE** 40 minutes
OVEN 400°F **MAKES** 8 servings

NUTRITION FACTS per serving

CALORIES 184
TOTAL FAT 11 g (2 g sat. fat)
CHOLESTEROL 58 mg
SODIUM 132 mg
CARBOHYDRATE 2 g
FIBER 1 g
PROTEIN 20 g
EXCHANGES 3 Lean Meat

- 1 2-pound fresh or frozen salmon fillet
- 1 tablespoon snipped fresh chives
- 1 tablespoon snipped fresh thyme or 1 teaspoon dried thyme, crushed
- ½ teaspoon black pepper
- ¼ teaspoon salt
- 1 lemon, cut into ⅛-inch slices and seeded

1 Thaw salmon, if frozen. Rinse fish; pat dry with paper towels. Preheat oven to 400°F. Line a large baking sheet with foil. Place salmon, skin side down, on prepared baking sheet. Sprinkle salmon with chives, thyme, pepper, and salt. Top with lemon slices.

2 Cover salmon with foil. Bake for 20 minutes. Uncover and bake for 20 to 25 minutes more or until salmon flakes easily when tested with a fork. Serve immediately.

Salmon with Asparagus and Mushrooms

START TO FINISH 45 minutes
MAKES 4 servings

NUTRITION FACTS per serving

CALORIES 371
TOTAL FAT 20 g (4 g sat. fat)
CHOLESTEROL 67 mg
SODIUM 289 mg
CARBOHYDRATE 12 g
FIBER 3 g
PROTEIN 28 g
EXCHANGES 1½ Vegetable, ½ Other Carbo., 3½ Lean Meat, 2½ Fat

- 4 fresh or frozen skinless salmon fillets, about 1 inch thick (about 1 pound total)
- Kosher salt
- Freshly ground black pepper
- 2 tablespoons olive oil
- 2 cups sliced assorted fresh mushrooms (such as button, cremini, and/or stemmed shiitake)
- 1 cup chopped onion (1 large)
- 6 cloves garlic, minced
- 1 tablespoon snipped fresh thyme
- 1 cup dry white wine
- 1 cup clam juice or chicken broth
- 2 cups 1½-inch-long pieces asparagus
- 1 cup cherry tomatoes, halved
- 1 tablespoon snipped fresh Italian (flat-leaf) parsley
- 1 teaspoon lemon juice

1 Thaw fish, if frozen. Rinse fish; pat dry with paper towels. Measure thickness of fish. Sprinkle fish with salt and pepper. Set aside.

2 In a large skillet heat 1 tablespoon of the oil over medium heat. Add mushrooms; cook for 5 minutes. Add onion, garlic, and thyme; cook until mushrooms are tender, stirring occasionally. Add wine. Bring to boiling; reduce heat. Simmer, uncovered, about 15 minutes or until liquid is reduced to ¼ cup.

3 Add clam juice. Return to boiling; reduce heat. Simmer, uncovered, about 15 minutes more or until liquid is reduced to ¾ cup. Add the asparagus. Cook, covered, about 3 minutes or until asparagus is crisp-tender. Stir in tomatoes, parsley, and lemon juice. Season with kosher salt and pepper. Transfer to a platter and keep warm.

4 In the same skillet heat the remaining 1 tablespoon olive oil over medium heat. Add salmon; cook for 4 to 6 minutes per ½-inch thickness of salmon or until salmon flakes easily when tested with a fork, turning once halfway through cooking. Serve salmon over vegetable mixture. If desired, garnish with fresh *thyme*.

Salmon with Roasted Tomatoes and Shallots

PREP 20 minutes **ROAST** 30 minutes
OVEN 400°F **MAKES** 4 servings

- 1 1-pound fresh or frozen salmon fillet, skinned if desired
- 1/8 teaspoon salt
- 1/8 teaspoon black pepper
- Nonstick cooking spray
- 4 cups grape tomatoes
- 1/2 cup thinly sliced shallots
- 6 cloves garlic, minced
- 2 tablespoons snipped fresh oregano or 1 1/2 teaspoons dried oregano, crushed
- 1 tablespoon olive oil
- 1/4 teaspoon salt
- 1/4 teaspoon black pepper

1 Thaw fish, if frozen. Rinse salmon; pat dry with paper towels. Sprinkle salmon with the 1/8 teaspoon salt and the 1/8 teaspoon pepper. Preheat oven to 400°F.

2 Lightly coat a 3-quart baking dish with cooking spray. In the baking dish combine tomatoes, shallots, garlic, oregano, olive oil, the 1/4 teaspoon salt, and the 1/4 teaspoon pepper. Toss to coat.

3 Roast, uncovered, for 15 minutes. Place salmon, skin side down, on the tomato-shallot mixture. Roast, uncovered, for 15 to 18 minutes or until salmon flakes easily when tested with a fork.

4 Use 2 large pancake turners to transfer salmon to a serving platter. Top with tomato mixture.

NUTRITION FACTS per serving

CALORIES 320
TOTAL FAT 19 g (4 g sat. fat)
CHOLESTEROL 62 mg
SODIUM 297 mg
CARBOHYDRATE 12 g
FIBER 2 g
PROTEIN 26 g
EXCHANGES 1 1/2 Vegetable, 3 1/2 Lean Meat, 2 1/2 Fat

Citrus Salsa Salmon

PREP 10 minutes **BROIL** 8 minutes
MAKES 4 servings

NUTRITION FACTS per serving

CALORIES 357
TOTAL FAT 15 g (3 g sat. fat)
CHOLESTEROL 62 mg
SODIUM 221 mg
CARBOHYDRATE 31 g
FIBER 3 g
PROTEIN 25 g
EXCHANGES 1 Fruit, 1 Other Carbo., 3½ Lean Meat, 1½ Fat

- 4 fresh or frozen skinless salmon fillets, ¾ to 1 inch thick (1 to 1¼ pounds)
- ¼ teaspoon salt
- ⅛ teaspoon black pepper
- ¼ cup red jalapeño jelly
- 2 medium oranges, peeled, seeded, and coarsely chopped
- 1 medium grapefruit, peeled and sectioned
- 1 cup grape or cherry tomatoes, halved
- Salt and black pepper

1 Thaw salmon, if frozen. Rinse fish; pat dry with paper towels. Preheat broiler. Sprinkle salmon with salt and pepper. In a small saucepan melt jelly over low heat. Brush 2 tablespoons of the melted jelly on the salmon; reserve remaining jelly. Place salmon on the unheated rack of a broiler pan. Broil 4 inches from heat for 8 to 10 minutes or until salmon flakes easily when tested with a fork.

2 Meanwhile, for fresh citrus salsa, in a medium bowl combine chopped oranges, grapefruit sections, halved tomatoes, and the remaining jelly. Season with salt and pepper. Serve salmon with citrus salsa.

Basil-Buttered Salmon

PREP 15 minutes **BROIL** 8 minutes
MAKES 4 servings

- 4 fresh or frozen skinless salmon, halibut, or sea bass fillets (about 1¼ pounds)
- ½ teaspoon salt-free lemon-pepper seasoning
- 2 tablespoons butter, softened
- 1 teaspoon snipped fresh lemon basil, basil, or dill; or ¼ teaspoon dried basil, crushed, or dried dill
- 1 teaspoon snipped fresh parsley or cilantro
- ¼ teaspoon finely shredded lemon peel or lime peel

1 Thaw fish, if frozen. Rinse fish; pat dry with paper towels. Sprinkle fish with lemon-pepper seasoning.

2 Place fish on the greased unheated rack of a broiler pan. Tuck under any thin portions to make uniform thickness. Broil 4 inches from the heat for 5 minutes. Carefully turn fish over. Broil for 3 to 7 minutes more or until fish flakes easily when tested with a fork.

3 Meanwhile, in a small bowl stir together butter, basil, parsley, and lemon peel. To serve, spoon 1 teaspoon of the butter mixture on each fish piece. Cover and chill remaining butter mixture for another use.

Grilling Directions: For a charcoal grill, place fish on the greased rack of an uncovered grill directly over medium coals. Grill for 8 to 12 minutes or until fish flakes easily when tested with a fork, carefully turning once halfway through grilling. (For a gas grill, preheat grill. Reduce heat to medium. Place fish on grill rack over heat. Cover and grill as above.)

NUTRITION FACTS per serving

CALORIES 294
TOTAL FAT 19 g (5 g sat. fat)
CHOLESTEROL 94 mg
SODIUM 113 mg
CARBOHYDRATE 0 g
FIBER 0 g
PROTEIN 28 g
EXCHANGES 4 Lean Meat, 1½ Fat

Cod Amandine

PREP 20 minutes
BAKE 4 to 6 minutes per ½-inch thickness
OVEN 450°F
MAKES 4 servings

NUTRITION FACTS per serving

CALORIES 191
TOTAL FAT 7 g (1 g sat. fat)
CHOLESTEROL 49 mg
SODIUM 245 mg
CARBOHYDRATE 7 g
FIBER 1 g
PROTEIN 23 g
EXCHANGES ½ Starch, 3 Lean Meat, 1 Fat

- 4 4-ounce fresh or frozen skinless cod, tilapia, trout, or halibut fillets, ½ to 1 inch thick
- ¼ cup buttermilk
- ½ cup panko (Japanese-style bread crumbs) or fine dry bread crumbs
- 2 tablespoons snipped fresh parsley or 2 teaspoons dried parsley flakes
- ½ teaspoon dry mustard
- ¼ teaspoon salt
- ⅛ teaspoon black pepper
- ¼ cup sliced almonds, coarsely chopped
- 1 tablespoon olive oil
- Lemon wedges (optional)

1 Thaw fish, if frozen. Grease a shallow baking pan; set aside. Preheat oven to 450°F. Rinse fish; pat dry with paper towels. Measure thickness of fish.

2 Pour buttermilk in a shallow dish. In another shallow dish combine bread crumbs, parsley, dry mustard, salt, and pepper. Dip fish into buttermilk, then coat fish with crumb mixture. Place coated fish in prepared baking pan.

3 Sprinkle fish with almonds. Drizzle olive oil over fish. Bake for 4 to 6 minutes per ½-inch thickness of fish or until fish flakes easily when tested with a fork. If desired, serve fish with lemon wedges.

Parmesan-Crusted Fish

START TO FINISH 20 minutes **OVEN** 450°F
MAKES 4 servings

- 4 fresh or frozen skinless cod fillets (about 1½ pounds total)
- Nonstick cooking spray
- Salt and black pepper
- ⅓ cup panko (Japanese-style bread crumbs)
- ¼ cup finely shredded Parmesan cheese
- ½ cup water
- 1 10-ounce package julienned fresh carrots (3 cups)
- 1 tablespoon butter
- ¾ teaspoon ground ginger
- Mixed fresh salad greens

1 Thaw fish, if frozen. Preheat oven to 450°F. Lightly coat a baking sheet with cooking spray. Rinse fish; pat dry with paper towels. Place fish on the prepared baking sheet. Sprinkle with salt and pepper.

2 In small bowl stir together bread crumbs and cheese; sprinkle on fish. Bake, uncovered, for 4 to 6 minutes for each ½-inch thickness of fish or until fish flakes easily when tested with a fork and crumbs are golden.

3 Meanwhile, in a large skillet bring water to boiling; add carrots. Reduce heat. Cook, covered, for 5 minutes. Uncover; cook for 2 minutes more or until liquid is evaporated. Add butter and ginger; toss to coat. Serve fish and carrots with greens.

NUTRITION FACTS per serving

CALORIES 233
TOTAL FAT 6 g (3 g sat. fat)
CHOLESTEROL 84 mg
SODIUM 407 mg
CARBOHYDRATE 11 g
FIBER 2 g
PROTEIN 34 g
EXCHANGES 1 Vegetable, ½ Starch, 4 Lean Meat

Provençal Fish Fillets

PREP 20 minutes
BROIL 4 to 6 minutes per ½-inch thickness
MAKES 4 servings

NUTRITION FACTS per serving

CALORIES 161
TOTAL FAT 5 g (1 g sat. fat)
CHOLESTEROL 48 mg
SODIUM 292 mg
CARBOHYDRATE 7 g
FIBER 2 g
PROTEIN 21 g
EXCHANGES 1 Vegetable, 3 Very Lean Meat, 1 Fat

- 4 4-ounce fresh or frozen skinless cod, catfish, pollock, or tilapia fish fillets, ½ to 1 inch thick
- 1 tablespoon olive oil
- 1 medium onion, thinly sliced
- 2 cloves garlic, minced
- 1 14.5-ounce can whole tomatoes, drained and chopped
- 2 teaspoons snipped fresh thyme or ½ teaspoon dried thyme, crushed
- 8 oil-cured Greek olives, pitted and halved, or 8 pitted ripe olives, halved
- 1 teaspoon capers, drained
- Fresh thyme sprigs (optional)

1 Thaw fish, if frozen. Rinse fish; pat dry with paper towels. Set aside. For sauce, in a small saucepan heat oil over medium heat. Add onion and garlic; cook about 5 minutes or until tender, stirring occasionally. Add tomatoes, the snipped or dried thyme, olives, and capers. Heat to boiling; reduce heat to medium. Simmer, uncovered, about 10 minutes or until most of the liquid has evaporated.

2 Meanwhile, preheat broiler. Measure thickness of fish. Place fish on the greased unheated rack of a broiler pan, folding under any thin edges. Broil 3 to 4 inches from heat for 4 to 6 minutes per ½-inch thickness of fish or until fish flakes easily when tested with a fork, turning fish once if fillets are 1 inch thick. Serve with sauce. If desired, garnish with fresh thyme sprigs.

Poached Halibut and Peppers

PREP 27 minutes
COOK 4 to 6 minutes per ½-inch thickness
MAKES 4 servings

NUTRITION FACTS per serving

CALORIES 260
TOTAL FAT 6 g (1 g sat. fat)
CHOLESTEROL 36 mg
SODIUM 402 mg
CARBOHYDRATE 9 g
FIBER 1 g
PROTEIN 25 g
EXCHANGES ½ Vegetable, ½ Other Carbo., 3½ Lean Meat, 1 Fat

- 4 fresh or frozen halibut, cod, or other whitefish fillets (1 to 1½ pounds total)
- 1½ cups dry white wine (Sauvignon Blanc or Pinot Grigio) or reduced-sodium chicken broth
- 1 cup water
- 1½ cups chopped yellow and/or red sweet peppers (2 medium)
- 3 tablespoons drained capers
- 4 cloves garlic, minced
- ¼ to ½ teaspoon crushed red pepper
- ¼ teaspoon salt
- ⅛ teaspoon freshly ground black pepper
- 1 tablespoon olive oil
- Coarsely chopped fresh basil

1 Thaw fish, if frozen. Rinse fish; pat dry with paper towels.

2 In a large skillet combine wine, water, sweet peppers, capers, garlic, and crushed red pepper. Bring to boiling; reduce heat. Simmer, uncovered, for 7 minutes, stirring occasionally.

3 Place fish in a single layer in the wine mixture in the skillet. Sprinkle fish with salt and pepper. Spoon liquid over fish. Return to simmering. Cook, covered, for 4 to 6 minutes per ½-inch thickness of fish or until fish flakes easily when tested with a fork. Remove fish to serving platter and pour poaching liquid into a small serving pitcher. Drizzle cooked fish with olive oil and a little of the poaching liquid. Sprinkle with basil. Serve with remaining poaching liquid.

Grilled Snapper with Red Pepper Sauce

PREP 25 minutes **COOK** 10 minutes
GRILL 4 to 6 minutes per ½-inch thickness
MAKES 4 servings

NUTRITION FACTS per serving

CALORIES 194
TOTAL FAT 8 g (1 g sat. fat)
CHOLESTEROL 41 mg
SODIUM 223 mg
CARBOHYDRATE 4 g
FIBER 1 g
PROTEIN 26 g
EXCHANGES 1 Vegetable, 3½ Lean Meat, 1½ Fat

- 4 4- to 6-ounce fresh or frozen skinless red snapper fillets
- 2 tablespoons olive oil
- 1 cup chopped red sweet pepper (1 large)
- 1 cup chopped, seeded, peeled tomatoes
- 2 tablespoons white wine vinegar
- ¼ teaspoon salt
- Dash cayenne pepper
- 1 tablespoon fresh snipped basil or oregano or ½ teaspoon dried basil or oregano, crushed
- Red and/or yellow cherry tomatoes (optional)
- Fresh basil or oregano sprigs (optional)

1 Thaw fish, if frozen. Rinse fish; pat dry with paper towels. Measure thickness of fish.

2 For red pepper sauce, in a small skillet heat 1 tablespoon of the oil over medium heat. Add sweet pepper; cook for 3 to 5 minutes or until tender, stirring occasionally. Stir in chopped tomatoes, 1 tablespoon of the vinegar, the salt, and cayenne pepper. Cook about 5 minutes or until tomatoes soften, stirring occasionally. Cool slightly. Transfer tomato-pepper mixture to a food processor or blender. Cover and process or blend until smooth. Return sauce to skillet; keep warm over low heat.

3 In a small bowl stir together the remaining 1 tablespoon oil, the remaining 1 tablespoon vinegar, and the snipped or dried basil; brush onto fish.

4 For a charcoal grill, place fish on the lightly greased rack of an uncovered grill directly over medium coals. Grill for 4 to 6 minutes per ½-inch thickness of fish or until fish flakes easily when tested with a fork, turning once halfway through grilling. (For a gas grill, preheat grill. Reduce heat to medium. Place fish on greased grill rack over heat. Cover and grill as above.)

5 Divide red pepper sauce evenly among four plates. Place a fish fillet on each plate. If desired, garnish with cherry tomatoes and fresh basil sprigs.

Chile-Lime Catfish with Corn Sauté

PREP 25 minutes
COOK 4 to 6 minutes per ½-inch thickness
MAKES 4 servings

NUTRITION FACTS per serving

CALORIES 288
TOTAL FAT 13 g (2 g sat. fat)
CHOLESTEROL 53 mg
SODIUM 216 mg
CARBOHYDRATE 25 g
FIBER 3 g
PROTEIN 21 g
EXCHANGES 1½ Starch, 2½ Lean Meat, 1 Fat

- 4 4- to 5-ounce fresh or frozen skinless catfish, sole, or tilapia fillets
- 1 tablespoon lime juice
- 1 teaspoon ground ancho chile pepper or chili powder
- ¼ teaspoon salt
- 1 tablespoon canola oil
- 2⅔ cups frozen gold and white whole kernel corn, thawed
- ¼ cup finely chopped red onion
- 2 teaspoons finely chopped, seeded fresh jalapeño*
- 2 cloves garlic, minced
- 1 tablespoon snipped fresh cilantro
- Lime wedges (optional)

1 Thaw fish, if frozen. Rinse fish; pat dry with paper towels. In a small bowl stir together lime juice, ancho chile pepper, and salt. Brush mixture evenly over both sides of each fish fillet. Measure thickness of fish.

2 In a large nonstick skillet heat 2 teaspoons of the oil over medium-high heat. Add fish fillets to hot oil; cook for 4 to 6 minutes per ½-inch thickness or until fish flakes easily when tested with a fork, turning once halfway through cooking. Remove from skillet. Cover and keep warm.

3 In the same skillet cook corn, onion, jalapeño, and garlic in the remaining 1 teaspoon oil about 2 minutes or until vegetables are heated through and just starting to soften, stirring occasionally. Remove from heat. Stir in cilantro.

4 To serve, divide corn mixture among 4 serving plates. Top with fish. If desired, serve with lime wedges.

***Note:** Because chile peppers contain volatile oils that can burn your skin and eyes, avoid direct contact with them as much as possible. When working with chile peppers, wear plastic or rubber gloves. If your bare hands do touch the peppers, wash your hands and nails well with soap and warm water.

Tilapia Puttanesca

START TO FINISH 25 minutes
MAKES 4 servings

NUTRITION FACTS per serving

CALORIES 182
TOTAL FAT 6 g (1 g sat. fat)
CHOLESTEROL 56 mg
SODIUM 431 mg
CARBOHYDRATE 8 g
FIBER 2 g
PROTEIN 24 g
EXCHANGES 1 Vegetable, 3 Lean Meat, ½ Fat

- 1 pound fresh or frozen skinless tilapia fillets
- ⅛ teaspoon salt
- 1 tablespoon olive oil
- ½ of a medium red onion, cut into wedges
- 2 cloves garlic, minced
- 1 14.5-ounce can diced tomatoes, undrained
- 2 teaspoons dried oregano, crushed
- ¼ teaspoon crushed red pepper
- ¼ cup pitted kalamata olives
- 1 tablespoon capers, drained (optional)
- 2 tablespoons snipped fresh Italian (flat-leaf) parsley

1 Thaw fish, if frozen. Rinse fish fillets; pat dry with paper towels. Sprinkle fish with salt; set aside.

2 For sauce, in a large skillet heat oil over medium heat. Add onion; cook until tender, stirring occasionally. Stir in garlic. Add undrained tomatoes, oregano, and crushed red pepper. Bring to boiling; reduce heat. Simmer, uncovered, for 5 minutes.

3 Add olives and, if desired, capers to sauce. Top with fish. Return sauce to boiling; reduce heat. Cook, covered, for 6 to 10 minutes or until fish flakes easily when tested with a fork. Remove fish. Simmer sauce, uncovered, for 1 to 2 minutes more to thicken. To serve, spoon sauce over fish. Sprinkle with parsley.

Tilapia with Herbed Shiitake Sauce

PREP 20 minutes
BAKE 4 to 6 minutes per ½-inch thickness
OVEN 450°F **MAKES** 6 servings

NUTRITION FACTS per serving

CALORIES 220
TOTAL FAT 4 g (1 g sat. fat)
CHOLESTEROL 75 mg
SODIUM 369 mg
CARBOHYDRATE 11 g
FIBER 1 g
PROTEIN 32 g
EXCHANGES ½ Starch, 4 Lean Meat, 1 Fat

- 6 fresh or frozen skinless tilapia, pollock, or cod fillets, ½ to ¾ inch thick (about 2 pounds total)
- Nonstick cooking spray
- 2 teaspoons lemon juice
- ¼ cup fine dry bread crumbs
- ¼ to ½ teaspoon black pepper
- ¼ teaspoon salt
- 2 teaspoons olive oil
- 1½ cups shiitake mushrooms, stemmed and thinly sliced
- 2 tablespoons finely chopped shallots or sweet onion
- 1 tablespoon all-purpose flour
- ½ cup dry white wine or reduced-sodium chicken broth
- ¾ cup reduced-sodium chicken broth
- 1 tablespoon snipped fresh chives
- 1 tablespoon snipped fresh parsley
- 2 teaspoons snipped fresh thyme or ½ teaspoon dried thyme, crushed

1 Thaw fish, if frozen. Preheat oven to 450°F. Lightly coat a shallow baking pan with cooking spray; set aside. Rinse fish; pat dry with paper towels. Measure thickness of fish. Brush fish with lemon juice. Place fish, skinned sides down, in prepared pan. In a bowl combine bread crumbs, pepper, and salt. Sprinkle evenly onto fish. Coat fish generously with cooking spray.

2 Bake 4 to 6 minutes per ½-inch thickness of fish or until fish flakes easily when tested with a fork.

3 Meanwhile, for sauce, in a large skillet heat oil over medium-high heat. Add mushrooms and shallots; cook about 3 minutes or until tender, stirring occasionally. Stir in flour. Add white wine; cook and stir until thickened and bubbly. Add chicken broth. Bring to boiling; reduce heat. Simmer, uncovered, for 4 minutes, stirring occasionally. Stir in chives, parsley, and snipped or dried thyme.

4 Serve sauce over fish. If desired, garnish with fresh *thyme sprigs* and *lemon slices.*

Grilled Sea Bass with Tomatoes

PREP 15 minutes **MARINATE** 15 minutes
GRILL 4 to 6 minutes per ½-inch thickness
MAKES 4 servings

NUTRITION FACTS per serving

CALORIES 252
TOTAL FAT 9 g (2 g sat. fat)
CHOLESTEROL 69 mg
SODIUM 580 mg
CARBOHYDRATE 8 g
FIBER 2 g
PROTEIN 33 g
EXCHANGES 1½ Vegetable, 4½ Lean Meat, 1½ Fat

- 4 6-ounce fresh or frozen sea bass or halibut fillets, ¾ to 1 inch thick
- 4 cloves garlic, minced
- 1 tablespoon grated fresh ginger
- 2 teaspoons toasted sesame oil
- ¾ teaspoon salt
- ½ teaspoon ground cardamom
- 1 medium red onion, cut into ¼-inch slices
- 1 tablespoon olive oil
- 2 fresh jalapeño, seeded and finely chopped (about 3 tablespoons) (see note, page 199)
- 3 small yellow or red tomatoes, halved and cut into wedges
- 1 tablespoon snipped fresh oregano
- ¾ teaspoon snipped fresh thyme
- ¼ teaspoon black pepper

1 Thaw fish, if frozen. Rinse fish; pat dry with paper towels. Measure thickness of fish. Set aside.

2 For paste, stir together half of the garlic, the ginger, sesame oil, ½ teaspoon of the salt, and the cardamom. Rub both sides of fish evenly with paste. Cover and chill for 15 minutes.

3 For a charcoal grill, place fish on the greased rack of an uncovered grill directly over medium coals. Grill for 4 to 6 minutes per ½-inch thickness or until fish flakes easily with a fork, turning once halfway through grilling time. (For a gas grill, preheat grill. Reduce heat to medium. Place fish on greased grill rack over heat. Cover and grill as above.)

4 Meanwhile, in a heavy large skillet cook onion slices in hot olive oil over medium-high heat until tender, stirring frequently. Add remaining garlic and the jalapeños; cook until onions are golden. Add tomatoes, oregano, thyme, black pepper, and the remaining ¼ teaspoon salt. Stir gently until heated through.

5 To serve, place fish on serving plates; top with tomato-onion mixture.

Cuban-Style Swordfish

PREP 20 minutes **MARINATE** 30 minutes
GRILL 8 minutes **MAKES** 4 servings

NUTRITION FACTS per serving

CALORIES 190
TOTAL FAT 8 g (2 g sat. fat)
CHOLESTEROL 43 mg
SODIUM 254 mg
CARBOHYDRATE 6 g
FIBER 3 g
PROTEIN 24 g
EXCHANGES 1 Vegetable, 3 Lean Meat, 1½ Fat

- 1 pound fresh or frozen swordfish steaks, cut 1 inch thick
- 1 large clove garlic, halved
- 2 tablespoons lime juice
- ½ teaspoon ground cumin
- ¼ teaspoon black pepper
- ⅛ teaspoon salt
- 1 recipe Fresh Tomato Salsa

1 Thaw fish, if frozen. Rinse fish; pat dry with paper towels. Cut fish into 4 serving-size pieces. Rub fish on both sides with cut sides of halved garlic clove. Place fish in a shallow glass dish; drizzle with lime juice. Cover and marinate in the refrigerator for 30 minutes, turning once. Drain fish. In a small bowl combine cumin, black pepper, and salt; sprinkle over fish.

2 For a charcoal grill, place fish on the greased rack of an uncovered grill directly over medium coals. Grill for 8 to 12 minutes or until fish flakes easily when tested with a fork, turning once halfway through grilling. (For a gas grill, preheat grill. Reduce heat to medium. Place fish on greased grill rack over heat.) Serve swordfish with Fresh Tomato Salsa.

Fresh Tomato Salsa: In a medium bowl combine 1 cup chopped red and/or yellow tomato; ¼ cup chopped tomatillo; ¼ cup chopped avocado; 2 tablespoons snipped fresh cilantro; 1 medium fresh jalapeño, seeded and finely chopped;* 1 clove garlic, minced; 1 tablespoon lime juice; ⅛ teaspoon salt; and ⅛ teaspoon black pepper. Serve immediately or cover and chill for up to 4 hours.

***Note:** Because chile peppers contain volatile oils that can burn your skin and eyes, avoid direct contact with them as much as possible. When working with chile peppers, wear plastic or rubber gloves. If your bare hands do touch the peppers, wash your hands and fingernails well with soap and warm water.

Catfish and Turkey Sausage Jambalaya

PREP 30 minutes **COOK** 10 minutes
STAND 5 minutes **MAKES** 4 servings

NUTRITION FACTS per serving

CALORIES 263
TOTAL FAT 9 g (2 g sat. fat)
CHOLESTEROL 44 mg
SODIUM 548 mg
CARBOHYDRATE 29 g
FIBER 4 g
PROTEIN 18 g
EXCHANGES 1 Vegetable, 1½ Starch, 2 Lean Meat, ½ Fat

- 8 ounces fresh or frozen skinless catfish fillets
- 1 teaspoon olive oil or vegetable oil
- 4 ounces uncooked turkey hot Italian sausage links, cut into ½-inch pieces
- ½ cup chopped onion (1 medium)
- ½ cup chopped green sweet pepper
- ½ cup chopped celery (1 stalk)
- 3 cloves garlic, minced
- 1 14.5-ounce can no-salt-added diced tomatoes, drained
- 1 14.5-ounce can reduced-sodium chicken broth
- 1½ cups instant brown rice
- 1½ teaspoons paprika
- 1 tablespoon snipped fresh oregano or 1 teaspoon dried oregano, crushed
- 1½ teaspoons snipped fresh thyme or ½ teaspoon dried thyme, crushed
- ⅛ to ¼ teaspoon cayenne pepper
- Fresh oregano (optional)

1 Thaw fish, if frozen. Rinse fish; pat dry with paper towels. Cut fish into ¾-inch chunks. Set aside.

2 In a large saucepan heat oil over medium heat. Add sausage pieces; cook for 3 to 4 minutes or until browned. Add onion, sweet pepper, celery, and garlic; cook about 10 minutes or until vegetables are tender and sausage is no longer pink, stirring occasionally.

3 Stir in tomatoes, chicken broth, uncooked rice, paprika, dried oregano (if using), dried thyme (if using), and cayenne pepper. Bring to boiling; reduce heat. Simmer, covered, for 5 minutes. Stir in fish pieces, fresh oregano (if using), and fresh thyme (if using); cook about 5 minutes more or until liquid is nearly absorbed and rice is tender. Remove from heat. Cover and let stand for 5 minutes. Using a slotted spoon, spoon into shallow bowls. If desired, garnish with fresh oregano.

Shrimp with Vermicelli

START TO FINISH 35 minutes
MAKES 4 servings

- 12 ounces fresh or frozen medium shrimp, peeled and deveined
- 4 ounces dried multigrain angel hair pasta
- 2 tablespoons butter
- 1 large onion, halved and thinly sliced
- ¼ to ½ teaspoon crushed red pepper
- 1 8-ounce can tomato sauce with basil, garlic, and oregano
- 1 medium yellow summer squash or zucchini, halved lengthwise and thinly sliced
- ⅛ teaspoon salt
- 4 cups prewashed baby spinach
- 1 cup cherry tomatoes, halved
- 2 tablespoons finely shredded Parmesan cheese

1 Thaw shrimp, if frozen. Rinse shrimp; pat dry with paper towels. Cook pasta according to package directions; drain.

2 Meanwhile, in a very large skillet melt butter over medium heat. Add onion; cook until tender. Add shrimp and crushed red pepper; cook and stir for 1 minute. Add tomato sauce, squash, and salt. Bring to boiling; reduce heat. Simmer, covered, for 5 minutes.

3 Stir drained pasta, spinach, and cherry tomatoes into skillet. Toss gently over medium heat until heated through. Sprinkle with Parmesan cheese.

NUTRITION FACTS per serving

CALORIES 279
TOTAL FAT 8 g (4 g sat. fat)
CHOLESTEROL 114 mg
SODIUM 588 mg
CARBOHYDRATE 31 g
FIBER 5 g
PROTEIN 21 g
EXCHANGES 2 Vegetable, 1½ Starch, 2 Lean Meat

Basil-Lemon Shrimp Linguine

START TO FINISH 30 minutes
MAKES 4 servings

NUTRITION FACTS per serving

CALORIES 338
TOTAL FAT 6 g (1 g sat. fat)
CHOLESTEROL 172 mg
SODIUM 463 mg
CARBOHYDRATE 39 g
FIBER 4 g
PROTEIN 31 g
EXCHANGES 1 Vegetable, 2 Starch, 3 Lean Meat, 1 Fat

- 1 pound fresh or frozen large shrimp in shells or 12 ounces fresh or frozen sea scallops
- 6 ounces dried linguine or fettuccine
- ½ teaspoon salt
- 8 ounces fresh asparagus spears, trimmed and cut diagonally into 2-inch pieces
- Nonstick cooking spray
- 2 cloves garlic, minced
- 1 cup thin red, yellow, and/or green sweet pepper strips
- ¼ cup snipped fresh basil or 1 tablespoon dried basil, crushed
- 1 teaspoon finely shredded lemon peel
- ¼ teaspoon black pepper
- ¼ cup sliced green onions (2)
- 2 tablespoons lemon juice
- 1 tablespoon olive oil
- Lemon wedges (optional)

1 Thaw shrimp, if frozen. Peel and devein shrimp, leaving tails intact if desired. Rinse shrimp; pat dry with paper towels.

2 Cook pasta according to package directions in water with ¼ teaspoon of the salt, adding asparagus the last 3 minutes of cooking; drain and return to pan. Cover and keep warm.

3 Meanwhile, lightly coat a large nonstick skillet with cooking spray. Heat over medium heat. Add garlic; cook and stir for 15 seconds. Add sweet pepper strips; cook and stir for 2 minutes or until crisp-tender. Add shrimp, dried basil (if using), lemon peel, the remaining ¼ teaspoon salt, and the black pepper. Cook and stir about 3 minutes or until shrimp turn opaque. Remove from heat.

4 Add shrimp mixture to pasta mixture. Add snipped fresh basil (if using), the green onions, lemon juice, and oil; toss gently to coat. Transfer to serving plates. If desired, garnish with lemon wedges.

Szechwan Shrimp

START TO FINISH 30 minutes
MAKES 4 servings

NUTRITION FACTS per serving

CALORIES 249
TOTAL FAT 5 g (1 g sat. fat)
CHOLESTEROL 129 mg
SODIUM 372 mg
CARBOHYDRATE 30 g
FIBER 0 g
PROTEIN 19 g
EXCHANGES 2 Starch, 2 Lean Meat, ½ Fat

- 1 pound fresh or frozen medium shrimp in shells
- 3 tablespoons water
- 2 tablespoons ketchup
- 1 tablespoon reduced-sodium soy sauce
- 1 tablespoon rice wine or water
- 2 teaspoons cornstarch
- 1 teaspoon honey
- 1 teaspoon grated fresh ginger or ¼ teaspoon ground ginger
- ½ teaspoon crushed red pepper
- 1 tablespoon peanut oil or vegetable oil
- ½ cup sliced green onions (4)
- 4 cloves garlic, minced
- 2 cups rice noodles or hot cooked rice
- 2 small fresh red chile peppers, sliced* (optional)

1 Thaw shrimp, if frozen. Peel and devein shrimp; cut in half lengthwise. Rinse shrimp; pat dry with paper towels. Set aside.

2 For sauce, in a small bowl stir together the 3 tablespoons water, ketchup, soy sauce, rice wine, cornstarch, honey, ground ginger (if using), and crushed red pepper. Set aside.

3 Pour oil into a large skillet or wok. Heat over medium-high heat. Add green onions, garlic, and grated fresh ginger (if using); stir-fry for 30 seconds.

4 Add shrimp. Stir-fry for 2 to 3 minutes or until shrimp are opaque; push to side of skillet. Stir sauce; add to center of skillet. Cook and stir until thickened and bubbly. Cook and stir for 2 minutes more. Serve with rice noodles. If desired, garnish with sliced red chile peppers.

***Note:** Because chile peppers contain volatile oils that can burn your skin and eyes, avoid direct contact with them as much as possible. When working with chile peppers, wear plastic or rubber gloves. If your bare hands do touch the peppers, wash your hands and fingernails well with soap and warm water.

Soy-Lime Scallops with Leeks

PREP 10 minutes **MARINATE** 30 minutes
GRILL 8 minutes **MAKES** 4 servings

NUTRITION FACTS per serving

CALORIES 130
TOTAL FAT 1 g (0 g sat. fat)
CHOLESTEROL 37 mg
SODIUM 478 mg
CARBOHYDRATE 9 g
FIBER 1 g
PROTEIN 20 g
EXCHANGES ½ Vegetable, ½ Other Carbo., 2½ Lean Meat

- 1 pound fresh or frozen sea scallops
- ¼ cup reduced-sodium soy sauce
- ¼ cup rice vinegar
- 4 baby leeks
- 8 medium green scallions, red scallions, or green onions
- 1 medium lime, halved

1 Thaw scallops, if frozen. Rinse scallops; pat dry with paper towels. For marinade, in a small bowl combine soy sauce and rice vinegar; set aside.

2 Trim root ends and green tops from leeks. Rinse leeks thoroughly to remove any grit.

3 Place leeks, scallops, and scallions in a resealable plastic bag set in a shallow dish. Pour marinade over scallops and vegetables. Seal bag; turn to coat scallops and vegetables. Marinate in refrigerator for 30 minutes.

4 Remove, leeks, scallops, and scallions from bag. Discard marinade. For a charcoal grill, place leeks, scallops, scallions, and lime halves (cut sides down) on the rack of an uncovered grill directly over medium coals. Grill for 8 to 10 minutes or until scallops are opaque, turning scallops and vegetables occasionally. Remove scallions from grill rack before they overbrown. (For a gas grill, preheat grill. Reduce heat to medium. Place leeks, scallops, scallions, and lime halves [cut sides down] on grill rack over heat. Cover and grill as above.)

5 To serve, transfer leeks and scallions to four dinner plates. Top with scallops. Using grilling tongs, remove limes from grill and squeeze over scallops.

Chapter 11

Meatless

On the opener: White Bean and Cumin Chili *(see recipe, page 216)*

GRAINS/BEANS

PASTA

VEGETABLE SANDWICHES

SOY

Asparagus-Leek Risotto

START TO FINISH 45 minutes
OVEN 450°F **MAKES** 4 servings

NUTRITION FACTS per serving

CALORIES 256
TOTAL FAT 9 g (2 g sat. fat)
CHOLESTEROL 6 mg
SODIUM 683 mg
CARBOHYDRATE 36 g
FIBER 3 g
PROTEIN 10 g
EXCHANGES 1 Vegetable, 2 Starch, 1 Lean Meat, 2½ Fat

- 12 ounces asparagus spears, trimmed
- 2 tablespoons olive oil
- Salt and black pepper
- 1½ cups sliced leeks
- 1 cup Arborio rice
- 3 cups reduced-sodium chicken broth
- ⅓ cup freshly grated Parmesan cheese
- 2 tablespoons snipped fresh parsley
- ½ teaspoon finely shredded lemon peel
- 1 tablespoon lemon juice
- ¼ teaspoon freshly ground coarse black pepper
- Lemon slices
- Lemon peel strips

1 Preheat oven to 450°F. Place asparagus in single layer on a baking sheet. Brush with 1 tablespoon olive oil; lightly sprinkle with salt and black pepper. Bake, uncovered, about 10 minutes or until crisp-tender. Cool slightly. Cut two-thirds of the asparagus into 2-inch pieces; set aside all asparagus.

2 Meanwhile, in a large saucepan heat the remaining 1 tablespoon olive oil. Add leeks; cook until tender. Stir in uncooked rice. Cook and stir over medium heat about 5 minutes or until rice begins to turn golden brown.

3 In another saucepan bring broth to boiling. Reduce heat to simmer. Carefully stir 1 cup of hot broth into rice mixture. Cook, stirring frequently, over medium heat until liquid is absorbed. Then add ½ cup broth at a time, stirring frequently until broth is absorbed before adding more broth (about 22 minutes).

4 Stir in any remaining broth. Cook and stir just until rice is tender and creamy.

5 Stir in asparagus pieces, cheese, parsley, lemon peel, lemon juice, and pepper. Top with asparagus spears, lemon slices, and lemon peel strips.

Pasta with Ricotta and Vegetables

START TO FINISH 25 minutes
MAKES 4 servings

NUTRITION FACTS per serving

CALORIES 361
TOTAL FAT 9 g (2 g sat. fat)
CHOLESTEROL 17 mg
SODIUM 408 mg
CARBOHYDRATE 55 g
FIBER 7 g
PROTEIN 16 g
EXCHANGES 1½ Vegetable, 3 Starch, 1 Lean Meat, ½ Fat

- 8 ounces dried cut ziti or penne pasta
- 1½ cups 1-inch pieces fresh asparagus or green beans
- 2½ cups broccoli florets
- 1 cup ricotta cheese
- ¼ cup snipped fresh basil
- 1 tablespoon snipped fresh thyme
- 1 tablespoon balsamic vinegar
- 1 tablespoon olive oil
- 1 clove garlic, minced
- ½ teaspoon salt
- ½ teaspoon black pepper
- 1⅓ cups chopped, seeded red and/or yellow tomatoes
- Shaved Parmesan or Romano cheese (optional)
- Fresh thyme sprigs (optional)

1 Cook pasta according to package directions, adding green beans (if using) with pasta for the entire cooking time and adding broccoli and asparagus (if using) the last 3 minutes of cooking time. Drain well. Return to hot pan; cover and keep warm.

2 Meanwhile, in a large bowl combine ricotta cheese, basil, snipped thyme, vinegar, oil, garlic, salt, and pepper. Gently stir in tomatoes.

3 Add the drained pasta mixture to the tomato mixture; toss gently to combine. If desired, top with Parmesan cheese and garnish with thyme sprigs.

Summer Vegetable Pilaf

PREP 25 minutes **COOK** 20 minutes
STAND 5 minutes **MAKES** 4 servings

NUTRITION FACTS per serving

CALORIES 275
TOTAL FAT 6 g (2 g sat. fat)
CHOLESTEROL 8 mg
SODIUM 495 mg
CARBOHYDRATE 44 g
FIBER 11 g
PROTEIN 12 g
EXCHANGES 1½ Vegetable, 2½ Starch, 1 Fat

- 1 14.5-ounce can vegetable broth
- ½ cup chopped onion (1 medium)
- ½ cup dry lentils, rinsed and drained
- ½ cup uncooked long grain white rice
- ¼ cup water
- 1 teaspoon finely shredded lemon peel
- 1½ cups small fresh broccoli florets, sliced zucchini or yellow summer squash, and/or fresh snow or sugar snap pea pods
- 1 medium carrot, cut into thin strips
- 2 teaspoons olive oil
- ½ of a small eggplant, peeled and diced
- 2 cloves garlic, minced
- 3 plum tomatoes, chopped
- ¼ cup snipped fresh basil
- ¼ cup finely shredded Asiago or Parmesan cheese (1 ounce)

1 In a 3-quart saucepan combine the broth, onion, lentils, rice, water, and lemon peel. Bring to boiling; reduce heat. Simmer, covered, for 20 minutes, adding broccoli and carrot during the last 3 to 5 minutes of cooking.

2 Meanwhile, in a large skillet heat oil over medium heat. Add the eggplant and garlic; cook about 5 minutes or until eggplant is soft.

3 Remove lentil mixture from heat; let stand, covered, for 5 minutes. Carefully stir in the eggplant mixture, tomatoes, and basil. To serve, sprinkle with cheese.

Crispy Tofu and Vegetables

PREP 20 minutes **STAND** 1 hour
COOK 16 minutes **MAKES** 4 servings

NUTRITION FACTS per serving

CALORIES 198
TOTAL FAT 10 g (1 g sat. fat)
CHOLESTEROL 0 mg
SODIUM 410 mg
CARBOHYDRATE 14 g
FIBER 3 g
PROTEIN 16 g
EXCHANGES 1½ Vegetable, ½ Starch, 1 Lean Meat, 1 Fat

- 1 10.5-ounce package light extra-firm tofu (fresh bean curd), drained
- 3 tablespoons reduced-sodium soy sauce
- 8 green onions
- 2 cups snow pea pods, strings and tips removed
- 1 tablespoon toasted sesame oil
- 1 teaspoon grated fresh ginger or ½ teaspoon ground ginger
- 1 clove garlic, minced
- 1 red sweet pepper, seeded and cut into long, thin strips
- 1 yellow sweet pepper, seeded and cut into long, thin strips
- 3 tablespoons cornmeal
- 1 tablespoon white or black sesame seeds, toasted (optional)

1 Cut tofu crosswise into 8 slices. Arrange slices in 1 layer on a large plate or 15×10×1-inch baking pan. Pour soy sauce over tofu; turn slices to coat. Let stand for 1 hour.

2 Meanwhile, cut root ends off green onions. Cut off dark green portion of onions, leaving 3 inches of white and light green. Cut green onions in half lengthwise, forming 16 long strips. Set aside. Cut pea pods in half lengthwise. Set aside.

3 Heat sesame oil in a large nonstick skillet over medium-high heat. Add fresh ginger (if using) and garlic; stir-fry for 30 seconds. Add sweet pepper strips; stir-fry for 1 minute. Add green onions and pea pods; stir-fry for 2 to 3 minutes more or until crisp-tender.

4 Drain tofu, reserving soy sauce. Stir reserved soy sauce and ground ginger (if using) into cooked vegetables; transfer vegetable mixture to a serving platter. Cover and keep warm. Carefully dip tofu slices in cornmeal to lightly coat both sides. Cook in same skillet for 3 minutes on each side or until crisp and hot, using a spatula to turn carefully. (You may need to cook tofu slices in 2 batches; do not crowd skillet.) Serve tofu slices with vegetables. If desired, sprinkle with sesame seeds.

Garden Vegetables Lasagna

PREP 25 minutes **BAKE** 45 minutes
STAND 10 minutes **OVEN** 375°F
MAKES 8 servings

Nonstick cooking spray
- 3 cups broccoli florets
- 2 red sweet peppers, seeded and cut into bite-size strips (2 cups)
- 2 medium zucchini and/or yellow summer squash, sliced (about 2½ cups)
- 2 15-ounce cartons light ricotta cheese
- ½ cup snipped fresh basil or 1 tablespoon dried basil, crushed
- 1 tablespoon snipped fresh thyme or 1 teaspoon dried thyme, crushed
- 3 cloves garlic, minced
- ½ teaspoon salt
- ¼ teaspoon black pepper
- ¼ teaspoon bottled hot pepper sauce
- 9 dried whole grain or regular lasagna noodles, cooked and drained
- 2 cups shredded reduced-fat mozzarella cheese (8 ounces)
- ¼ cup shredded fresh basil (optional)

1 Preheat oven to 375°F. Lightly coat a 3-quart rectangular baking dish with cooking spray; set aside. Place a steamer basket in a 4-quart Dutch oven. Add water to just below the bottom of the basket. Bring to boiling. Add broccoli, sweet peppers, and zucchini; cover and reduce heat. Steam for 6 to 8 minutes or until vegetables are crisp-tender. Remove from heat.

2 In a large bowl combine ricotta cheese, the ½ cup basil, the thyme, garlic, salt, black pepper, and hot pepper sauce. Layer 3 of the cooked noodles in the prepared baking dish. Spread with one-third of the ricotta cheese mixture. Top with one-third of the vegetable mixture and ⅔ cup of the mozzarella cheese. Repeat layers twice.

3 Bake, covered, for 45 to 55 minutes or until heated through. Uncover; let stand for 10 minutes before serving. If desired, sprinkle with the ¼ cup basil.

NUTRITION FACTS per serving

CALORIES 296
TOTAL FAT 9 g (5 g sat. fat)
CHOLESTEROL 41 mg
SODIUM 426 mg
CARBOHYDRATE 31 g
FIBER 6 g
PROTEIN 20 g
EXCHANGES 1 Vegetable, 1½ Starch, 2 Medium-Fat Meat

Red Bean Lasagna

PREP 45 minutes **BAKE** 45 minutes
STAND 10 minutes **OVEN** 375°F
MAKES 8 servings

NUTRITION FACTS per serving

CALORIES 243
TOTAL FAT 6 g (2 g sat. fat)
CHOLESTEROL 13 mg
SODIUM 631 mg
CARBOHYDRATE 29 g
FIBER 6 g
PROTEIN 18 g
EXCHANGES 1 Vegetable, 1½ Starch, 2 Lean Meat

- 1 cup chopped onion (1 large)
- ½ cup chopped carrot (1 medium)
- 1 clove garlic, minced
- 1 tablespoon vegetable oil
- 1 15- to 16-ounce can red beans, rinsed and drained
- 1 14.5-ounce can diced tomatoes, undrained
- ¼ cup snipped fresh parsley
- 1 tablespoon snipped fresh basil
- 2 teaspoons snipped fresh oregano
- 2 cups sliced fresh mushrooms
- 1 12-ounce carton low-fat cottage cheese, drained
- 1 cup shredded part-skim mozzarella cheese (4 ounces)
- ¼ cup refrigerated or frozen egg product, thawed
- ¼ cup grated Parmesan cheese
- 6 dried whole wheat lasagna noodles, cooked and drained
- 3 cups chopped fresh spinach

1 In a large skillet cook onion, carrot, and garlic in hot oil until tender. Add beans, undrained tomatoes, ¼ cup parsley, basil, and oregano. Bring to boiling; reduce heat. Simmer, covered, for 15 minutes. Mash beans slightly. Add mushrooms; simmer, uncovered, for 15 minutes more, stirring occasionally. Meanwhile, in a medium bowl combine cottage cheese, ½ cup of the mozzarella cheese, the egg, and Parmesan cheese; set aside.

2 Preheat oven to 375°F. Spread ½ cup of the bean mixture in a 2-quart rectangular baking dish. Arrange 2 noodles on top of the bean mixture. Spread with one-third of the cheese mixture. Top evenly with one-third of the remaining bean mixture. Top with half of the spinach. Repeat layers twice, first with noodles and ending with bean mixture.

3 Bake, covered, about 40 minutes or until heated through. Top with remaining ½ cup mozzarella cheese. Bake, uncovered, for 5 minutes more or until cheese is melted. Let stand for 10 minutes before serving. If desired, sprinkle with fresh *basil* and/or *oregano leaves*.

Three-Cheese Manicotti

PREP 30 minutes **BAKE** 40 minutes
STAND 10 minutes **OVEN** 350°F
MAKES 10 to 12 servings

- 20 dried manicotti shells
- 2½ cups low-fat ricotta cheese (24 ounces)
- 2 cups shredded part-skim mozzarella cheese (4 ounces)
- ½ cup refrigerated or frozen egg product, thawed, or 2 eggs
- ⅓ cup grated Romano or Asiago cheese
- ¼ cup snipped fresh parsley
- ¼ teaspoon black pepper
- 4 cups purchased light tomato basil pasta sauce
- Snipped fresh parsley (optional)

1 Cook manicotti shells according to package directions; set aside. For filling, in a large bowl combine ricotta cheese, 1 cup of the mozzarella cheese, the egg product, Romano cheese, ¼ cup parsley, and the pepper. Set aside.

2 Preheat oven to 350°F. Spread 1 cup of pasta sauce in bottom of a 3-quart rectangular baking dish. Spoon about 3 tablespoons of the filling into each cooked shell. Arrange filled shells on the sauce in the baking dish. Spoon remaining pasta sauce evenly over the filled shells.

3 Bake for 35 to 40 minutes or until heated through. Sprinkle with the remaining 1 cup mozzarella cheese. Bake for 5 minutes more or until cheese is melted. Let stand on a wire rack for 10 minutes before serving. If desired, sprinkle with additional parsley.

Make-Ahead Directions: Prepare as directed through Step 2. Cover and chill up to 24 hours. To serve, preheat oven to 350°F. Uncover baking dish; bake for 40 to 45 minutes or until heated through. Sprinkle with remaining 1 cup mozzarella cheese. Bake about 5 minutes more or until cheese is melted. Let stand on a wire rack for 10 minutes before serving. If desired, sprinkle with additional parsley.

NUTRITION FACTS per serving

CALORIES 293
TOTAL FAT 8 g (4 g sat. fat)
CHOLESTEROL 36 mg
SODIUM 640 mg
CARBOHYDRATE 37 g
FIBER 3 g
PROTEIN 20 g
EXCHANGES ½ Vegetable, 2 Starch, 2 Medium-Fat Meat

Baked Stuffed Shells

PREP 40 minutes **BAKE** 37 minutes
STAND 10 minutes **OVEN** 350°F
MAKES 6 servings (2 shells per serving)

NUTRITION FACTS per serving

CALORIES 234
TOTAL FAT 5 g (2 g sat. fat)
CHOLESTEROL 10 mg
SODIUM 357 mg
CARBOHYDRATE 32 g
FIBER 3 g
PROTEIN 14 g
EXCHANGES 1 Vegetable, 2 Starch, 1 Lean Meat

- ½ cup chopped onion (1 medium
- 2 cloves garlic, minced
- 1 teaspoon olive oil
- 1 14.5-ounce can no-salt-added diced tomatoes, undrained
- 1 8-ounce can no-salt-added tomato sauce
- ¼ teaspoon salt
- 1 tablespoon snipped fresh basil
- 2 teaspoons snipped fresh oregano
- 1 12.3-ounce package extra-firm, silken-style tofu (fresh bean curd)
- ¼ cup refrigerated or frozen egg product, thawed, or 1 egg, lightly beaten
- ½ cup finely shredded Parmesan or Romano cheese
- ¼ teaspoon black pepper
- 12 dried jumbo shell macaroni, cooked and drained
- ½ cup shredded reduced-fat mozzarella cheese (2 ounces)

1 Preheat oven to 350°F. For sauce, in a medium saucepan cook onion and garlic in hot oil over medium heat. Add undrained tomatoes, tomato sauce, and salt. Bring to boiling; reduce heat. Simmer, uncovered, about 15 minutes or until desired consistency. Remove from heat; stir in basil and oregano. Set aside ¾ cup of the sauce; spoon the remaining sauce into a 2-quart rectangular baking dish. Set aside.

2 For filling, place tofu in a food processor or blender. Cover and process or blend until smooth. Add egg product, Parmesan cheese, and pepper; cover and process just until combined. Spoon about 3 tablespoons of the filling into each pasta shell. Arrange filled shells, filling sides up, on top of the sauce in dish. Spoon the reserved ¾ cup sauce over stuffed shells.

4 Bake, covered, about 35 minutes or until heated through. Uncover and sprinkle with mozzarella cheese. Bake, uncovered, about 2 minutes more or until cheese is melted. Let stand for 10 minutes. If desired, top with shredded *fresh basil.*

Lentil and Veggie Shepherd's Pie

PREP 45 minutes **BAKE** 35 minutes
OVEN 350°F **MAKES** 8 servings

NUTRITION FACTS per serving

CALORIES 234
TOTAL FAT 3 g (2 g sat. fat)
CHOLESTEROL 8 mg
SODIUM 386 mg
CARBOHYDRATE 41 g
FIBER 13 g
PROTEIN 12 g
EXCHANGES 2 Vegetable, 2 Starch, ½ Fat

- 1 14.5-ounce can vegetable broth or reduced-sodium chicken broth
- 1 cup water
- 1 cup dry brown lentils, rinsed and drained
- 3 cloves garlic, minced
- 4 medium carrots, peeled and bias-cut into ½-inch slices (2 cups)
- 3 small parsnips, peeled and bias-cut into ½-inch slices (1½ cups)
- 6 white boiling onions (8 ounces), quartered, or 1 medium onion, cut into thin wedges
- 4 cups coarsely shredded trimmed fresh chard or kale
- 1 14.5-ounce can no-salt-added diced tomatoes, undrained
- 2 tablespoons no-salt-added tomato paste
- 3 tablespoons snipped fresh basil
- 4 medium potatoes, peeled and cut up
- 4 cloves garlic, peeled
- 1 tablespoon butter
- 3 to 4 tablespoons fat-free milk
- ½ cup finely shredded Parmesan cheese

1 In a saucepan bring broth, the 1 cup water, lentils, and minced garlic to boiling; reduce heat. Simmer, covered, for 20 minutes. Add carrots, parsnips, and onions. Return to boiling; reduce heat. Simmer, covered, for 10 to 15 minutes more or until tender. Stir in chard; remove from heat. Stir in tomatoes, tomato paste, and 2 tablespoons of the fresh basil.

2 Preheat oven to 350°F. In a covered saucepan cook potatoes and whole garlic cloves in enough water to cover for 20 to 25 minutes or until tender; drain. Mash with a potato masher or beat with an electric mixer on low. Add butter. Beat in enough milk to make potatoes light and fluffy. Fold in cheese and the remaining basil. Spread lentil mixture into a 2- or 2½-quart casserole. Spread potato mixture evenly over lentil mixture. Bake, uncovered, about 35 minutes or until heated through.

White Bean and Cumin Chili

PREP 25 minutes
COOK 8 to 9 hours (low) or 4 to 4½ hours (high)
MAKES 6 servings

NUTRITION FACTS per serving

CALORIES 140
TOTAL FAT 1 g (1 g sat. fat)
CHOLESTEROL 4 mg
SODIUM 406 mg
CARBOHYDRATE 28 g
FIBER 7 g
PROTEIN 7 g
EXCHANGES 1 Vegetable, 1½ Starch

- 2 19-ounce cans cannellini beans (white kidney beans), rinsed and drained
- 2 14.5-ounce cans no-salt-added diced tomatoes, undrained
- 1½ cups peeled, seeded, and coarsely chopped butternut squash (about 12 ounces)
- 1½ cups chopped onions (3 medium)
- 1 12-ounce can light beer
- 1 canned chipotle pepper in adobo sauce, finely chopped (see note, page 203)
- 1 tablespoon cumin seeds, toasted and ground*
- 3 cloves garlic, minced
- ½ teaspoon salt
- ⅓ cup light sour cream
- 2 tablespoon lime juice
- 1 tablespoon snipped fresh chives
- Small lime wedges (optional)

1 In a 3½ or 4-quart slow cooker combine beans, undrained tomatoes, squash, onions, beer, chipotle pepper, cumin, garlic, and salt.

2 Cover and cook on low-heat setting for 8 to 9 hours or on high-heat setting for 4 to 4½ hours.

3 In a small bowl combine sour cream, lime juice, and chives. Spoon chili into bowls; top with sour cream mixture. If desired, garnish with lime wedges.

***Note:** To toast cumin seeds, place the seeds in a dry skillet over medium heat. Cook for 2 to 3 minutes or until fragrant, shaking skillet occasionally. (Avoid overcooking cumin seeds, which can make them bitter.) Remove from heat; allow to cool. Grind with a mortar and pestle or in a blender.

Ratatouille with Lentils

PREP 25 minutes
COOK 8 to 9 hours (low) or 4 to 4½ hours (high)
MAKES 6 servings

NUTRITION FACTS per serving

CALORIES 191
TOTAL FAT 1 g (0 g sat. fat)
CHOLESTEROL 0 mg
SODIUM 256 mg
CARBOHYDRATE 37 g
FIBER 16 g
PROTEIN 11 g
EXCHANGES 2 Vegetable, 2 Starch

- 1 cup dry lentils, rinsed and drained
- 1 small eggplant (12 ounces), peeled and cubed
- 2 14.5-ounce cans no-salt-added diced tomatoes, undrained
- 2 cups coarsely chopped onions (2 large)
- 2 medium yellow summer squash and/or zucchini, halved lengthwise and cut into ½-inch slices (about 2½ cups)
- ¾ cup chopped red sweet pepper (1 medium)
- ½ cup water
- 1 tablespoon dried Italian seasoning, crushed
- 2 cloves garlic, minced
- ½ teaspoon salt
- ¼ to ½ teaspoon black pepper

1 In a 3½- or 4-quart slow cooker combine lentils, eggplant, tomatoes, onions, summer squash, sweet pepper, the water, Italian seasoning, garlic, salt, and black pepper. Cover and cook on low-heat setting for 8 to 9 hours or on high-heat setting for 4 to 4½ hours.

Spinach Panini

PREP 20 minutes **COOK** 2 minutes per batch
MAKES 4 sandwiches

NUTRITION FACTS per sandwich

CALORIES 299
TOTAL FAT 7 g (3 g sat. fat)
CHOLESTEROL 13 mg
SODIUM 826 mg
CARBOHYDRATE 50 g
FIBER 8 g
PROTEIN 13 g
EXCHANGES 1½ Vegetable, 3 Starch, ½ Medium-Fat Meat

- Nonstick olive oil cooking spray
- 8 slices whole wheat bread or 2 whole wheat pita bread rounds, halved crosswise and split horizontally
- 4 cups fresh baby spinach leaves
- 8 thin tomato slices (1 medium tomato)
- ¼ cup thinly sliced red onion
- 2 tablespoons shredded fresh basil leaves
- ⅛ teaspoon freshly ground black pepper
- ½ cup crumbled feta cheese (2 ounces)

1 Lightly coat an unheated panini griddle, covered indoor electric grill, or large nonstick skillet with cooking spray; set aside.

2 Place 4 of the bread slices or 4 pita pieces on a work surface. Divide half of the spinach leaves among the bread slices. Top with tomato, red onion, and basil; sprinkle with black pepper. Sprinkle with feta cheese and top with the remaining spinach and bread. Press down on sandwiches firmly.

3 Preheat griddle, grill, or skillet over medium heat or heat according to manufacturer's directions. Add sandwiches, in batches if necessary. If using griddle or grill, close lid and grill for 2 to 3 minutes or until bread is toasted. (If using skillet, place a heavy plate or small skillet on top of sandwiches. Cook for 1 to 2 minutes or until bottoms are toasted. Carefully remove plate, which may be hot. Turn sandwiches and top again with the plate. Cook for 1 to 2 minutes more or until bread is toasted.)

Open-Face Ratatouille Sandwich

PREP 25 minutes **ROAST** 45 minutes
OVEN 400°F **MAKES** 4 servings

NUTRITION FACTS per serving

CALORIES 250
TOTAL FAT 7 g (1 g sat. fat)
CHOLESTEROL 0 mg
SODIUM 328 mg
CARBOHYDRATE 43 g
FIBER 8 g
PROTEIN 7 g
EXCHANGES 2 Starch, 2 Vegetable, 1 Fat

Nonstick cooking spray
1 small eggplant, cut into 1-inch pieces
1 small zucchini or yellow summer squash, cut into ¾-inch slices
1 medium red sweet pepper, cut into strips
½ of a small red onion, cut into ½-inch wedges
1 tablespoon olive oil
½ teaspoon herbes de Provence or dried thyme, crushed
⅛ teaspoon salt
⅛ teaspoon black pepper
2 medium plum tomatoes, each cut lengthwise into 6 wedges
8 small or 4 large ½-inch slices whole wheat or white French bread, toasted (about 8 ounces total)
1 clove garlic, halved
2 tablespoons balsamic vinegar
Fresh thyme sprigs (optional)

1 Preheat oven to 400°F. Coat a large shallow roasting pan with cooking spray. Add eggplant, zucchini, sweet pepper, and onion to prepared pan. Drizzle with olive oil; sprinkle with herbes de Provence, salt, and pepper. Toss to coat. Roast vegetables for 30 minutes, tossing once. Add tomatoes to roasting pan. Roast for 15 to 20 minutes more or until vegetables are tender and some surface areas are lightly browned.

2 Meanwhile, rub toasted bread with the cut sides of the garlic clove. Place 2 small slices or 1 large slice of bread on each of 4 serving plates. Sprinkle balsamic vinegar over vegetables; toss gently to coat. Spoon warm vegetables on bread. If desired, garnish with fresh thyme sprigs.

Open-Face Egg Sandwiches

START TO FINISH 15 minutes
MAKES 4 sandwiches

NUTRITION FACTS per sandwich

CALORIES 240
TOTAL FAT 14 g (3 g sat. fat)
CHOLESTEROL 212 mg
SODIUM 293 mg
CARBOHYDRATE 17 g
FIBER 6 g
PROTEIN 14 g
EXCHANGES 1 Starch, 2½ Medium-Fat Meat

- 1 cup frozen shelled sweet soybeans (edamame), thawed
- 1 small avocado, halved, seeded, and peeled
- 2 tablespoons lemon juice
- 2 cloves garlic, minced
- ¼ teaspoon salt
- ½ cup chopped red sweet pepper
- 4 very thin slices firm-texture whole wheat bread, toasted, or 2 whole wheat pita bread rounds, split in half horizontally
- 4 hard-cooked eggs, thinly sliced
- Freshly ground black pepper

1 In a medium bowl combine edamame, avocado, lemon juice, garlic, and salt; use a fork or potato masher to mash ingredients together until avocado is smooth and edamame are coarsely mashed. Stir in sweet pepper.

2 Spread edamame mixture on bread slices or pita halves. Arrange egg slices on edamame mixture. Sprinkle sandwiches with black pepper.

Cheese and Tomato Stack

START TO FINISH 15 minutes
MAKES 4 sandwiches

- 2 whole wheat English muffins, toasted
- 8 thin red and/or yellow tomato slices
- 4 ounces fresh mozzarella, cut into 4 slices
- 4 teaspoons snipped fresh basil
- 4 teaspoons olive oil
- ¼ teaspoon salt
- ¼ teaspoon cracked black pepper
- 4 grape tomatoes or cherry tomatoes, halved (optional)

1 On each English muffin half layer 1 tomato slice, 1 mozzarella slice, and 1 teaspoon of the basil. Repeat layers. In a small bowl combine olive oil, salt, and pepper. Drizzle sandwiches with half of the oil mixture. If desired, top with grape tomato halves.

NUTRITION FACTS per sandwich

CALORIES 203
TOTAL FAT 12 g (4 g sat. fat)
CHOLESTEROL 22 mg
SODIUM 531 mg
CARBOHYDRATE 16 g
FIBER 3 g
PROTEIN 10 g
EXCHANGES ½ Vegetable, 1 Starch, 1 Medium-Fat Meat, 1 Fat

Bean and Rice Salad

START TO FINISH 15 minutes
MAKES 4 servings

NUTRITION FACTS per serving

CALORIES 210
TOTAL FAT 4 g (1 g sat. fat)
CHOLESTEROL 4 mg
SODIUM 438 mg
CARBOHYDRATE 38 g
FIBER 8 g
PROTEIN 8 g
EXCHANGES 2 Vegetable, 2 Starch

1⅓ cups cooked brown rice
1⅓ cups canned pinto beans, black beans, or red beans, rinsed and drained
6 cups coarsely shredded mixed salad greens or fresh spinach
2 cups chopped tomatoes (2 large)
½ cup chopped onion (1 medium)
¼ cup shredded carrot
¼ cup sliced pitted ripe olives, halved
¼ cup purchased salsa
¼ cup light sour cream
½ of a medium avocado, peeled and sliced (optional)

1 Divide rice among 4 serving plates. Top with beans, greens, tomatoes, onion, carrot, olives, salsa, and sour cream. If desired, garnish with avocado slices.

Confetti Barley Salad

PREP 15 minutes **COOK** 45 minutes
MAKES 6 servings

NUTRITION FACTS per serving

CALORIES 247
TOTAL FAT 8 g (1 g sat. fat)
CHOLESTEROL 0 mg
SODIUM 363 mg
CARBOHYDRATE 38 g
FIBER 5 g
PROTEIN 6 g
EXCHANGES 2½ Starch, 1 Fat

- 5 cups water
- 1 cup regular barley
- 2 cups frozen succotash,* thawed
- ¼ cup white wine vinegar
- 3 tablespoons olive oil
- 1 tablespoon Dijon mustard
- 2 teaspoons snipped fresh oregano or ½ teaspoon dried oregano, crushed
- 2 cloves garlic, minced
- ½ teaspoon salt
- ¼ teaspoon black pepper
- 1 cup finely chopped red sweet pepper (1 large)
- ⅓ cup sliced pitted ripe olives
- Fresh herb sprigs (optional)

1 In a large saucepan bring the water to boiling. Stir in barley; reduce heat. Simmer, covered, for 45 to 50 minutes or just until tender, adding succotash the last 10 minutes of cooking time; drain. Rinse with cold water; drain again.

2 Meanwhile, for dressing, in a screw-top jar combine vinegar, oil, mustard, oregano, garlic, salt, and black pepper. Cover and shake well. Set aside.

3 In a large bowl combine barley mixture, sweet pepper, and olives. Shake dressing; pour over barley mixture. Toss to coat. Serve immediately or cover and chill up to 24 hours. If desired, garnish with fresh herb sprigs.

***Note:** If you can't find frozen succotash, substitute 1 cup thawed frozen corn and 1 cup thawed frozen lima beans.

Italian Beans with Pesto

PREP 15 minutes **COOK** 15 minutes
CHILL up to 3 days **MAKES** 6 servings

NUTRITION FACTS per serving

CALORIES 251
TOTAL FAT 10 g (0 g sat. fat)
CHOLESTEROL 2 mg
SODIUM 267 mg
CARBOHYDRATE 33 g
FIBER 8 g
PROTEIN 10 g
EXCHANGES 1 Vegetable, 1½ Starch, 1 Lean Meat, 1½ Fat

- 1 14.5-ounce can reduced-sodium chicken broth or vegetable broth
- ¾ cup bulgur
- ¾ cup chopped red sweet pepper (1 medium)
- ⅓ cup refrigerated basil pesto
- ¼ cup thinly sliced green onions (2)
- 2 tablespoons balsamic vinegar
- 2 cups cooked or canned red kidney beans, pinto beans, Christmas lima beans, and/or other white beans*
- Black pepper
- 12 butterhead lettuce leaves

1 In a large saucepan combine broth and bulgur. Bring to boiling; reduce heat. Simmer, covered, about 15 minutes or until bulgur is tender. Remove from heat. Stir in sweet pepper, pesto, green onions, and balsamic vinegar. Stir in beans. Season with black pepper. Cover and chill up to 3 days.

2 To serve, spoon bean mixture evenly into lettuce leaves. Roll up.

***Note:** To cook dried beans, rinse ¾ cup dried beans. In a large saucepan combine rinsed beans and 5 cups water. Bring to boiling; reduce heat. Simmer, uncovered, for 2 minutes. Remove from heat. Cover and let stand for 1 hour. Drain; rinse beans and return to saucepan. Add 5 cups fresh water. Bring to boiling; reduce heat. Simmer, covered, for 1¼ to 1½ hours or until beans are tender; drain.

Chapter 12

Sides

On the opener: Sweet Potato Fries *(see recipe, page 232)*

FRUIT

GRAINS & BEANS

VEGETABLES

Thyme-Roasted Asparagus

PREP 10 minutes **BROIL** 8 minutes
STAND 20 minutes **ROAST** 10 minutes
OVEN 400°F **MAKES** 4 servings

NUTRITION FACTS per serving

CALORIES 110
TOTAL FAT 9 g (2 g sat. fat)
CHOLESTEROL 5 mg
SODIUM 269 mg
CARBOHYDRATE 5 g
FIBER 2 g
PROTEIN 4 g
EXCHANGES 1 Vegetable, 2 Fat

- 1 medium red sweet pepper
- 1 pound fresh asparagus
- 2 tablespoons olive oil
- 1 teaspoon snipped fresh thyme
- ¼ teaspoon salt
- ¼ teaspoon freshly ground black pepper
- 1 ounce Parmesan cheese, shaved
- 2 tablespoons snipped fresh parsley
- Olive oil (optional)
- Cracked black pepper (optional)

1 Preheat broiler. Line a baking sheet with foil; set aside. Halve sweet pepper lengthwise; discard stem, membranes, and seeds. Place sweet pepper, cut sides down, on prepared baking sheet. Broil 4 to 5 inches from heat for 8 to 10 minutes or until blackened and blistered. Carefully bring foil up and around pepper halves to enclose. Let stand about 20 minutes or until cool enough to handle. Peel skin off sweet pepper. Cut sweet pepper into ½-inch-wide strips. Set strips aside.

2 Preheat oven to 400°F. Snap off and discard woody bases from asparagus. If desired, scrape off scales. In a small bowl combine oil, thyme, salt, and freshly ground black pepper; pour over asparagus spears. Toss lightly to coat. Arrange spears in a single layer in a 15×10×1-inch baking pan. Roast, uncovered, for 10 to 12 minutes or until lightly browned and tender, turning asparagus once.

3 Arrange asparagus spears and sweet pepper strips on a warm serving platter. Top with Parmesan cheese and parsley. If desired, drizzle with olive oil and sprinkle with cracked black pepper. Serve immediately.

Broccoli and Cauliflower Sauté

START TO FINISH 20 minutes
MAKES 4 servings

NUTRITION FACTS per serving

CALORIES 47
TOTAL FAT 2 g (0 g sat. fat)
CHOLESTEROL 0 mg
SODIUM 88 mg
CARBOHYDRATE 4 g
FIBER 1 g
PROTEIN 1 g
EXCHANGES 1 Vegetable, ½ Fat

2 teaspoons olive oil
1 cup broccoli florets
1 cup cauliflower florets
1 clove garlic, thinly sliced
¼ cup dry white wine or reduced-sodium chicken broth
3 tablespoons water
⅛ teaspoon salt
⅛ teaspoon black pepper

1 In a large skillet heat oil over medium-high heat. Add broccoli, cauliflower, and garlic; cook for 2 minutes, stirring occasionally. Carefully add wine, the water, salt, and pepper; reduce heat to low. Cover and cook for 2 minutes. Uncover; increase heat to medium. Cook for 2 minutes or until vegetables are tender.

Classic Succotash

PREP 15 minutes **COOK** 32 minutes
MAKES 8 servings

NUTRITION FACTS per serving

CALORIES 125
TOTAL FAT 5 g (3 g sat. fat)
CHOLESTEROL 13 mg
SODIUM 222 mg
CARBOHYDRATE 18 g
FIBER 3 g
PROTEIN 5 g
EXCHANGES 1 Starch, 1 Fat

- 2 cups fresh shelled butter or lima beans*
- ¼ teaspoon salt
- 2 large ears fresh corn (about 2 cups)
- 2 tablespoons butter
- ⅛ teaspoon salt
- ⅛ teaspoon freshly ground black pepper
- ¼ cup half-and-half or light cream
- ¼ cup finely chopped lean country ham

1 Place butter beans in a large saucepan. Cover with water; add ¼ teaspoon salt. Bring to boiling. Skim surface until clear. Cook, partially covered, for 30 to 40 minutes or until tender. Drain beans and set aside.

2 Shuck corn. Using a clean terry cloth kitchen towel, gently rub corn to remove silks. Using a sharp knife, cut kernels from cobs.

3 In a large skillet heat butter over medium-high heat until melted and foaming. Add corn, the ⅛ teaspoon salt, and the pepper, stirring to coat corn in butter. Cook for 1 to 2 minutes. Add beans. Cook for 1 minute more, taking care not to overcook corn and beans.

4 Add half-and-half and ham. Cook just until heated through and slightly reduced.

***Note:** If fresh lima beans are not available, substitute 2 cups frozen baby lima beans. Cook beans according to package directions.

Savory Pea Pods and Apples

START TO FINISH 20 minutes
MAKES 8 to 10 servings

NUTRITION FACTS per serving

CALORIES 78
TOTAL FAT 2 g (0 g sat. fat)
CHOLESTEROL 4 mg
SODIUM 115 mg
CARBOHYDRATE 11 g
FIBER 2 g
PROTEIN 2 g
EXCHANGES 1 Vegetable, ½ Fruit, ½ Fat

- 2 teaspoons vegetable oil
- 3 slices turkey bacon, cut crosswise into thin strips
- ⅔ cup chopped leeks (2 medium)
- 3 tart red cooking apples (such as Jonathan), cut into ½-inch slices
- 4 cups fresh pea pods, trimmed and strings removed
- ⅛ teaspoon salt
- ⅛ teaspoon cracked black pepper

1 In a very large skillet heat oil over medium heat. Add turkey bacon; cook for 2 to 3 minutes or just until crisp, stirring occasionally. Add leeks and apples to bacon. Cook and stir for 3 to 4 minutes or just until apples are tender. Add pea pods. Cover and cook for 2 to 3 minutes more or until pea pods are crisp-tender. Sprinkle with salt and pepper.

Ginger-Vegetable Stir-Fry

START TO FINISH 20 minutes
MAKES 6 servings

- ½ cup cold water
- 1 tablespoon reduced-sodium soy sauce
- 1 teaspoon cornstarch
- ½ teaspoon ground ginger
- 1 tablespoon canola oil or vegetable oil
- 2 cups broccoli and/or cauliflower florets
- ½ cup thinly bias-sliced carrot (1 medium)
- ¼ cup chopped onion
- 1 clove garlic, minced
- ½ cup fresh sugar snap peas, tips and strings removed (about 2 ounces)
- ½ of a large red or green sweet pepper, seeded and cut into strips
- ½ of a 14-ounce can baby corn, drained and halved crosswise
- ½ of an 8-ounce can sliced water chestnuts, drained

1 In a small bowl stir together the water, soy sauce, cornstarch, and ginger; set aside.

2 In a wok or large skillet heat oil over medium-high heat. Add broccoli and/or cauliflower, carrot, onion, and garlic; stir-fry for 6 to 8 minutes or just until tender. Add sugar snap peas, sweet pepper, baby corn, and water chestnuts; stir-fry for 2 minutes.

3 Stir cornstarch mixture; add to vegetables in wok. Cook and stir until thickened and bubbly. Cook and stir for 2 minutes more.

NUTRITION FACTS per serving

CALORIES 56
TOTAL FAT 2 g (0 g sat. fat)
CHOLESTEROL 0 mg
SODIUM 120 mg
CARBOHYDRATE 7 g
FIBER 2 g
PROTEIN 2 g
EXCHANGES 1½ Vegetable, ½ Fat

Sweet Potato Fries

PREP 15 minutes **BAKE** 20 minutes
OVEN 400°F **MAKES** 6 servings

NUTRITION FACTS per serving

CALORIES 114
TOTAL FAT 5 g (1 g sat. fat)
CHOLESTEROL 0 mg
SODIUM 145 mg
CARBOHYDRATE 17 g
FIBER 3 g
PROTEIN 1 g
EXCHANGES 1 Starch, 1 Fat

- 4 medium sweet potatoes, peeled (if desired)
- 2 tablespoons olive oil
- ¼ teaspoon salt
- ⅛ teaspoon black pepper
- Snipped fresh parsley (optional)

1 Preheat oven to 400°F. Line 2 baking sheets with foil; set aside.

2 Cut sweet potatoes lengthwise into ½-inch-thick wedges. Place sweet potato wedges in a large bowl. Drizzle with oil; toss to coat. Arrange sweet potato wedges in a single layer on prepared baking sheets.

3 Bake for 10 to 15 minutes. Turn potatoes over and bake for 10 to 15 minutes more or until golden brown. Sprinkle with salt and pepper. If desired, sprinkle with snipped parsley.

Skillet Squash

PREP 20 minutes **COOK** 8 minutes
MAKES 6 servings

- 2 teaspoons olive oil
- 2 cups chopped zucchini (2 medium)
- 2 cups chopped yellow summer squash (2 medium)
- 1 medium onion, thinly sliced
- 1 4-ounce can diced green chiles, undrained
- 1 cup chopped tomatoes (2 medium)
- 2 teaspoons snipped fresh oregano or ½ teaspoon dried oregano, crushed
- ¼ teaspoon black pepper
- ⅛ teaspoon salt

1 In a large nonstick skillet heat oil over medium heat. Add zucchini, yellow squash, and onion. Cook for 8 to 10 minutes or just until onion is tender, stirring occasionally.

2 Add undrained green chiles, tomatoes, and dried oregano (if using). Heat through, stirring occasionally. Stir in fresh oregano (if using), black pepper, and salt. Serve immediately.

NUTRITION FACTS per serving

CALORIES 49
TOTAL FAT 2 g (0 g sat. fat)
CHOLESTEROL 0 mg
SODIUM 112 mg
CARBOHYDRATE 8 g
FIBER 2 g
PROTEIN 2 g
EXCHANGES 1½ Vegetable

Cheesy Squash Bake

PREP 30 minutes **BAKE** 25 minutes
OVEN 350°F **MAKES** 6 servings

NUTRITION FACTS per serving

CALORIES 72
TOTAL FAT 3 g (1 g sat. fat)
CHOLESTEROL 7 mg
SODIUM 169 mg
CARBOHYDRATE 8 g
FIBER 1 g
PROTEIN 5 g
EXCHANGES 1 Vegetable, ½ Medium-Fat Meat

- 1 pound yellow summer squash, thinly sliced
- ½ cup chopped onion (1 medium)
- 1 tablespoon lower-fat margarine
- 1 tablespoon all-purpose flour
- ½ cup fat-free milk
- ½ cup shredded reduced-fat cheddar cheese (2 ounces)
- ¼ teaspoon black pepper
- ⅛ teaspoon salt
- Nonstick cooking spray
- ½ cup soft whole wheat bread crumbs, toasted

1 Preheat oven to 350°F. In a large saucepan cook squash and onion in a small amount of boiling water for 5 to 10 minutes or until tender; drain and set aside.

2 Meanwhile, in a medium saucepan melt margarine over medium heat. Stir in flour. Gradually stir in milk; cook and stir until thickened and bubbly. Remove from heat. Stir in cheese, pepper, and salt until cheese is melted. Add squash mixture; toss to coat.

3 Coat a 1- to 1½-quart baking dish, casserole, or soufflé dish with cooking spray. Spoon squash mixture into prepared dish. Sprinkle with bread crumbs. Bake about 25 minutes or until golden brown and heated through.

Zucchini Bread Pudding

PREP 40 minutes **BAKE** 35 minutes
STAND 10 minutes **OVEN** 350°F
MAKES 12 servings

NUTRITION FACTS per serving

CALORIES 191
TOTAL FAT 7 g (2 g sat. fat)
CHOLESTEROL 7 mg
SODIUM 414 mg
CARBOHYDRATE 22 g
FIBER 2 g
PROTEIN 10 g
EXCHANGES ½ Vegetable, 1 Starch, 1 Lean Meat, 1 Fat

- Nonstick cooking spray
- 2 tablespoons olive oil
- 2 medium zucchini, cut into ¼-inch slices
- ½ cup fresh or frozen whole kernel corn
- ½ cup chopped bottled roasted red sweet peppers
- 6 cloves garlic, minced (1 tablespoon)
- 2 tablespoons snipped fresh basil or 2 teaspoons dried basil, crushed
- 1 tablespoon snipped fresh parsley or 1 teaspoon dried parsley flakes, crushed
- 1 tablespoon snipped fresh sage or 1 teaspoon dried sage, crushed
- 5 cups 1-inch sourdough or Italian bread cubes (about 13 ounces)
- 1 cup shredded Italian-blend cheeses (4 ounces)
- ¼ cup chopped pecans
- 2 cups fat-free milk
- 1¼ cups refrigerated or frozen egg product, thawed, or 5 eggs, lightly beaten
- ½ teaspoon salt
- ¼ teaspoon black pepper

1 Preheat oven to 350°F. Coat a 2-quart rectangular or oval baking dish with cooking spray; set aside. In a large skillet heat olive oil over medium heat. Add zucchini and corn; cook for 3 minutes. Stir in sweet peppers and garlic. Cook and stir about 2 minutes more or until zucchini is tender. Stir in basil, parsley, and sage. Stir in bread cubes.

2 Place half the mixture in prepared dish. Sprinkle with half the cheese. Repeat layers. Sprinkle with nuts. In a medium bowl whisk together milk, egg product, salt, and black pepper. Carefully pour over bread mixture.

3 Bake, uncovered, about 35 minutes or until a knife inserted near the center comes out clean. Let stand for 10 minutes before serving.

Tomato Sauté

START TO FINISH 30 minutes
MAKES 4 servings

NUTRITION FACTS per serving

CALORIES 88
TOTAL FAT 6 g (2 g sat. fat)
CHOLESTEROL 11 mg
SODIUM 168 mg
CARBOHYDRATE 6 g
FIBER 2 g
PROTEIN 4 g
EXCHANGES 1 Vegetable, ½ High-Fat Meat, ½ Fat

- 2½ cups whole red grape tomatoes, yellow pear tomatoes, cherry tomatoes, and/or small yellow tomatoes
- 2 teaspoons olive oil
- ¼ cup finely chopped onion
- 1 clove garlic, minced
- 1 teaspoon snipped fresh thyme or ¼ teaspoon dried thyme, crushed
- ¼ teaspoon salt
- ¼ teaspoon black pepper
- 2 ounces fresh mozzarella cheese, cut into ½-inch cubes

1 Halve the grape, pear, and/or cherry tomatoes or cut small yellow tomatoes into wedges; set aside. In a large skillet heat oil over medium heat. Add onion, garlic, and thyme; cook and stir for 2 to 3 minutes or until onion is tender.

2 Add the tomatoes, salt, and pepper. Cook and stir for 1 to 2 minutes or just until tomatoes are warmed. Remove from heat. Stir in mozzarella cheese.

Tomatoes with Crispy Bread Topping

PREP 20 minutes **BAKE** 15 minutes
OVEN 400°F **MAKES** 4 servings

NUTRITION FACTS per serving

CALORIES 75
TOTAL FAT 4 g (1 g sat. fat)
CHOLESTEROL 0 mg
SODIUM 152 mg
CARBOHYDRATE 9 g
FIBER 3 g
PROTEIN 2 g
EXCHANGES 1½ Vegetable, 1 Fat

- 8 plum tomatoes, cored and cut in half lengthwise (about 1⅓ pounds)
- Kosher salt
- Freshly ground black pepper
- ½ cup soft whole wheat bread crumbs
- ¼ cup thinly sliced green onions (2)
- 2 tablespoons snipped fresh thyme
- 1 tablespoon snipped fresh Italian (flat-leaf) parsley
- 1 tablespoon snipped fresh tarragon
- 1 tablespoon olive oil
- 2 cloves garlic, minced
- 1 tablespoon grated Parmesan cheese (optional)

1 Preheat oven to 400°F. Sprinkle the cut sides of the tomatoes with salt and pepper. Arrange tomatoes, cut sides up, in a shallow baking pan. Set aside.

2 In a small bowl combine bread crumbs, onions, thyme, parsley, tarragon, oil, garlic, and, if desired, cheese. Sprinkle over tomato halves. Bake, uncovered, for 15 to 20 minutes or until the tomatoes are heated through and the bread crumbs are browned and crisp.

Roasted Vegetable Couscous

PREP 20 minutes **ROAST** 45 minutes
STAND 20 minutes **OVEN** 375°F
MAKES 6 to 8 servings

NUTRITION FACTS per serving

CALORIES 141
TOTAL FAT 3 g (0 g sat. fat)
CHOLESTEROL 0 mg
SODIUM 105 mg
CARBOHYDRATE 25 g
FIBER 3 g
PROTEIN 4 g
EXCHANGES 1 Vegetable, 1 Starch, ½ Fat

- Nonstick cooking spray
- 1 Japanese eggplant or 1 small eggplant, halved lengthwise
- 1 small sweet onion (such as Walla Walla or Vidalia), halved
- 1 carrot, halved lengthwise
- 1 yellow or red sweet pepper,* halved lengthwise and seeded
- 1 or 2 yellow banana peppers, halved lengthwise and seeded
- 1 cup water
- ¾ cup quick-cooking couscous
- 1 recipe Balsamic-Mustard Dressing
- Butterhead lettuce leaves (optional)

1 Preheat oven to 375°F. Lightly coat a shallow baking pan with cooking spray. Place vegetables, cut sides down, in prepared baking pan. Roast for 45 to 60 minutes or until tender.

2 Wrap eggplant and peppers in foil; let stand for 20 minutes. Set remaining vegetables aside. Peel eggplant and peppers. Cut all vegetables into bite-size pieces.

3 In a medium saucepan bring the water to boiling. Stir in couscous. Remove from heat; let stand, covered, for 5 minutes.

4 In a large bowl combine vegetables, couscous, and Balsamic-Mustard Dressing. Toss gently to coat. If desired, line a shallow serving bowl with lettuce leaves. Spoon couscous mixture into bowl. Serve chilled or at room temperature.

Balsamic-Mustard Dressing: In a screw-top jar combine ¼ cup white or regular balsamic vinegar, 1 tablespoon canola oil, 1½ teaspoons Dijon mustard, ¼ teaspoon salt, ¼ teaspoon pepper seasoning blend, and ¼ teaspoon garlic powder. Cover and shake well.

***Note:** If you like, use half of a yellow sweet pepper and half of a red sweet pepper.

Red Lentil, Quinoa, and Flaxseed Pilaf

PREP 15 minutes **COOK** 28 minutes
STAND 5 minutes **MAKES** 5 servings

NUTRITION FACTS per serving

CALORIES 152
TOTAL FAT 5 g (1 g sat. fat)
CHOLESTEROL 0 mg
SODIUM 198 mg
CARBOHYDRATE 20 g
FIBER 4 g
PROTEIN 7 g
EXCHANGES 1½ Starch, 1 Fat

- ⅓ cup dry red lentils
- ⅓ cup quinoa
- 1 tablespoon olive oil
- ⅓ cup finely chopped shallots or onion
- 2 cloves garlic, minced
- 2 tablespoons flaxseeds
- 1 14.5-ounce can reduced-sodium chicken broth
- 1 cup chopped red or green sweet pepper (1 large)
- 1 teaspoon snipped fresh thyme or ¼ teaspoon dried thyme, crushed
- Fresh thyme sprigs (optional)

1 Rinse and drain lentils; set aside. Rinse and drain quinoa; set aside.

2 In a medium saucepan heat oil over medium heat. Add shallots and garlic; cook and stir for 3 minutes. Add quinoa and flaxseeds; cook and stir about 5 minutes or until quinoa is lightly browned.

3 Add lentils and chicken broth. Bring to boiling; reduce heat. Simmer, covered, for 15 minutes. Stir in sweet pepper and snipped or dried thyme. Cover and cook about 5 minutes more or until quinoa and lentils are tender. Let stand, covered, for 5 minutes. If desired, garnish with thyme sprigs.

Asparagus, Haricots Verts, and Snow Peas

PREP 15 minutes **STAND** 10 minutes
MAKES 6 to 8 servings

NUTRITION FACTS per serving

CALORIES 59
TOTAL FAT 1 g (0 g sat. fat)
CHOLESTEROL 0 mg
SODIUM 109 mg
CARBOHYDRATE 11 g
FIBER 3 g
PROTEIN 3 g
EXCHANGES 2 Vegetable

- 8 ounces fresh snow pea pods, trimmed (2½ cups)
- 8 ounces fresh haricots verts or green beans, trimmed and cut into 2-inch pieces (2 cups)
- 8 ounces fresh asparagus spears, trimmed and cut into 2-inch pieces (1¼ cups)
- ⅓ cup bottled fat-free raspberry vinaigrette salad dressing
- ½ teaspoon Jamaican jerk seasoning
- 1 tablespoon white sesame seeds, toasted

1 In a large saucepan bring 6 cups water to boiling. Add snow peas, haricots verts, and asparagus. Return to boiling. Boil gently, uncovered, for 2 minutes. Immediately remove vegetables from boiling water with a slotted spoon; plunge into a large bowl half-filled with ice water. Let stand for 10 minutes. Drain vegetables well; pat dry. Transfer vegetables to the large bowl.

2 In a small bowl combine salad dressing and Jamaican jerk seasoning; pour over vegetables, tossing to coat. Transfer vegetables to a serving platter; sprinkle with sesame seeds.

Pepper and Four-Bean Salad

PREP 25 minutes **CHILL** 4 to 24 hours
MAKES 14 servings

NUTRITION FACTS per serving

CALORIES 117
TOTAL FAT 4 g (1 g sat. fat)
CHOLESTEROL 0 mg
SODIUM 146 mg
CARBOHYDRATE 17 g
FIBER 5 g
PROTEIN 5 g
EXCHANGES 1½ Vegetable, ½ Starch, 1 Fat

- 4 cups fresh green and/or wax beans, trimmed and cut into 1½-inch pieces, or one 16-ounce package frozen cut green beans
- 1 15- to 16-ounce can kidney beans, rinsed and drained
- 1 15- to 16-ounce can garbanzo beans (chickpeas), rinsed and drained
- 3 medium green, red, and/or yellow sweet peppers, cut into thin strips
- 1 small red or white onion, thinly sliced and separated into rings
- ½ cup vinegar
- ¼ cup olive oil
- 1 tablespoon sugar
- 2 teaspoons snipped fresh tarragon or thyme or ½ teaspoon dried tarragon or thyme, crushed
- ½ teaspoon black pepper
- Lettuce leaves

1 In a covered large saucepan cook fresh green and/or wax beans in a small amount of boiling water for 8 to 10 minutes or just until tender. (If using frozen green beans, cook according to package directions.) Drain beans; plunge into a large bowl half-filled with ice water to cool quickly. Drain well.

2 In a large bowl combine green and/or wax beans, kidney beans, garbanzo beans, sweet peppers, and onion. For marinade, in a medium bowl combine vinegar, olive oil, sugar, tarragon, and black pepper. Whisk until combined. Pour marinade over the bean mixture. Toss gently to coat. Cover and chill for 4 to 24 hours, stirring occasionally.

3 Using a slotted spoon, spoon bean mixture into a serving bowl and garnish with lettuce leaves. Or serve bean mixture on lettuce leaves.

Spinach Salad with Glazed Almonds

START TO FINISH 35 minutes
MAKES 8 servings

NUTRITION FACTS per serving

CALORIES 113
TOTAL FAT 10 g (1 g sat. fat)
CHOLESTEROL 0 mg
SODIUM 110 mg
CARBOHYDRATE 6 g
FIBER 2 g
PROTEIN 2 g
EXCHANGES 1½ Vegetable, 1½ Fat

Nonstick cooking spray
⅓ cup sliced almonds
2 teaspoons sugar
1 10-ounce package prewashed spinach
1 cup sliced fresh strawberries
⅔ cup sliced celery
¼ cup sliced green onions (2)
¼ cup olive oil
¼ cup red wine vinegar
1 teaspoon sugar
¼ teaspoon salt
2 drops bottled hot pepper sauce

1 For glazed almonds, line a baking sheet with foil. Coat foil with cooking spray. In a heavy small skillet combine almonds and the 2 teaspoons sugar. Cook over medium-high heat until sugar begins to melt, shaking skillet occasionally. Do not stir. Reduce heat to low. Continue cooking until sugar is golden brown, stirring occasionally. Remove skillet from heat. Pour nut mixture onto the prepared baking sheet. Cool completely. Break into clusters.

2 Meanwhile, in a very large bowl combine spinach, strawberries, celery, and green onions. For dressing, in a small bowl whisk together oil, vinegar, the 1 teaspoon sugar, the salt, and hot pepper sauce.

3 Drizzle dressing over spinach mixture. Toss to coat. Divide spinach mixture among 8 salad plates. Sprinkle with glazed almonds.

Grapefruit and Avocado Salad

START TO FINISH 15 minutes
MAKES 6 servings

NUTRITION FACTS per serving

CALORIES 106
TOTAL FAT 7 g (1 g sat. fat)
CHOLESTEROL 0 mg
SODIUM 122 mg
CARBOHYDRATE 11 g
FIBER 4 g
PROTEIN 2 g
EXCHANGES 1 Vegetable, ½ Fruit, 1 Fat

- 4 cups packaged fresh baby spinach
- 1 grapefruit, peeled and sectioned
- 1 small avocado, halved, seeded, peeled, and sliced
- 1 cup canned sliced beets
- 1 tablespoon sliced almonds, toasted
- 1 recipe Orange Vinaigrette

1 Divide spinach among 4 salad plates. Arrange grapefruit sections, avocado slices, and beets on spinach. Top with almonds. Drizzle with Orange Vinaigrette.

Orange Vinaigrette: In a screw-top jar combine 1 teaspoon finely shredded orange peel, ⅓ cup orange juice, 2 teaspoons red wine vinegar, 2 teaspoons salad oil, ⅛ teaspoon salt, and a dash black pepper. Cover and shake well.

Fresh Fruit Salad with Creamy Lime Topping

START TO FINISH 35 minutes
MAKES 12 servings

NUTRITION FACTS per serving

CALORIES 64
TOTAL FAT 1 g (1 g sat. fat)
CHOLESTEROL 3 mg
SODIUM 61 mg
CARBOHYDRATE 13 g
FIBER 2 g
PROTEIN 1 g
EXCHANGES 1 Fruit

- ½ cup light sour cream
- ⅓ cup fat-free mayonnaise dressing or light mayonnaise
- 1 teaspoon finely shredded lime peel
- 2 tablespoons powdered sugar
- 2 tablespoons lime juice
- 1 tablespoon fat-free milk (optional)
- 6 cups assorted fresh fruit (such as clementine segments, cut-up mango, raspberries, carambola [star fruit] slices, pineapple chunks, cut-up kiwifruit, and/or halved strawberries)
- Lime peel (optional)

1 In a small bowl stir together sour cream, mayonnaise dressing, the 1 teaspoon lime peel, powdered sugar, and lime juice. If desired, stir in milk to make desired consistency.

2 Divide fruit among 12 salad dishes. Spoon sour cream mixture over fruit. If desired, garnish with additional lime peel.

Note: To serve fewer than 12, use ½ cup fruit per serving; top each serving with about 1 tablespoon of the sour cream mixture. Cover and chill remaining sour cream mixture up to 5 days.

Chapter 13

Appetizers & Snacks

On the opener: Sweet Potato Wontons *(see recipe, page 257)*

SAVORY

SPREADS & DIPS

SWEET

Roasted Vegetable Dip

PREP 20 minutes **ROAST** 40 minutes
OVEN 425°F **MAKES** 8 servings

NUTRITION FACTS per serving

CALORIES 136
TOTAL FAT 4 g (0 g sat. fat)
CHOLESTEROL 0 mg
SODIUM 217 mg
CARBOHYDRATE 24 g
FIBER 3 g
PROTEIN 3 g
EXCHANGES ½ Vegetable, 1 Starch, 1 Fat

- 4 medium carrots, cut into 1-inch pieces
- 2 large red sweet peppers, seeded and cut into 1-inch pieces
- 2 medium shallots, halved
- 3 cloves garlic
- 1 tablespoon olive oil
- ½ teaspoon freshly ground black pepper
- ¼ teaspoon salt
- 2 tablespoons balsamic vinegar
- 1 teaspoon snipped fresh rosemary
- Fresh rosemary sprigs (optional)
- 48 water crackers or 8 cups assorted vegetable dippers (such as broccoli florets, cauliflower florets, and/or zucchini sticks)

1 Preheat oven to 425°F. Line a shallow roasting pan with foil. Place carrots, sweet peppers, shallots, and garlic in prepared pan. Drizzle with olive oil and sprinkle with black pepper and salt. Cover with foil.

2 Roast for 20 minutes. Uncover and stir vegetables. Roast, uncovered, for 20 to 25 minutes more or until vegetables are tender and lightly browned. Cool slightly on a wire rack.

3 Transfer vegetable mixture to a food processor. Add vinegar and the 1 teaspoon rosemary. Cover and process until smooth. If desired, garnish with rosemary sprigs. Serve with crackers or vegetable dippers.

Sweet Pepper Dip

PREP 30 minutes **CHILL** 4 to 12 hours
MAKES 10 servings

NUTRITION FACTS per serving

CALORIES 116
TOTAL FAT 7 g (4 g sat. fat)
CHOLESTEROL 17 mg
SODIUM 239 mg
CARBOHYDRATE 11 g
FIBER 3 g
PROTEIN 4 g
EXCHANGES 1½ Vegetable, 1½ Fat

- 4 large red, green, yellow, or orange sweet peppers, seeded and cut up
- 1 small onion, cut up
- ¼ cup water
- 1 8-ounce package reduced-fat cream cheese (Neufchâtel), softened
- ¼ cup low-fat mayonnaise dressing
- 2 tablespoons lemon juice
- 2 teaspoons olive oil or vegetable oil
- 1 teaspoon prepared horseradish
- ¼ teaspoon salt
- Few dashes bottled hot pepper sauce
- Freshly ground black pepper (optional)
- 7½ cups assorted vegetable dippers (such as carrot sticks, sweet pepper strips, sliced zucchini, and/or celery sticks)

1 In a blender or large food processor combine about one-third of the cut-up sweet peppers, the onion, and the water. Cover and blend or process until smooth. Add the remaining cut-up peppers; cover and blend or process until smooth.

2 Place pureed vegetable mixture in a fine sieve; press mixture gently to drain off excess liquid. Set aside.

3 In a medium mixing bowl combine cream cheese, mayonnaise dressing, lemon juice, oil, horseradish, salt, and hot pepper sauce. Beat with an electric mixer on medium until smooth. Beat in pureed vegetable mixture. Cover and chill for 4 to 12 hours.

4 If desired, sprinkle dip with black pepper. Serve with vegetable dippers.

Tomato and Basil Chèvre Spread

PREP 15 minutes **STAND** 10 minutes
CHILL 2 to 4 hours **MAKES** 10 servings

- ⅓ cup dried tomatoes (not oil-packed)
- Boiling water
- 4 ounces soft goat cheese (chèvre)
- ½ of an 8-ounce package reduced-fat cream cheese (Neufchâtel), softened
- ¼ cup snipped fresh basil or 2 teaspoons dried basil, crushed
- 3 cloves garlic, minced
- ⅛ teaspoon black pepper
- 1 to 2 tablespoons fat-free milk
- Miniature toasts and/or assorted reduced-fat crackers

1 Place dried tomatoes in a small bowl. Add enough boiling water to cover; let stand for 10 minutes. Drain tomatoes, discarding liquid. Finely snip tomatoes.

2 In a medium bowl stir together snipped tomatoes, goat cheese, cream cheese, basil, garlic, and pepper. Stir in enough of the milk to make mixture spreading consistency. Cover and chill for 2 to 4 hours. Serve with miniature toasts and/or crackers.

NUTRITION FACTS per serving

CALORIES 66
TOTAL FAT 5 g (3 g sat. fat)
CHOLESTEROL 14 mg
SODIUM 125 mg
CARBOHYDRATE 2 g
FIBER 0 g
PROTEIN 4 g
EXCHANGES ½ High-Fat Meat

Curried Carrot Spread

PREP 20 minutes **COOK** 15 minutes
CHILL 4 hours to 3 days **MAKES** 24 servings

NUTRITION FACTS per serving

CALORIES 40
TOTAL FAT 1 g (0 g sat. fat)
CHOLESTEROL 0 mg
SODIUM 84 mg
CARBOHYDRATE 6 g
FIBER 2 g
PROTEIN 2 g
EXCHANGES ½ Starch

- 3 cups sliced carrots (6 medium)
- 2 tablespoons olive oil or vegetable oil
- ¾ cup chopped onion
- 3 cloves garlic, minced
- 1 tablespoon curry powder
- 1 teaspoon ground cumin
- 1 15-ounce can cannellini beans (white kidney beans), rinsed and drained
- ¾ teaspoon salt
- Thinly sliced green onion (optional)
- Crackers, melba toast, toasted French bread baguette slices, or vegetable dippers

1 In a covered medium saucepan cook carrots in a small amount of boiling water about 15 minutes or until very tender. Drain.

2 Meanwhile, in a small skillet heat oil over medium heat. Add onion and garlic; cook until tender. Stir in curry powder and cumin. Transfer carrots and onion mixture to a food processor; add beans and salt. Cover and process until smooth. Transfer to a serving bowl; cover and chill for 4 hours to 3 days.

3 If desired, garnish spread with green onion. Serve with crackers, melba toast, toasted French bread slices, or vegetable dippers.

Edamame-Lemongrass Hummus

START TO FINISH 25 minutes
MAKES 10 servings

NUTRITION FACTS per serving

CALORIES 51
TOTAL FAT 3 g (0 g sat. fat)
CHOLESTEROL 0 mg
SODIUM 180 mg
CARBOHYDRATE 4 g
FIBER 2 g
PROTEIN 3 g
EXCHANGES 1 Vegetable, ½ Fat

- 2 green onions
- 1 10-ounce package (2 cups) frozen sweet soybeans (edamame)
- ½ cup fresh Italian (flat-leaf) parsley sprigs
- ½ cup water
- 2 tablespoons lemon juice
- 1 tablespoon chopped fresh lemongrass or ½ teaspoon finely shredded lemon peel
- 1 tablespoon canola oil
- 2 cloves garlic, quartered
- 1 teaspoon finely chopped fresh ginger or ¼ teaspoon ground ginger
- ¾ teaspoon salt
- ¼ teaspoon crushed red pepper (optional)
- 40 Belgian endive leaves and/or 10 cups assorted dippers, such as radishes, red sweet pepper strips, Belgian endive leaves, and/or peeled jicama sticks

1 Thinly slice green onions, keeping green tops separate from white bottoms; set aside. Cook edamame according to package directions, except omit salt. Drain; rinse with cold water. Drain again.

2 In a food processor combine white parts of green onions, cooked edamame, parsley, the water, lemon juice, lemongrass, oil, garlic, ginger, salt, and, if desired, crushed red pepper. Cover and process until nearly smooth. Stir in green onion tops. Serve with vegetable dippers.

Make-Ahead Directions: Prepare as directed. Cover and chill up to 24 hours.

Pumpkin-Shrimp Bruschetta

START TO FINISH 35 minutes
MAKES 20 appetizers

NUTRITION FACTS per appetizer

CALORIES 114
TOTAL FAT 5 g (1 g sat. fat)
CHOLESTEROL 37 mg
SODIUM 142 mg
CARBOHYDRATE 10 g
FIBER 1 g
PROTEIN 8 g
EXCHANGES ½ Starch, 1 Lean Meat, ½ Fat

20 fresh or frozen jumbo shrimp in shells
1 cup canned pumpkin
½ cup crumbled goat cheese, at room temperature (2 ounces)
1 tablespoon lemon juice
1 tablespoon honey
1 cup arugula
½ cup finely chopped red onion (1 medium)
½ cup toasted pumpkin seeds*
¼ cup bottled light Italian vinaigrette salad dressing
20 ¾-inch slices baguette-style French bread
2 tablespoons olive oil
2 ounces Parmesan cheese, shaved (optional)

1 Thaw shrimp, if frozen. Peel and devein shrimp, leaving tails intact if desired. Rinse shrimp. In a large skillet cook shrimp in a large amount of boiling water for 2 to 3 minutes or until shrimp are opaque. Drain well.

2 Preheat broiler. In a medium bowl whisk together pumpkin, goat cheese, lemon juice, and honey; set aside.

3 In a large bowl combine shrimp, arugula, onion, pumpkin seeds, and salad dressing. Toss to mix; set aside.

4 Brush both sides of baguette slices lightly with olive oil. Arrange on a large baking sheet. Broil 3 to 4 inches from the heat about 2 minutes or until toasted, turning bread over once.

5 Spread pumpkin mixture on 1 side of toasted baguette slices. Top each with a shrimp and some of the arugula mixture. If desired, top each with shaved Parmesan cheese.

***Note:** To toast pumpkin seeds, place seeds in a dry large skillet; cover. Heat over medium heat about 5 minutes or until seeds are toasted, shaking skillet occasionally.

Hummus and Cucumber Bruschetta

PREP 25 minutes **BAKE** 10 minutes
OVEN 400°F **MAKES** 4 servings

NUTRITION FACTS per serving

CALORIES 126
TOTAL FAT 3 g (0 g sat. fat)
CHOLESTEROL 0 mg
SODIUM 296 mg
CARBOHYDRATE 21 g
FIBER 1 g
PROTEIN 5 g
EXCHANGES 1½ Starch

- 12 ¼-inch slices baguette-style French bread
- Olive oil nonstick cooking spray
- 1½ teaspoons Italian seasoning, crushed
- ¼ teaspoon garlic powder
- ⅓ cup finely chopped English cucumber
- 2 tablespoons plain low-fat yogurt
- 1½ teaspoons lemon juice
- 1½ teaspoons snipped fresh oregano or ½ teaspoon dried oregano, crushed
- ⅓ cup hummus
- ¼ cup chopped bottled roasted red sweet pepper
- Snipped fresh oregano (optional)

1 Preheat oven to 400°F. Arrange baguette slices in a single layer on a large baking sheet. Lightly coat baguette slices with cooking spray. Combine Italian seasoning and garlic powder; sprinkle on bread. Bake about 10 minutes or until crisp and lightly toasted. Cool.

2 Meanwhile, in a small bowl combine cucumber, yogurt, lemon juice, and the 1½ teaspoons fresh or ½ teaspoon dried oregano. Spread some of the hummus on each toasted baguette slice; top with cucumber mixture and roasted red pepper. If desired, sprinkle with additional fresh oregano.

Four-Cheese Stuffed Mushrooms

PREP 20 minutes **BAKE** 20 minutes
STAND 10 minutes **OVEN** 350°F/450°F
MAKES 24 servings

NUTRITION FACTS per serving

CALORIES 42
TOTAL FAT 3 g (1 g sat. fat)
CHOLESTEROL 8 mg
SODIUM 105 mg
CARBOHYDRATE 2 g
FIBER 0 g
PROTEIN 3 g
EXCHANGES ½ Medium-Fat Meat

24 large fresh mushrooms (1½ to 2 inches in diameter)
1 tablespoon olive oil
8 dried tomatoes (not oil-packed)
Boiling water
1 cup light ricotta cheese
½ cup finely chopped fresh spinach
½ cup shredded Monterey Jack cheese (2 ounces)
3 tablespoons freshly grated Parmesan cheese
1 tablespoon snipped fresh basil
2 cloves garlic, minced
¼ teaspoon salt
¼ teaspoon black pepper
½ cup crumbled feta cheese (2 ounces)
Fresh basil leaves (optional)

1 Preheat oven to 350°F. Remove and discard mushroom stems. Brush mushroom caps with oil. Arrange in a shallow baking pan, stem sides down. Bake for 12 minutes. Drain off any liquid. Increase oven temperature to 450°F.

2 Meanwhile, in a small bowl cover dried tomatoes with boiling water; let stand for 10 minutes. Drain tomatoes, discarding liquid. Coarsely snip tomatoes.

3 In a medium bowl combine snipped tomatoes, ricotta cheese, spinach, Monterey Jack cheese, Parmesan cheese, snipped basil, garlic, salt, and pepper. Turn mushroom caps stem sides up; fill caps with ricotta mixture. Sprinkle feta cheese over tops.

4 Bake for 8 to 10 minutes or until heated through and lightly browned. If desired, garnish with basil leaves.

Make-Ahead Directions: Prepare as directed through Step 3. Cover and chill up to 24 hours. Preheat oven to 450°F. Bake mushrooms as directed in Step 4.

Gingered Turkey Meatballs with Sesame-Lime Sauce

PREP 30 minutes **BAKE** 15 minutes
OVEN 425°F **MAKES** 28 meatballs

- 1 egg, lightly beaten
- 1 cup panko (Japanese-style bread crumbs)
- ½ cup canned sliced water chestnuts, drained and finely chopped
- ½ cup finely snipped fresh cilantro
- 1 tablespoon grated fresh ginger
- 1 tablespoon reduced-sodium soy sauce
- 1 tablespoon sesame oil
- 2 cloves garlic, minced
- ½ teaspoon salt
- ¼ teaspoon cayenne pepper
- 1½ pounds uncooked ground turkey
- 1 cup sliced almonds, finely chopped
- 1 recipe Sesame-Lime Sauce

1 Preheat oven to 425°F. In a large bowl combine egg, panko, water chestnuts, cilantro, ginger, soy sauce, sesame oil, garlic, salt, and cayenne pepper. Add turkey. Mix well.

2 Shape into 28 meatballs. Roll meatballs in almonds. Place meatballs in a single layer in a 15×10×1-inch baking pan.

3 Bake, uncovered, for 15 to 20 minutes or until done (165°F).* Serve warm with Sesame-Lime Sauce.

Sesame-Lime Sauce: In a small bowl combine ¼ cup reduced-sodium soy sauce, ¼ cup water, 2 tablespoons lime juice, 2 teaspoons sesame oil, and 2 teaspoons sugar. Stir until sugar is dissolved.

***Note:** The internal color of a meatball is not a reliable doneness indicator. A poultry meatball cooked to 165°F is safe, regardless of color. To measure doneness, insert an instant-read thermometer into centers of meatballs.

NUTRITION FACTS per meatball

CALORIES 78
TOTAL FAT 5 g (1 g sat. fat)
CHOLESTEROL 27 mg
SODIUM 177 mg
CARBOHYDRATE 3 g
FIBER 1 g
PROTEIN 6 g
EXCHANGES 1 Medium-Fat Meat

Sloppy Joe Meatball Minis

PREP 35 minutes **BAKE** 25 minutes
COOK 5 minutes **OVEN** 350°F
MAKES 21 servings

NUTRITION FACTS per serving

CALORIES 154
TOTAL FAT 5 g (1 g sat. fat)
CHOLESTEROL 25 mg
SODIUM 324 mg
CARBOHYDRATE 19 g
FIBER 1 g
PROTEIN 8 g
EXCHANGES 1 Starch, ½ Medium-Fat Meat, ½ Fat

- 1 egg, lightly beaten
- ½ cup finely chopped onion (1 medium)
- ¼ cup fine dry bread crumbs
- ¼ teaspoon dried oregano, crushed
- ¼ teaspoon salt
- 1 pound lean ground beef
- 1 tablespoon vegetable oil
- ½ cup chopped green sweet pepper
- 1 15-ounce can tomato sauce
- 2 tablespoons packed brown sugar
- 1 tablespoon yellow mustard
- 1 teaspoon chili powder
- ¼ teaspoon garlic powder
- ¼ teaspoon black pepper
- Dash bottled hot pepper sauce (optional)
- 21 baby spinach leaves
- 21 2- to 2½-inch cocktail rolls, split and toasted

1 Preheat oven to 350°F. In a large bowl combine egg, ¼ cup of the onion, the bread crumbs, oregano, and salt. Add beef and mix well.

2 Shape into 21 meatballs. Place in a single layer in a 15×10×1-inch baking pan. Bake, uncovered, about 25 minutes or until done (160°F).* Drain well.

3 Meanwhile, in a large saucepan heat the oil over medium heat. Cook the remaining ¼ cup onion and the sweet pepper in hot oil until tender. Stir in tomato sauce, brown sugar, mustard, chili powder, garlic powder, black pepper, and, if desired, hot pepper sauce. Bring to boiling; reduce heat. Simmer for 5 minutes. Add meatballs to sauce and heat through.

4 Place a spinach leaf on each roll bottom. Top with a meatball, a little sauce, and roll top.

***Note:** The internal color of a meatball is not a reliable doneness indicator. A beef meatball cooked to 160°F is safe, regardless of color. To measure doneness, insert an instant-read thermometer into the center of a meatball.

Sweet Potato Wontons

PREP 25 minutes **BAKE** 10 minutes
OVEN 350°F **MAKES** 24 wontons

NUTRITION FACTS per wonton

CALORIES 61
TOTAL FAT 2 g (0 g sat. fat)
CHOLESTEROL 2 mg
SODIUM 69 mg
CARBOHYDRATE 10 g
FIBER 1 g
PROTEIN 1 g
EXCHANGES ½ Starch, ½ Fat

- 24 wonton wrappers
- Nonstick cooking spray
- 3 tablespoons mango chutney
- 2 tablespoons canola oil
- ⅓ cup finely chopped onion (1 small)
- 2 teaspoons curry powder
- 1 teaspoon minced fresh ginger
- 1 clove garlic, minced
- 1 tablespoon all-purpose flour
- 1½ cups chopped, cooked sweet potato
- ⅓ cup half-and-half
- Carrots, cut into thin bite-size strips and sautéed (optional)

1 Preheat oven to 350°F. Lightly coat wonton wrappers with cooking spray. Press wrappers, coated sides down, into twenty-four 1¾-inch muffin cups, pleating as necessary. Bake about 10 minutes or until golden brown.

2 Meanwhile, cut up any large pieces of fruit in chutney; set aside. In a large heavy skillet heat the canola oil over medium heat. Add onion, curry powder, ginger, and garlic; cook until onion is tender. Stir in flour. Stir in cooked sweet potato, half-and-half, and chutney. Cook and stir until thickened. Cook and stir for 1 minute more.

3 Spoon sweet potato mixture into wonton shells. Serve immediately. If desired, sprinkle with carrot strips.

Light 'n' Crisp Egg Rolls

PREP 30 minutes **BAKE** 15 minutes
OVEN 450°F **MAKES** 8 egg rolls

NUTRITION FACTS per egg roll

CALORIES 167
TOTAL FAT 4 g (1 g sat. fat)
CHOLESTEROL 22 mg
SODIUM 282 mg
CARBOHYDRATE 23 g
FIBER 1 g
PROTEIN 10 g
EXCHANGES 1½ Starch, 1 Lean Meat

Nonstick cooking spray
2 teaspoons toasted sesame oil or canola oil
8 ounces lean pork loin, cut into ½-inch pieces, or ground pork
½ cup chopped red sweet pepper
1 teaspoon grated fresh ginger or ¼ teaspoon ground ginger
1 clove garlic, minced
¾ cup finely chopped bok choy or Chinese (napa) cabbage
½ cup chopped canned water chestnuts
½ cup coarsely shredded carrot (1 medium)
¼ cup sliced green onions (2)
¼ cup bottled light Asian sesame-ginger vinaigrette
8 egg roll wrappers

1 Preheat oven to 450°F. Lightly coat a large baking sheet with cooking spray; set aside. For filling, in a medium nonstick skillet heat oil over medium-high heat. Add pork, sweet pepper, ginger, and garlic. Cook for 3 to 4 minutes or until pork is no longer pink, stirring occasionally. If using ground pork, drain off fat. Add bok choy, water chestnuts, carrot, and green onions to pork mixture in skillet. Cook and stir about 1 minute more or until any liquid is evaporated. Stir in vinaigrette. Cool filling slightly.

2 For each egg roll, place 1 egg roll wrapper on a flat surface with a corner pointing toward you. Spoon about ⅓ cup of the filling across and just below center of each egg roll wrapper. Fold bottom corner over filling, tucking it under the opposite side. Fold side corners over filling, forming an envelope shape. Roll egg roll toward remaining corner. Moisten top corner with water; press firmly to seal.

3 Place egg rolls, seam sides down, on the prepared baking sheet. Coat tops and sides of egg rolls with cooking spray. Bake for 15 to 18 minutes or until golden brown and crisp. Cool slightly before serving.

Peanut Butter-Cereal Bars

PREP 20 minutes **BAKE** 28 minutes
OVEN 325°F **MAKES** 16 bars

NUTRITION FACTS per bar

CALORIES 181
TOTAL FAT 8 g (1 g sat. fat)
CHOLESTEROL 27 mg
SODIUM 91 mg
CARBOHYDRATE 26 g
FIBER 2 g
PROTEIN 4 g
EXCHANGES 1 Starch, 1 Other Carbo., 1 Fat

Nonstick cooking spray
- 4 cups sweetened oat cereal flakes with raisins
- ¾ cup quick-cooking rolled oats
- ½ cup all-purpose flour
- ½ cup snipped dried apples
- 2 eggs
- ⅓ cup honey
- ⅓ cup chunky peanut butter
- ¼ cup canola oil or butter, melted

1 Preheat oven to 325°F. Line a 9×9×2-inch baking pan with foil. Coat foil with cooking spray; set aside. In a large bowl combine oat cereal flakes, rolled oats, flour, and dried apples. Set aside.

2 In a small bowl beat eggs with a fork; stir in honey, peanut butter, and oil. Pour over cereal mixture. Mix well. Transfer cereal mixture to prepared pan. Using the back of a large spoon, press mixture firmly into pan. Bake for 28 to 30 minutes or until edges are browned. Cool completely in pan on a wire rack. Using a serrated knife, cut into bars.

To Store: Wrap cooled bars individually in plastic wrap. Chill up to 3 days. For longer storage, place individually wrapped bars in a freezer container or freezer bag; freeze up to 3 months. To serve, thaw bars in refrigerator overnight.

Strawberries with Lime Dipping Sauce

START TO FINISH 10 minutes
MAKES 8 servings

NUTRITION FACTS per serving

CALORIES 44
TOTAL FAT 0 g
CHOLESTEROL 3 mg
SODIUM 41 mg
CARBOHYDRATE 10 g
FIBER 1 g
PROTEIN 1 g
EXCHANGES ½ Fruit

1 8-ounce carton fat-free or light sour cream
2 tablespoons powdered sugar
2 teaspoons finely shredded lime peel
1 tablespoon lime juice
3 cups fresh strawberries

1 For lime dipping sauce, in a small bowl stir together sour cream, powdered sugar, lime peel, and lime juice. Cover tightly with plastic wrap; chill until serving.

2 Wash strawberries but do not remove stems or caps. Drain strawberries on several layers of paper towels. Serve berries with lime dipping sauce.

Chapter 14

Desserts

On the opener: Chocolate-Peanut Butter Molten Cupcakes *(see recipe, page 273)*

CAKES

CHILLED DESSERTS

COOKIES

FROZEN DESSERTS

FRUIT DESSERTS

PIES & TARTS

Caramel Apple Crisp

START TO FINISH 20 minutes
MAKES 6 servings

- 1 pound small cooking apples, cut into ½-inch slices (about 5 cups)
- ¼ cup low-calorie cranberry juice or water
- 1 teaspoon finely shredded lemon peel
- ¼ teaspoon ground allspice
- 1 cup low-fat granola
- ¼ cup chopped pecans, toasted (see note, page 275)
- ¼ cup fat-free caramel ice cream topping
- Light or low-fat vanilla ice cream or frozen yogurt (optional)

1 In a large skillet combine apple slices, cranberry juice, and lemon peel. Cook, stirring occasionally, over medium-high heat for 6 to 8 minutes or until apples are crisp-tender. Remove from heat. Sprinkle allspice over apples.

2 Spoon apple mixture into dessert dishes. Sprinkle with granola and nuts. Drizzle with caramel topping. If desired, serve with ice cream.

NUTRITION FACTS per serving

CALORIES 172
TOTAL FAT 4 g (1 g sat. fat)
CHOLESTEROL 0 mg
SODIUM 76 mg
CARBOHYDRATE 34 g
FIBER 3 g
PROTEIN 2 g
EXCHANGES 1 Fruit, 1 Other Carbo., 1 Fat

Strawberry-Rhubarb Crisp

PREP 15 minutes **BAKE** 40 minutes
COOL 20 minutes **OVEN** 375°F
MAKES 6 to 8 servings

NUTRITION FACTS per serving

CALORIES 117
TOTAL FAT 1 g (0 g sat. fat)
CHOLESTEROL 0 mg
SODIUM 7 mg
CARBOHYDRATE 26 g
FIBER 3 g
PROTEIN 2 g
EXCHANGES ½ Fruit, 1 Other Carbo.

- ⅓ cup low-sugar strawberry preserves
- ⅛ teaspoon ground cinnamon or nutmeg
- 2 cups sliced fresh strawberries
- 2 cups sliced fresh rhubarb
- 3 tablespoons all-purpose flour
- ½ cup quick-cooking rolled oats
- 2 tablespoons cornmeal
- 2 tablespoons honey
- 1 teaspoon vanilla

1. Preheat oven to 375°F. In a large bowl stir together preserves and cinnamon. Add strawberries and rhubarb; stir gently to coat. Add flour; stir gently until combined. Spoon into a 9-inch pie plate. Bake, uncovered, for 20 minutes.

2. Meanwhile, in a small bowl stir together rolled oats and cornmeal. Stir in honey and vanilla until combined. Sprinkle over strawberry mixture. Bake, uncovered, about 20 minutes or until topping is golden brown and fruit is tender and bubbly.

3. Cool about 20 minutes before serving. Serve warm.

Peach-Blueberry Ginger-Oat Crisp

PREP 25 minutes **BAKE** 35 minutes
COOL 30 minutes **OVEN** 375°F
MAKES 8 servings

- 4 cups sliced fresh peaches or frozen unsweetened peach slices, thawed and undrained
- 3 tablespoons packed brown sugar
- 2 tablespoons all-purpose flour
- ½ teaspoon ground ginger
- 1 cup fresh or frozen unsweetened blueberries, thawed
- ¼ cup water
- 8 gingersnaps
- ⅔ cup quick-cooking rolled oats
- ¼ cup chopped pecans (optional)
- 2 tablespoons butter, melted
- 1 cup frozen light whipped dessert topping, thawed (optional)

1 Preheat oven to 375°F. In a large bowl toss together peach slices, brown sugar, flour, and ginger. Add blueberries and the water; toss to combine. Spoon fruit mixture into a 2-quart square baking dish. Bake, uncovered, for 20 minutes.

2 Meanwhile, place gingersnaps in a heavy resealable plastic bag; seal bag. Using the flat side of a meat mallet or a rolling pin, crush cookies into ¼- to ½-inch pieces. Transfer crumbs to a medium bowl. Stir in rolled oats and, if desired, chopped pecans. Stir in butter until well mixed. Sprinkle over partially baked fruit mixture.

3 Bake for 15 to 20 minutes more or until fruit is bubbly and topping is lightly browned. Cool on a wire rack for 30 minutes. Serve warm. If desired, top with whipped topping.

NUTRITION FACTS per serving

CALORIES 153
TOTAL FAT 4 g (2 g sat. fat)
CHOLESTEROL 8 mg
SODIUM 68 mg
CARBOHYDRATE 29 g
FIBER 3 g
PROTEIN 2 g
EXCHANGES ½ Fruit, 1½ Other Carbo., 1 Fat

Peachy Raspberry Cobblers

PREP 25 minutes **BAKE** 15 minutes
OVEN 400°F **MAKES** 8 servings

NUTRITION FACTS per serving

CALORIES 160
TOTAL FAT 4 g (2 g sat. fat)
CHOLESTEROL 35 mg
SODIUM 120 mg
CARBOHYDRATE 28 g
FIBER 4 g
PROTEIN 4 g
EXCHANGES ½ Fruit, 1 Starch, ½ Other Carbo., ½ Fat

- 1 cup all-purpose flour
- 1½ teaspoons baking powder
- ¼ teaspoon ground ginger or ground cinnamon
- ⅛ teaspoon salt
- 2 tablespoons butter or margarine
- ¼ cup sugar
- 4 teaspoons cornstarch
- ⅓ cup water
- 3 cups fresh or frozen unsweetened peach slices
- 2 cups fresh or frozen unsweetened raspberries
- ⅓ cup plain fat-free yogurt
- 1 egg, lightly beaten

1 Preheat oven to 400°F. For topping, in a bowl stir together flour, baking powder, ¼ teaspoon ginger, and salt. Using a pastry blender, cut in butter until mixture resembles coarse crumbs. Set aside.

2 For filling, in a large saucepan stir together sugar and cornstarch. Stir in the water. Add peach slices and raspberries. Cook and stir until thickened and bubbly. Keep filling hot while finishing topping.

3 To finish topping, stir together yogurt and egg. Add yogurt mixture to flour mixture, stirring just until moistened.

4 Divide filling among eight 6-ounce custard cups or four 10- to 12-ounce casseroles.* Drop the topping from a spoon onto hot filling, one mound into each custard cup or two mounds into each casserole. Place custard cups or casseroles on a baking sheet.

5 Bake for 15 to 20 minutes or until a wooden toothpick inserted into topping comes out clean. Cool slightly; serve warm.

***Note:** To make a large cobbler, transfer hot filling to a 2-quart square baking dish. Drop topping from a spoon into 8 mounds on top of hot filling. Bake in a 400°F oven about 20 minutes or until a wooden toothpick inserted into topping comes out clean.

Peach Crumble Tart

PREP 35 minutes **BAKE** 63 minutes
OVEN 450°F/375°F **MAKES** 12 servings

NUTRITION FACTS per serving

CALORIES 177
TOTAL FAT 7 g (2 g sat. fat)
CHOLESTEROL 5 mg
SODIUM 65 mg
CARBOHYDRATE 27 g
FIBER 2 g
PROTEIN 3 g
EXCHANGES 1 Fruit, 1 Other Carbo., 1½ Fat

- 1 recipe Oil Pastry (see recipe, page 304)
- ½ cup regular rolled oats
- ¼ cup all-purpose flour
- 2 tablespoons packed brown sugar
- ½ teaspoon ground cinnamon
- 2 tablespoons butter or margarine, melted
- ¼ cup granulated sugar
- 1 tablespoon all-purpose flour
- 1 teaspoon ground cinnamon
- 6 cups thinly sliced, peeled peaches or nectarines (6 medium) or two 16-ounce package frozen unsweetened peach slices, thawed and undrained (7 cups)
- Fresh peach or nectarine slices (optional)
- Frozen light whipped dessert topping, thawed (optional)

1 Preheat oven to 450°F. Prepare Oil Pastry. On a lightly floured surface slightly flatten pastry; roll from center to edges into a 12-inch circle. To transfer pastry, wrap it around rolling pin (be careful; pastry will be very tender); unroll into a 10-inch tart pan with removable bottom. Press pastry into fluted sides of tart pan. Trim pastry to edge of pan. Do not prick pastry. Line pastry with a double thickness of foil. Bake for 8 minutes. Remove foil. Bake for 5 to 6 minutes more or until golden brown. Cool on a wire rack. Reduce oven temperature to 375°F.

2 Meanwhile, for topping, in a small bowl combine oats, the ¼ cup flour, brown sugar, and ½ teaspoon cinnamon. Stir in melted butter. Set aside.

3 For filling, in a large bowl stir together granulated sugar, 1 tablespoon flour, and 1 teaspoon cinnamon. Add peaches; toss gently to coat.

4 Spread filling evenly in tart shell. Sprinkle with topping. Bake about 50 minutes or until edge is bubbly and topping is browned. Serve warm or cool. If desired, top with additional nectarine or peach slices and whipped topping.

Plum-Pear Phyllo Bundles

PREP 25 minutes **BAKE** 15 minutes
STAND 30 minutes **OVEN** 375°F
MAKES 2 bundles

NUTRITION FACTS per bundle

CALORIES 141
TOTAL FAT 5 g (1 g sat. fat)
CHOLESTEROL 5 mg
SODIUM 98 mg
CARBOHYDRATE 23 g
FIBER 2 g
PROTEIN 2 g
EXCHANGES ½ Fruit, 1 Other Carbo., 1 Fat

- 1 teaspoon butter
- ½ of a medium pear, cored and coarsely chopped
- ¼ cup coarsely chopped fresh plums or 2 tablespoons coarsely chopped pitted dried plums
- 1½ teaspoons honey
- ¼ teaspoon ground cardamom or ginger
- 1 tablespoon coarsely chopped pistachio nuts
- 3 sheets frozen phyllo dough (14×9-inch rectangles), thawed
- Nonstick cooking spray

1 In a small nonstick skillet melt butter over medium heat. Add pear, plums, honey, and cardamom; cook and stir about 5 minutes or until fruit begins to soften. Remove from heat; let cool. Stir in pistachio nuts.

2 Preheat oven to 375°F. Line a baking sheet with foil; set aside. Unfold phyllo dough; remove 1 sheet of the phyllo dough. (As you work, cover the remaining phyllo dough with plastic wrap to prevent it from drying out.) Lightly coat the phyllo sheet with cooking spray. Place a second sheet of phyllo dough on top of the first; lightly coat with cooking spray. Layer the third sheet of phyllo dough and lightly coat with cooking spray. Cut phyllo stack in half crosswise to form two 9×7-inch rectangles.

3 Divide fruit mixture between phyllo rectangles, placing fruit in center of each rectangle. For each bundle, bring together the 4 corners of a phyllo rectangle; pinch gently and twist slightly to make a bundle. Place on prepared baking sheet. Lightly coat the tops of bundles with cooking spray.

4 Bake for 15 to 20 minutes or until golden. Transfer bundles to a wire rack; cool slightly. Serve warm or cool.

Berry Pudding Cakes

PREP 20 minutes **BAKE** 20 minutes
OVEN 400°F **MAKES** 6 servings

NUTRITION FACTS per serving

CALORIES 141
TOTAL FAT 2 g (1 g sat. fat)
CHOLESTEROL 71 mg
SODIUM 86 mg
CARBOHYDRATE 26 g
FIBER 3 g
PROTEIN 5 g
EXCHANGES ½ Fruit, 1½ Other Carbo.

- Nonstick cooking spray
- 2 eggs, lightly beaten
- ¼ cup granulated sugar
- 1 teaspoon vanilla
- Dash salt
- 1 cup fat-free milk
- ½ cup all-purpose flour
- ½ teaspoon baking powder
- 3 cups fresh berries (such as raspberries, blueberries, and/or sliced strawberries)
- 2 teaspoons powdered sugar (optional)

1 Preheat oven to 400°F. Lightly coat six 6-ounce individual quiche dishes with cooking spray. Arrange in a 15×10×1-inch baking pan; set aside. In a medium bowl combine eggs, granulated sugar, vanilla, and salt; whisk until light and frothy. Whisk in milk until combined. Add flour and baking powder; whisk until smooth.

2 Divide berries among prepared dishes. Pour batter over berries. (Batter will not cover berries completely.) Bake about 20 minutes or until puffed and golden brown. Serve warm. If desired, sprinkle with powdered sugar.

Plum Clafouti Tarts

PREP 25 minutes **BAKE** 20 minutes
COOL 15 minutes **OVEN** 375°F
MAKES 4 servings

NUTRITION FACTS per serving

CALORIES 162
TOTAL FAT 3 g (2 g sat. fat)
CHOLESTEROL 9 mg
SODIUM 138 mg
CARBOHYDRATE 28 g
FIBER 1 g
PROTEIN 5 g
EXCHANGES 2 Other Carbo., ½ Fat

Nonstick cooking spray
4 sheets frozen phyllo dough (14×9-inch rectangles), thawed
⅓ cup refrigerated or frozen egg product, thawed, or 1 egg and 1 egg white, lightly beaten
3 tablespoons granulated sugar
1 tablespoon fat-free milk
¼ teaspoon vanilla
Dash salt
½ cup light sour cream
⅓ cup all-purpose flour
2 small ripe plums, halved and pitted

1 Preheat oven to 375°F. Lightly coat four 6-ounce custard cups or ramekins with cooking spray; set aside. Unfold phyllo dough; cover with plastic wrap, removing sheets as needed. Lay 1 sheet of phyllo dough on a flat surface; lightly coat with cooking spray. Top with a second phyllo sheet; lightly coat with cooking spray. Using a sharp knife or pizza cutter, cut phyllo stack lengthwise into two 14-inch-long strips. Cut each strip crosswise into 2 rectangles, making 4 rectangles total. Repeat with remaining phyllo sheets and cooking spray to make 4 more rectangles.

2 Gently press 1 phyllo rectangle into a prepared custard cup, pressing dough into the side of the cup. Place another phyllo rectangle crosswise over the first rectangle, pressing it into the side of the custard cup. Repeat with remaining phyllo rectangles and custard cups. Set aside.

3 For batter, in a medium bowl whisk together egg product, granulated sugar, milk, vanilla, and salt. Whisk in the sour cream until mixture is smooth. Add flour, whisking until mixture is smooth. Divide batter among phyllo-lined custard cups. Place a plum half, cut side up, in the center of each cup.

4 Bake for 20 to 25 minutes or until batter around plums is set. Cool on wire rack about 15 minutes before serving. If desired, sprinkle with *powdered sugar;* serve warm.

Raspberry-Lemonade Shortcakes

PREP 35 minutes **STAND** 30 minutes
BAKE 20 minutes **OVEN** 350°F
MAKES 12 servings

NUTRITION FACTS per serving

CALORIES 175
TOTAL FAT 3 g (1 g sat. fat)
CHOLESTEROL 35 mg
SODIUM 49 mg
CARBOHYDRATE 35 g
FIBER 5 g
PROTEIN 3 g
EXCHANGES ½ Fruit, 2 Other Carbo.

- 2 eggs
- 1 cup all-purpose flour
- 1 teaspoon baking powder
- 1 teaspoon finely shredded lemon peel
- ¾ cup sugar
- ½ cup fat-free milk
- 2 tablespoons tub-style 60% to 70% vegetable oil spread
- 1 recipe Raspberry-Lemonade Sauce

1 Allow eggs to stand at room temperature for 30 minutes. Meanwhile, grease a 9×9×2-inch baking pan; line with waxed paper. Grease and flour waxed paper; set pan aside. In a small bowl stir together flour, baking powder, and lemon peel; set aside.

2 Preheat oven to 350°F. In a medium bowl beat eggs with an electric mixer on high about 4 minutes or until thick. Gradually add sugar, beating on medium for 4 to 5 minutes or until light and fluffy. Add flour mixture; beat on low to medium just until combined. In a small saucepan heat and stir milk and vegetable spread until spread is melted; add to batter, beating until combined. Pour batter into prepared pan.

4 Bake for 20 to 25 minutes or until a toothpick inserted near center comes out clean. Cool in pan on wire rack for 10 minutes. Invert cake onto wire rack lined with waxed paper; carefully peel off waxed paper; cool completely.

5 Cut cake into 12 pieces. Split each piece horizontally. Spoon half the Raspberry-Lemonade Sauce on cake bottoms. Layer tops, then remaining sauce. If desired, garnish with *lemon wedges* and *mint.*

Raspberry-Lemonade Sauce: Place 3 cups fresh or frozen raspberries in a medium bowl. (Thaw frozen raspberries in the bowl if using; do not drain.) Mash berries. In a small saucepan combine ⅓ cup sugar, ¾ teaspoon cornstarch, and ½ teaspoon finely shredded lemon peel. Add mashed raspberries. Cook and stir until thickened and bubbly; cook and stir 2 minutes more. Remove from heat. Cool about 10 minutes. Stir in 4 cups fresh or frozen (thawed and drained) raspberries. Makes about 3½ cups.

Banana Split Cake Roll

PREP 35 minutes **STAND** 30 minutes
BAKE 15 minutes **COOL** 1 hour **CHILL** 2 to 48 hours **OVEN** 375°F **MAKES** 10 servings

NUTRITION FACTS per serving

CALORIES 168
TOTAL FAT 4 g (3 g sat. fat)
CHOLESTEROL 69 mg
SODIUM 164 mg
CARBOHYDRATE 28 g
FIBER 1 g
PROTEIN 4 g
EXCHANGES 2 Other Carbo., ½ Fat

- 3 eggs
- ¾ cup all-purpose flour
- 1 teaspoon baking powder
- ¼ teaspoon salt
- ¼ teaspoon ground nutmeg
- ¼ teaspoon ground cinnamon
- ¾ cup granulated sugar
- ⅔ cup mashed ripe bananas
- 1 teaspoon lemon juice
- Powdered sugar
- 1 recipe Strawberry-Cheese Filling
- Whole strawberries (optional)

1 Let eggs stand at room temperature for 30 minutes. Meanwhile, grease a 15×10×1-inch baking pan. Line bottom of pan with waxed paper; grease and flour paper. Set aside. Stir together flour, baking powder, salt, nutmeg, and cinnamon; set aside.

2 Preheat oven to 375°F. In a large mixing bowl beat eggs with electric mixer on high for 5 minutes. Gradually add granulated sugar, beating until well mixed. Stir in bananas and lemon juice. Fold flour mixture into banana mixture. Spread evenly in prepared pan.

3 Bake about 15 minutes or until top springs back when touched. Immediately loosen edges of cake from pan; turn cake out onto a towel sprinkled with powdered sugar. Peel off waxed paper. From a short side, roll up cake with towel. Cool on a wire rack for 1 hour.

4 Unroll cake; remove towel. Spread with Strawberry-Cheese Filling to within 1 inch of edges. Reroll cake and filling. Trim ends. Cover and chill for 2 to 48 hours. If desired, sprinkle cake with powdered sugar and garnish with whole strawberries.

Strawberry-Cheese Filling: In a small mixing bowl beat ½ cup light tub-style cream cheese with an electric mixer on medium until smooth. Add ½ cup frozen light whipped dessert topping, thawed; fold in until well mixed. Fold in another ½ cup dessert topping, thawed. Fold in 1 cup chopped fresh strawberries.

Chocolate-Peanut Butter Molten Cupcakes

PREP 25 minutes **BAKE** 12 minutes
COOL 5 minutes **CHILL** 30 minutes
MAKES 6 servings

- 2 ounces milk chocolate, chopped
- 1 tablespoon creamy peanut butter (not reduced-fat or natural)
- ¼ cup refrigerated or frozen egg product, thawed, or 1 egg, lightly beaten
- ¼ cup sugar
- 2 tablespoons water
- 2 tablespoons canola oil
- ¼ teaspoon baking powder
- ¼ teaspoon vanilla
- ½ cup all-purpose flour
- 3 tablespoons unsweetened cocoa powder

1 For filling, in a small microwave-safe bowl combine chopped chocolate and peanut butter. Microwave on medium-low for 1½ to 2 minutes or until melted and smooth, stirring once halfway through cooking. Cover and chill until mixture is the consistency of thick frosting, stirring and checking every 5 to 10 minutes until consistency is reached (from 10 to 25 minutes). Mixture will set up quickly at the end; watch carefully. Use 2 spoons to drop mixture into 6 mounds on a wax paper-lined baking sheet, using about 2 teaspoons per mound. Return to the refrigerator until ready to use.

2 Preheat oven to 350°F. Grease six 2½-inch muffin cups; set aside. For chocolate batter, in a medium bowl whisk together egg product, sugar, water, oil, baking powder, and vanilla. Add flour and cocoa powder, stirring until smooth. Spoon about 1 tablespoon batter into each muffin cup. Set a chilled chocolate-peanut butter mound in center of chocolate batter in each muffin cup. Spoon remaining batter over peanut butter mounds.

3 Bake for 12 to 14 minutes or until tops spring back when lightly touched. Cool cakes in pan on a wire rack for 5 minutes. Run a thin sharp knife around the edge of each cake. Invert cakes onto serving plates. If desired, sprinkle with *powdered sugar* and garnish with fresh *raspberries* and/or *orange peel twists*. Serve immediately.

NUTRITION FACTS per serving

CALORIES 193
TOTAL FAT 9 g (3 g sat. fat)
CHOLESTEROL 2 mg
SODIUM 51 mg
CARBOHYDRATE 24 g
FIBER 1 g
PROTEIN 4 g
EXCHANGES 1½ Other Carbo., 1½ Fat

Chocolate-Almond Torte

PREP 25 minutes **STAND** 30 minutes
BAKE 25 minutes **OVEN** 350°F
MAKES 12 servings

NUTRITION FACTS per serving

CALORIES 144
TOTAL FAT 4 g (2 g sat. fat)
CHOLESTEROL 0 mg
SODIUM 81 mg
CARBOHYDRATE 25 g
FIBER 1 g
PROTEIN 4 g
EXCHANGES 1½ Other Carbo., ½ Fat

- ¾ cup fat-free milk
- ⅓ cup unsweetened cocoa powder
- 2 ounces unsweetened chocolate, chopped
- 1 tablespoon balsamic vinegar
- 3 egg whites
- Nonstick cooking spray
- ¾ cup all-purpose flour
- ⅔ cup granulated sugar
- ½ teaspoon baking powder
- ¼ teaspoon baking soda
- ⅛ teaspoon salt
- ¼ cup granulated sugar
- ¼ cup sliced almonds
- 1 to 2 teaspoons powdered sugar (optional)

1 In a small saucepan combine milk and cocoa powder. Heat over medium heat, whisking constantly, just until mixture comes to a boil. Remove from heat. Whisk in unsweetened chocolate and vinegar until smooth. Cool to room temperature. Meanwhile, in a medium mixing bowl allow egg whites to stand at room temperature for 30 minutes.

2 Preheat oven to 350°F. Lightly coat an 8×2-inch round tart pan with removable bottom or an 8-inch springform pan with cooking spray; set aside. In a large bowl stir together flour, the ⅔ cup granulated sugar, the baking powder, baking soda, and salt. Stir cooled chocolate mixture into flour mixture until well combined (batter will be thick); set aside.

3 Beat egg whites with an electric mixer on medium until soft peaks form (tips curl). Gradually add the ¼ cup granulated sugar, about 1 tablespoon at a time, beating on high until stiff peaks form (tips stand straight). Gently fold one-third of the beaten egg whites into the chocolate mixture. Fold in the remaining beaten egg whites just until combined. Spread batter in prepared pan. Sprinkle almonds on batter.

4 Bake for 25 to 28 minutes or until a wooden toothpick inserted near center comes out clean. Cool in pan on wire rack for 15 minutes. Remove side of pan. Cool completely. If desired, sprinkle lightly with powdered sugar before serving.

Hazelnut-Mocha Torte

PREP 30 minutes **BAKE** 10 minutes
COOL 1 hour **CHILL** 2 to 24 hours
OVEN 350°F **MAKES** 16 servings

NUTRITION FACTS per serving

CALORIES 144
TOTAL FAT 9 g (1 g sat. fat)
CHOLESTEROL 1 mg
SODIUM 63 mg
CARBOHYDRATE 13 g
FIBER 1 g
PROTEIN 3 g
EXCHANGES 1 Other Carbo., 1½ Fat

- 1½ cups hazelnuts or walnuts, toasted*
- 2 tablespoons all-purpose flour
- 2 teaspoons baking powder
- ¾ cup refrigerated or frozen egg product, thawed, or 3 eggs
- ⅓ cup sugar
- 1 recipe White Mocha Filling
- Chocolate curls (optional)

1 Preheat oven to 350°F. Grease and flour two 8×1½-inch round cake pans. Set pans aside. In a medium bowl combine nuts, flour, and baking powder; set aside.

2 In a blender or food processor combine egg product and sugar; cover and blend or process until combined. Add nut mixture. Cover and blend or process until nearly smooth, scraping side of container occasionally. Divide batter between the prepared pans; spread evenly.

3 Bake for 10 to 12 minutes or until a wooden toothpick inserted in center comes out clean. Cool cake layers in pans on wire racks for 10 minutes. Remove from pans. Cool completely on wire racks.

4 Place 1 cake layer on a serving plate. Spread top with half of White Mocha Filling. Top with second cake layer and remaining filling. Loosely cover. Chill for 2 to 24 hours. If desired, garnish with chocolate curls.

White Mocha Filling: Place three-fourths of an 8-ounce container frozen fat-free whipped dessert topping in a medium bowl; thaw. In a small saucepan combine 2 ounces white baking chocolate (with cocoa butter), chopped; 1 tablespoon instant sugar-free, fat-free Swiss mocha or French vanilla-style coffee powder; and 1 tablespoon fat-free milk. Cook and stir over low heat until melted and smooth. Remove from heat. Stir in ½ cup of the whipped topping (topping will melt). Cool mixture about 5 minutes. Then fold in remaining whipped topping.

***Note:** To toast nuts, preheat oven to 350°F. Place the nuts in a shallow baking pan. Bake about 10 minutes or until toasted. Cool nuts slightly. If using hazelnuts, place warm nuts on a clean kitchen towel. Rub nuts with towel to remove loose skins.

Apple Cake with Hot Coconut-Brown Sugar Topping

PREP 40 minutes **BAKE** 45 minutes
COOL 45 minutes **OVEN** 325°F
MAKES 2 loaf cakes (16 servings)

NUTRITION FACTS per serving

CALORIES 186
TOTAL FAT 9 g (4 g sat. fat)
CHOLESTEROL 19 mg
SODIUM 113 mg
CARBOHYDRATE 26 g
FIBER 1 g
PROTEIN 2 g
EXCHANGES 1½ Other Carbo., 2 Fat

Nonstick cooking spray
- ¾ cup granulated sugar
- ½ cup vanilla fat-free yogurt
- ¼ cup vegetable oil
- 1 egg or ¼ cup refrigerated or frozen egg product, thawed
- 1 teaspoon ground cinnamon
- 1 teaspoon vanilla
- ½ teaspoon baking powder
- ¼ teaspoon salt
- ¼ teaspoon baking soda
- ¼ teaspoon ground ginger
- ¼ teaspoon ground nutmeg
- 1¼ cups all-purpose flour
- 1 pound green cooking apples, cored and coarsely chopped (3 cups)
- 1 cup flaked coconut
- 3 tablespoons butter
- 3 tablespoons packed brown sugar
- 2 tablespoons fat-free milk
- ½ teaspoon ground cinnamon

1 Preheat oven to 325°F. Line two 8×4×2-inch loaf pans with foil; coat foil with cooking spray. Set aside.

2 In a large bowl stir together granulated sugar, yogurt, oil, egg product, the 1 teaspoon cinnamon, the vanilla, baking powder, salt, baking soda, ginger, and nutmeg. Stir in flour just until combined. Fold in apples (batter will be thick and chunky).

3 Spread batter evenly into prepared pans. Bake about 45 minutes or until a toothpick inserted near centers comes out clean and tops are browned.

4 Meanwhile, in a small saucepan combine coconut, butter, brown sugar, milk, and the ½ teaspoon cinnamon. Cook and stir over low heat until butter is melted. After removing cakes from oven, preheat broiler. Evenly and gently spread coconut mixture on cakes. Broil 4 inches from heat for 2 to 3 minutes or until topping is bubbly and lightly browned. Cool in pans on wire racks for 45 minutes. Use foil to lift cakes from pans; remove foil. Serve warm.

Zucchini-Banana Snack Cake

PREP 20 minutes **BAKE** 20 minutes
OVEN 350°F **MAKES** 24 servings

NUTRITION FACTS per serving

CALORIES 118
TOTAL FAT 5 g (0 g sat. fat)
CHOLESTEROL 0 mg
SODIUM 80 mg
CARBOHYDRATE 16 g
FIBER 1 g
PROTEIN 2 g
EXCHANGES 1 Other Carbo., 1 Fat

Nonstick cooking spray
1 cup all-purpose flour
1 cup whole wheat flour
¼ cup flaxseed meal or wheat germ
¼ cup unsweetened cocoa powder
2 teaspoons baking powder
½ teaspoon salt
½ cup refrigerated or frozen egg product, thawed, or 2 eggs, lightly beaten
¾ cup sugar
½ cup canola oil
⅓ cup fat-free milk
1 cup peeled (if desired) and shredded zucchini
½ cup mashed ripe banana (1 medium)
½ cup miniature semisweet chocolate pieces (optional)

1 Preheat oven to 350°F. Lightly coat a 13×9×2-inch baking pan with cooking spray; set aside. In a large bowl combine all-purpose flour, whole wheat flour, flaxseed meal, cocoa powder, baking powder, and salt. Make a well in center of flour mixture; set aside.

2 In a medium bowl whisk together egg product, sugar, canola oil, and milk until well mixed. Stir in zucchini and banana. Add zucchini mixture all at once to flour mixture. Stir just until moistened. Fold in chocolate pieces. Pour batter into prepared pan, spreading evenly.

3 Bake for 20 to 25 minutes or until top springs back when lightly touched. Cool completely on a wire rack. Cut into rectangles.

Almond Sandwich Cookies

PREP 30 minutes **BAKE** 10 minutes per batch
OVEN 325°F **MAKES** about 30 filled cookies

NUTRITION FACTS per cookie

CALORIES 118
TOTAL FAT 7 g (3 g sat. fat)
CHOLESTEROL 12 mg
SODIUM 58 mg
CARBOHYDRATE 14 g
FIBER 1 g
PROTEIN 1 g
EXCHANGES 1 Other Carbo., 1½ Fat

Nonstick cooking spray
1 cup rolled oats
¾ cup sugar
2 tablespoons all-purpose flour
1 teaspoon ground cardamom
¼ teaspoon salt
¼ teaspoon baking powder
¼ cup refrigerated or frozen egg product, thawed, or 1 egg, lightly beaten
½ cup butter, melted
1 teaspoon vanilla
1 cup slivered almonds
1 recipe Vanilla Cream

1 Preheat oven to 325°F. Line a cookie sheet with foil and lightly coat foil with cooking spray; set aside.

2 In a large bowl combine oats, sugar, flour, cardamom, salt, and baking powder. In a medium bowl whisk together the egg product, butter, and vanilla until well combined. Add egg mixture to flour mixture; stir until well combined. Add almonds; stir until almonds are evenly distributed.

3 Drop level teaspoons of dough 3 inches apart on prepared cookie sheet. Bake for 10 to 12 minutes or until edges are brown. Cool cookies completely then peel from foil. Repeat with remaining dough.

4 For each sandwich cookie, spread bottom side of a cookie with a rounded teaspoon of Vanilla Cream. Place another cookie, top side up, on filling.

Vanilla Cream: In a large mixing bowl combine ¼ cup butter, softened, and 1 cup powdered sugar. Beat with an electric mixer on medium until smooth. Beat in 1 teaspoon vanilla. Gradually beat in an additional ½ cup powdered sugar until filling is smooth.

Whole Grain Chocolate Chip Cookies

PREP 30 minutes **BAKE** 8 minutes per batch
OVEN 375°F **MAKES** about 48 cookies

- 2 eggs or ½ cup refrigerated or frozen egg product, thawed
- 1 cup sugar
- ¾ cup vegetable oil
- 1 teaspoon vanilla
- 1 cup whole wheat flour
- 1 cup regular rolled oats
- ½ cup barley flour
- ½ cup oat bran
- ¼ cup wheat bran
- 3 tablespoons nonfat dry milk powder
- 1½ teaspoons baking powder
- ¼ teaspoon baking soda
- ½ cup miniature semisweet chocolate pieces
- ½ cup chopped walnuts
- ¼ cup unsweetened shredded coconut (optional)

1 Preheat oven to 375°F. In a medium bowl beat egg product lightly with a fork; stir in sugar, oil, and vanilla. Set aside.

2 In a large bowl combine whole wheat flour, oats, barley flour, oat bran, wheat bran, dry milk powder, baking powder, and baking soda.

3 Add egg mixture to flour mixture; stir with a wooden spoon until combined. Stir in chocolate pieces, walnuts, and, if desired, coconut.

4 Drop dough by rounded teaspoons 2 inches apart onto an ungreased cookie sheet. Bake for 8 to 10 minutes or until edges are set and bottoms are lightly browned. Transfer cookies to a wire rack; to cool.

NUTRITION FACTS per cookie

CALORIES 94
TOTAL FAT 5 g (1 g sat. fat)
CHOLESTEROL 9 mg
SODIUM 19 mg
CARBOHYDRATE 11 g
FIBER 1 g
PROTEIN 2 g
EXCHANGES 1 Other Carbo., 1 Fat

Cranberry-Oatmeal Streusel Bars

PREP 25 minutes **BAKE** 20 minutes
OVEN 350°F **MAKES** 20 bars

NUTRITION FACTS per bar

CALORIES 175
TOTAL FAT 8 g (2 g sat. fat)
CHOLESTEROL 5 mg
SODIUM 55 mg
CARBOHYDRATE 23 g
FIBER 2 g
PROTEIN 4 g
EXCHANGES 1½ Starch, 1½ Fat

- 1½ cups quick-cooking rolled oats
- 1 cup all-purpose flour
- ⅔ cup packed brown sugar
- ¼ cup whole wheat pastry flour or all-purpose flour
- ¼ cup flaxseed meal or wheat germ
- ½ teaspoon baking soda
- ½ cup fat-free milk
- ⅓ cup canola oil or vegetable oil
- 2 egg whites, lightly beaten
- 1 teaspoon vanilla or ½ teaspoon maple flavoring or almond extract
- ¼ cup snipped dried cranberries
- 3 tablespoons butter
- ¼ cup chopped pecans or almonds

1. Preheat oven to 350°F. Line a 9×9×2-inch baking pan with foil; set aside. In a medium bowl stir together rolled oats, all-purpose flour, brown sugar, whole wheat pastry flour, and flaxseed meal. Set aside ½ cup of the oat mixture for streusel topping. Stir baking soda into the remaining oat mixture.

2. In another medium bowl whisk together milk, oil, egg whites, and vanilla; add to oat mixture, stirring until combined. Stir in cranberries. Pat into prepared baking pan.

3. Using a pasty blender, cut butter into reserved streusel topping until mixture resembles coarse crumbs; stir in pecans. Sprinkle over mixture in pan.

4. Bake for 20 to 25 minutes or until center is set. Cool on a wire rack. Use foil to lift out of pan; cut into bars.

Raspberry-Oatmeal Wedges

PREP 25 minutes **BAKE** 30 minutes
OVEN 350°F **MAKES** 12 servings

NUTRITION FACTS per serving

CALORIES 153
TOTAL FAT 4 g (1 g sat. fat)
CHOLESTEROL 0 mg
SODIUM 64 mg
CARBOHYDRATE 26 g
FIBER 2 g
PROTEIN 3 g
EXCHANGES 1½ Other Carbo., 1 Fat

- 2 tablespoons granulated sugar
- 1 teaspoon cornstarch
- 2 cups frozen red raspberries, thawed and drained, or fresh red raspberries
- ½ cup packed brown sugar
- ⅓ cup tub-style 60 to 70% vegetable oil spread
- ¼ teaspoon baking soda
- ¼ teaspoon ground cinnamon, nutmeg, or allspice
- 1 egg white
- ½ cup all-purpose flour
- ½ cup white whole wheat flour or whole wheat flour
- 1 cup quick-cooking rolled oats
- ¾ cup frozen light whipped dessert topping, thawed (optional)
- Fresh raspberries (optional)

1 In a medium bowl combine granulated sugar and cornstarch. Add the 2 cups raspberries; toss to coat. Using a potato masher or fork, lightly mash berries; set aside for 15 minutes. Meanwhile, preheat oven to 350°F. Lightly grease a 9-inch tart pan with removable bottom or a 9-inch springform pan.

2 In a medium mixing bowl beat brown sugar, vegetable oil spread, baking soda, and cinnamon with an electric mixer on medium until well mixed, scraping bowl occasionally. Beat in egg white. Beat in all-purpose flour and whole wheat flour until combined. Stir in oats.

3 Set aside ½ cup of the oat mixture for topping. Press the remaining oat mixture into the bottom of the prepared pan. Bake for 10 to 12 minutes or just until crust begins to brown on the edges. Spread raspberry mixture over partially baked crust. Crumble the reserved ½ cup topping on raspberry mixture.

4 Bake about 20 minutes or until the top is golden brown. Cool in pan on a wire rack. If using a tart pan, remove side of pan. If using a springform pan, run a thin metal spatula around the edge of the pan; remove side of pan. Cut into wedges to serve. If desired, top with whipped topping and fresh raspberries.

Ice Cream Sandwiches

PREP 45 minutes **BAKE** 6 minutes
FREEZE 3 hours **OVEN** 375°F
MAKES 13 sandwiches

NUTRITION FACTS per sandwich

CALORIES 126
TOTAL FAT 5 g (3 g sat. fat)
CHOLESTEROL 12 mg
SODIUM 78 mg
CARBOHYDRATE 19 g
FIBER 1 g
PROTEIN 2 g
EXCHANGES 1 Other Carbo., 1 Fat

- 1/4 cup butter, softened
- 1/4 cup sugar
- 1/2 teaspoon baking powder
- 1/2 teaspoon vanilla
- 1/8 teaspoon salt
- 2 tablespoons refrigerated or frozen egg product, thawed, or 1 egg white
- 1 1/4 cups cake flour or all-purpose flour
- 2 cups low-fat or light chocolate, vanilla, or fudge nut sundae ice cream
- 1/2 cup chopped toasted almonds or pecans (optional) (see note, page 275)

1 Preheat oven to 375°F. In a small mixing bowl beat butter with an electric mixer on medium for 30 seconds. Add sugar, baking powder, vanilla, and salt; beat until combined. Add egg product; beat until combined. Beat in as much of the flour as you can with the mixer. Using a wooden spoon, stir in any remaining flour (or knead gently until combined). Shape dough into a ball.

2 On a lightly floured surface roll dough to 1/8-inch thickness. Using a 2-inch square or round cutter with scalloped edges, cut out dough. Place 1 inch apart on ungreased cookie sheets.

3 Bake for 6 to 8 minutes or until edges are very lightly browned. Transfer cookies to wire racks; cool.

4 Meanwhile, scoop 13 ice cream balls, about 2 tablespoons each, and place on a waxed paper-lined baking sheet. Freeze until ready to assemble.

5 To assemble sandwiches, remove a few ice cream balls at a time. Place 1 ball on a cookie. Top with a second cookie, pressing gently together. Repeat with remaining ice cream and cookies. If desired, sprinkle and press nuts onto edges of ice cream.

6 Place sandwiches on a waxed paper-lined baking sheet. Freeze for 3 hours or until firm. To store, freeze up to 2 weeks in resealable plastic bags.

Pecan-Maple Sorbet Cups

PREP 45 minutes **STAND** 30 minutes
BAKE 5 minutes per batch **OVEN** 375°F
MAKES 10 sorbet cups

- 2 egg whites
- ½ cup ground pecans
- 3 tablespoons butter, melted
- ¼ teaspoon maple flavoring
- ½ cup sugar
- ½ cup all-purpose flour
- Nonstick cooking spray (optional)
- 3 cups any flavor sorbet (raspberry, lemon, and/or coconut)

1 In a medium mixing bowl let egg whites stand at room temperature for 30 minutes.

2 Preheat oven to 375°F. Line large cookie sheets with foil or parchment paper. If using foil, lightly grease foil; set aside. In a small bowl combine ground pecans, butter, and maple flavoring; set aside.

3 Beat egg whites with an electric mixer on medium until soft peaks form (tips curl). Gradually add sugar, beating on high until stiff peaks form (tips stand straight). Fold in about half the flour. Gently stir in pecan mixture. Fold in the remaining flour until thoroughly combined.

4 For each cookie cup, drop 2 rounded measuring tablespoons of batter onto prepared cookie sheet, leaving 4 inches between mounds (place only 2 or 3 mounds on each baking sheet). Using the back of a spoon, spread each mound to a 4-inch circle. If necessary, coat the back of the spoon with cooking spray to prevent sticking.

5 Bake for 5 to 7 minutes or until cookies are golden brown around edges and centers are lightly browned. Using a wide spatula, immediately remove the cookies and gently press each warm cookie into a 3½-inch (jumbo) muffin cup, pleating sides to form a cup. (Or wrap each warm cookie around the bottom of a 2½-inch muffin cup, pleating sides to form a cup.) Cool cookie cups until they hold their shape. Carefully remove from muffin cups. Cool completely on a wire rack.

6 To serve, place a small scoop of sorbet in each cookie cup. If desired, garnish with fresh *mint sprigs.*

NUTRITION FACTS per sorbet cup

CALORIES 194
TOTAL FAT 8 g (3 g sat. fat)
CHOLESTEROL 9 mg
SODIUM 42 mg
CARBOHYDRATE 32 g
FIBER 1 g
PROTEIN 2 g
EXCHANGES 2 Other Carbo., 1½ Fat

Tiramisu

PREP 30 minutes **CHILL** 4 to 24 hours
MAKES 15 servings

NUTRITION FACTS per serving

CALORIES 186
TOTAL FAT 8 g (5 g sat. fat)
CHOLESTEROL 67 mg
SODIUM 182 mg
CARBOHYDRATE 22 g
FIBER 0 g
PROTEIN 5 g
EXCHANGES 1½ Other Carbo., 1½ Fat

- 2 8-ounce cartons fat-free or light sour cream
- 2 8-ounce packages reduced-fat cream cheese (Neufchâtel), softened
- ⅔ cup sugar
- ¼ cup fat-free milk
- ½ teaspoon vanilla
- ½ cup strong coffee
- 2 tablespoons coffee liqueur or strong coffee
- 2 3-ounce packages ladyfingers, split
- 2 tablespoons sifted unsweetened cocoa powder
- Unsweetened cocoa powder (optional)
- White and/or dark chocolate curls (optional)

1 In a large mixing bowl combine sour cream, cream cheese, sugar, milk, and vanilla. Beat with an electric mixer on high until smooth. In a bowl combine the ½ cup coffee and the coffee liqueur.

2 In a 2-quart rectangular baking dish layer 1 package of ladyfingers, cut sides up. Brush with half the coffee mixture. Spread with half the cream cheese mixture. Repeat layering with remaining ladyfingers, coffee mixture, and cream cheese mixture.

3 Sprinkle with the 2 tablespoons cocoa powder. Cover and chill for 4 to 24 hours. If desired, sprinkle serving platter with additional unsweetened cocoa powder. Cut dessert into squares; arrange on platter. If desired, garnish with chocolate curls.

Almond-Apple Trifles

START TO FINISH 20 minutes
MAKES 4 servings

- ½ cup pomegranate juice or low-calorie cranberry juice
- ½ teaspoon almond extract
- 1 cup coarsely snipped dried apples
- 1 6-ounce carton plain low-fat or fat-free yogurt
- ⅓ cup frozen light whipped dessert topping, thawed
- ¼ teaspoon almond extract
- 1 cup lightly sweetened multigrain clusters
- ¼ cup sliced almonds, toasted (see note, page 275)

1 In a small saucepan heat pomegranate juice just until boiling; remove from heat. Stir in the ½ teaspoon almond extract. Stir in apples. Cover; cool completely.

2 In a small bowl gently stir together yogurt, whipped topping, and the ¼ teaspoon almond extract.

3 Divide half the apple mixture among four 6-ounce dessert dishes or custard cups. Sprinkle with half the multigrain clusters. Spoon half the whipped topping mixture on apple layers. Sprinkle with half of the almonds. Repeat layering with apple mixture, multigrain clusters, whipped topping mixture, and almonds. Serve immediately.

NUTRITION FACTS per serving

CALORIES 210
TOTAL FAT 6 g (1 g sat. fat)
CHOLESTEROL 3 mg
SODIUM 101 mg
CARBOHYDRATE 34 g
FIBER 5 g
PROTEIN 7 g
EXCHANGES 1 Fruit, 1 Starch, 1 Fat

Triple-Chocolate-Hazelnut Frozen Mousse

PREP 45 minutes **FREEZE** 3 hours
MAKES 10 servings

NUTRITION FACTS per serving

CALORIES 195
TOTAL FAT 10 g (6 g sat. fat)
CHOLESTEROL 6 mg
SODIUM 257 mg
CARBOHYDRATE 18 g
FIBER 1 g
PROTEIN 7 g
EXCHANGES 1 Other Carbo., ½ Lean Meat, 2 Fat

- 1½ 8-ounce packages fat-free cream cheese, softened
- 2 ounces dark chocolate or bittersweet chocolate, melted and cooled slightly
- 1 8-ounce container frozen light whipped dessert topping, thawed
- 2 ounces white baking chocolate (with cocoa butter), melted and cooled slightly
- 2 ounces milk chocolate, melted and cooled slightly
- 3 tablespoons hazelnuts (filberts), toasted (see note, page 275) and chopped
- 1 ounce dark chocolate or bittersweet chocolate (optional)
- ½ teaspoon shortening (optional)

1 Line an 8×4×2-inch or 9×5×3-inch loaf pan with heavy foil, extending foil over pan; set aside. In a medium mixing bowl beat one-third of the cream cheese with an electric mixer on medium for 30 seconds. Beat in the 2 ounces dark chocolate. Fold in one-third of the dessert topping. Spread mixture evenly in prepared pan. Cover; freeze about 30 minutes or until firm.

2 Meanwhile, in a clean medium mixing bowl beat half of the remaining cream cheese with electric mixer on medium for 30 seconds. Beat in white chocolate. Fold in half of the remaining dessert topping. Spread evenly over frozen dark chocolate layer in pan. Cover and freeze about 30 minutes or until firm.

3 Meanwhile, place remaining cream cheese in a clean medium mixing bowl. Beat with electric mixer on medium for 30 seconds. Beat in milk chocolate until smooth. Fold in remaining dessert topping. Spread evenly over the frozen white chocolate layer in pan. Sprinkle with hazelnuts. Cover and freeze for 2 to 24 hours.

4 To serve, using the edges of the foil, lift the mousse from the pan. If necessary, let stand at room temperature about 20 minutes to soften slightly. Cut loaf crosswise into 10 wedges. If desired, melt together dark chocolate and shortening; drizzle over mousse slices.

Creamy Lime Mousse

PREP 15 minutes **COOL** 10 minutes
CHILL 2 to 24 hours **MAKES** 6 servings

NUTRITION FACTS per serving

CALORIES 128
TOTAL FAT 1 g (0 g sat. fat)
CHOLESTEROL 37 mg
SODIUM 148 mg
CARBOHYDRATE 26 g
FIBER 2 g
PROTEIN 5 g
EXCHANGES ½ Medium-Fat Meat, 1½ Fat

- 1 4-serving-size package sugar-free lime-flavored gelatin
- 1 cup boiling water
- ½ teaspoon finely shredded lime peel
- 2 tablespoons lime juice
- 1 recipe Tofu Sour Cream or one 8-ounce carton light sour cream
- 1 cup frozen light whipped dessert topping, thawed
- ½ cup frozen light whipped dessert topping, thawed (optional)
- Lime peel curls or lime slices (optional)

1 In a large bowl combine gelatin and the boiling water; stir about 2 minutes or until gelatin is dissolved. Stir in shredded lime peel and lime juice. Cool for 10 to 15 minutes or until cooled slightly but not set. Whisk in Tofu Sour Cream. Gently whisk in the 1 cup dessert topping. Pour into six 6- to 8-ounce stemmed dessert glasses. Cover and chill for 2 to 24 hours or until set.

2 If desired, garnish with the ½ cup dessert topping and lime peel curls or lime slices.

Tofu Sour Cream: In a blender combine half of a 12.3-ounce package extra-firm silken-style tofu (fresh bean curd), patted dry with paper towels; 3 tablespoons vegetable oil; 4 teaspoons lemon juice; ¼ teaspoon honey; and ⅛ teaspoon salt. Cover and blend on high until smooth and creamy, stopping to push mixture into blades as necessary. Makes about ¾ cup.

Melon-Mango Ice Cream

PREP 20 minutes
FREEZE according to manufacturer's directions
MAKES about 3 quarts (twenty four ½-cup servings)

NUTRITION FACTS per serving

CALORIES 76
TOTAL FAT 1 g (1 g sat. fat)
CHOLESTEROL 4 mg
SODIUM 60 mg
CARBOHYDRATE 15 g
FIBER 0 g
PROTEIN 2 g
EXCHANGES 1 Other Carbo.

- 2 cups whole milk
- 2 cups buttermilk
- 2 cups fat-free half-and-half
- 1 cup sugar
- 1 tablespoon vanilla
- 1½ cups chopped cantaloupe
- 1½ cups chopped mango
- Edible flowers (optional)

1 In a large bowl combine milk, buttermilk, fat-free half-and-half, sugar, and vanilla. Stir to dissolve sugar.

2 In a food processor or blender combine cantaloupe and mango. Cover and process or blend until smooth. Stir pureed fruit into milk mixture. Freeze in a 4- to 5-quart ice cream freezer according to manufacturer's directions. If desired, ripen for 4 hours.* If desired, garnish servings with edible flowers.

***Note:** Ripening homemade ice cream improves the texture and helps to keep it from melting too quickly when served. To ripen in a traditional-style ice cream freezer, after churning remove the lid and dasher and cover the top of the freezer can with waxed paper or foil. Plug the hole in the lid with a small piece of cloth; replace the lid. Pack the outer freezer bucket with enough ice and rock salt to cover the top of the freezer can (use 1 cup salt for each 4 cups ice.) Ripen about 4 hours. When using an ice cream freezer with an insulated freezer bowl, transfer the ice cream to a covered freezer container and ripen by freezing in a regular freezer about 4 hours (or follow the manufacturer's recommendations).

Chapter 15

Holiday

On the opener: Stuffed Pork Loin *(see recipe, page 291)*

BREADS

DESSERTS

MAIN DISHES

SALADS

VEGETABLES & SIDE DISHES

Stuffed Pork Loin

PREP 40 minutes **ROAST** 1 hour 40 minutes
STAND 15 minutes **OVEN** 325°F
MAKES 12 servings

- 3 ounces fresh spinach, coarsely chopped
- 1 tablespoon olive oil
- ½ cup chopped dried tart cherries
- ¾ cup cooked wild rice
- ¾ teaspoon dried sage, crushed
- ⅓ cup chopped pecans
- ¾ teaspoon salt
- ¼ teaspoon black pepper
- 1 3½-pound boneless pork center loin roast
- ½ teaspoon salt
- ½ teaspoon black pepper
- ¼ teaspoon ground dried sage
- ⅛ teaspoon ground dried thyme
- ½ cup low-sugar apricot preserves
- 3 tablespoons water

1 In a large skillet cook spinach in hot oil until wilted. Combine cooked spinach, cherries, rice, ¾ teaspoon crushed sage, nuts, ¾ teaspoon salt, and ¼ teaspoon pepper; set aside.

2 Preheat oven to 325°F. Trim fat from pork. To pinwheel the roast, start cutting lengthwise ½ inch under the fat cap on roast. As you cut, gently rotate the roast at the same time, allowing the roast to unroll as you cut. When roast is completely cut, it should be a rectangular piece of meat ½ to 1 inch thick.

3 Sprinkle cut surface of meat with ½ teaspoon salt, ½ teaspoon pepper, ¼ teaspoon ground sage, and the thyme. Spread spinach mixture over cut side. Roll up the loin tightly to resemble the initial roast. Tie securely with kitchen twine.

4 Place the roast on a rack in a roasting pan; insert a meat thermometer into thickest part. Roast for 1½ to 1¾ hours or until meat thermometer registers 140°F.

5 In a small saucepan melt apricot preserves and water together. Brush half the preserves on roast. Roast for 10 to 15 minutes or until thermometer registers 150°F. Remove from oven; brush with remaining preserves. Cover; let stand for 15 minutes before carving. The temperature of the meat after standing should be 160°F.

NUTRITION FACTS per serving

CALORIES 279
TOTAL FAT 12 g (3 g sat. fat)
CHOLESTEROL 73 mg
SODIUM 309 mg
CARBOHYDRATE 11 g
FIBER 1 g
PROTEIN 30 g
EXCHANGES 1 Other Carbo., 4 Lean Meat, 1 Fat

Herb-Roasted Turkey and Vegetables

PREP 30 minutes **ROAST** 1 hour 35 minutes
STAND 10 minutes **OVEN** 400°F/350°F
MAKES 8 to 10 servings

NUTRITION FACTS per serving

CALORIES 231
TOTAL FAT 3 g (1 g sat. fat)
CHOLESTEROL 69 mg
SODIUM 219 mg
CARBOHYDRATE 21 g
FIBER 3 g
PROTEIN 30 g
EXCHANGES ½ Vegetable, 1 Starch, 3½ Lean Meat, ½ Fat

- 2 tablespoons snipped fresh parsley
- 4 cloves garlic, minced
- 1 teaspoon snipped fresh rosemary
- 1 teaspoon snipped fresh thyme
- ½ teaspoon salt
- ½ teaspoon black pepper
- 1 2¾- to 3¼-pound turkey breast portion with bone, skin removed
- Nonstick cooking spray
- 3 cups tiny red potatoes, quartered (about 1 pound)
- 2 cups baby carrots, tops trimmed and halved lengthwise (about 8 ounces)
- 2 cups white and/or red pearl onions, trimmed and halved (about 8 ounces)
- 1 tablespoon olive oil

1 Preheat oven to 400°F. In a small bowl combine parsley, garlic, rosemary, thyme, salt, and pepper. Set aside 1 tablespoon of the herb mixture.

2 Place turkey breast portion, bone side down, on a roasting rack in a shallow roasting pan. Lightly coat with cooking spray. Sprinkle the remaining herb mixture evenly over turkey breast portion; rub in with your fingers. Roast, uncovered, for 20 minutes.

3 Meanwhile, in a large bowl combine potatoes, carrots, and pearl onions; add the reserved 1 tablespoon herb mixture and the olive oil and toss until vegetables are coated. Arrange vegetables around turkey in roasting pan.

4 Reduce oven temperature to 350°F. Roast for 1¼ to 1½ hours more or until juices run clear, turkey is no longer pink (170°F), and vegetables are tender, stirring vegetables once.

5 Transfer turkey to cutting board; tent with foil and let stand for 10 minutes before slicing. Serve the turkey with vegetables.

Savory Butternut Squash Dressing

PREP 30 minutes **COOK** 45 minutes
BAKE 40 minutes **STAND** 10 minutes
OVEN 350°F **MAKES** 10 to 12 servings

NUTRITION FACTS per serving

CALORIES 161
TOTAL FAT 4 g (2 g sat. fat)
CHOLESTEROL 89 mg
SODIUM 296 mg
CARBOHYDRATE 25 g
FIBER 2 g
PROTEIN 7 g
EXCHANGES 1½ Starch, 1 Fat

- 1 tablespoon butter
- 1 shallot, finely chopped
- ½ cup fresh cranberries
- 1 cup reduced-sodium chicken broth
- ¼ cup uncooked wild rice, rinsed
- Nonstick cooking spray
- 12 ounces butternut squash, peeled, seeded, and cut into ½- to ¾-inch cubes
- ½ cup chopped celery (1 stalk)
- ¼ cup finely chopped onion
- 1½ teaspoons snipped fresh thyme
- ⅛ teaspoon black pepper
- ¾ cup reduced-fat milk (2%)
- 4 eggs
- ¾ cup reduced-sodium chicken broth
- ¼ cup dried cranberries
- 1½ teaspoons snipped fresh sage
- 4 cups dried sourdough bread cubes*

1 In a medium saucepan melt half of the butter over medium heat. Add shallot; cook for 1 minute. Add fresh cranberries; cook for 1 minute more. Add the 1 cup broth and the rice. Bring to boiling; reduce heat. Simmer, covered, for 40 to 45 minutes or until rice is tender.

2 Meanwhile, preheat oven to 350°F. Lightly coat a 2-quart rectangular baking dish with cooking spray; set aside. Place a Dutch oven over medium heat. Add remaining butter and squash. Cook and stir for 5 minutes. Add celery, onion, and thyme. Cook and stir for 3 minutes more. Sprinkle with pepper; set aside.

3 In a large bowl whisk together milk, eggs, and the ¾ cup broth. Stir in cooked rice mixture, squash mixture, dried cranberries, sage, and bread cubes. Transfer to prepared baking dish. Bake, covered, for 20 minutes. Uncover; bake about 20 minutes more or until set. Let stand for 10 minutes before serving.

***Note:** To dry bread cubes, cut bread into ½-inch cubes (8 ounces of bread yields 4 cups cubes). Spread in a 15×10×1-inch baking pan. Bake for 10 to 15 minutes or until dry, stirring twice. Cool.

Herbed Corn Bread Dressing

PREP 30 minutes **BAKE** 20 minutes
OVEN 375°F **MAKES** 8 servings

NUTRITION FACTS per serving

CALORIES 226
TOTAL FAT 8 g (1 g sat. fat)
CHOLESTEROL 18 mg
SODIUM 492 mg
CARBOHYDRATE 32 g
FIBER 3 g
PROTEIN 7 g
EXCHANGES 2 Starch, 1½ Fat

Nonstick cooking spray
- 2 tablespoons olive oil or vegetable oil
- 1 cup sliced celery (2 stalks)
- ¾ cup chopped onion
- 2 cloves garlic, minced
- 4 cups crumbled corn bread
- 3 slices whole wheat bread, dried and crumbled
- ¼ cup snipped fresh parsley
- 1½ teaspoons dried sage, crushed, or 1 tablespoon finely snipped fresh sage
- 1 teaspoon dried thyme, crushed, or 2 teaspoons finely snipped fresh thyme
- ½ teaspoon dried marjoram, crushed, or 1 teaspoon finely snipped fresh marjoram
- ½ teaspoon black pepper
- ⅛ teaspoon salt
- ¾ cup refrigerated or frozen egg product, thawed, or 3 eggs, lightly beaten
- ½ to ¾ cup reduced-sodium chicken broth

1 Preheat oven to 375°F. Lightly coat a 2-quart rectangular baking dish with cooking spray. In a large skillet heat oil over medium heat. Add celery, onion, and garlic; cook about 10 minutes or until tender. In a very large bowl combine corn bread and whole wheat bread.

2 Add the onion mixture, parsley, sage, thyme, marjoram, pepper, and salt to the bread mixture and mix well.

3 Add egg product, tossing to coat. Add enough of the chicken broth to reach desired consistency. Spoon dressing into the prepared dish. Bake, uncovered, about 20 minutes or until hot in center (165°F).

Vegetable Gratin

START TO FINISH 40 minutes
MAKES 12 servings

NUTRITION FACTS per serving

CALORIES 65
TOTAL FAT 1 g (0 g sat. fat)
CHOLESTEROL 1 mg
SODIUM 98 mg
CARBOHYDRATE 10 g
FIBER 3 g
PROTEIN 3 g
EXCHANGES 1 Vegetable, ½ Starch

- 1 slice whole grain bread
- ¼ cup slivered almonds
- Nonstick cooking spray
- 4 medium carrots, peeled and cut crosswise into 1-inch pieces
- 3 cups broccoli florets
- 3 cups cauliflower florets
- ¾ cup chopped sweet onion (such as Vidalia or Walla Walla)
- 2 cloves garlic, minced
- ¼ teaspoon salt
- ¼ teaspoon black pepper
- 1¼ cups fat-free milk
- 3 tablespoons all-purpose flour
- 2 tablespoons dry white wine or fat-free milk

1 Place bread in a blender or small food processor; cover and blend or process to make coarse crumbs. In a small bowl combine bread crumbs and almonds; coat with cooking spray. Toss mixture; coat again with cooking spray. Coat unheated large nonstick skillet with cooking spray. Preheat skillet over medium heat for 2 minutes; add crumb mixture. Cook about 5 minutes or until nuts are toasted, stirring frequently. Remove from skillet; set aside.

2 In a 4-quart pot cook carrots, uncovered, in a large amount of boiling water for 3 minutes. Add broccoli and cauliflower; cook for 3 to 5 minutes more or just until vegetables are tender. Drain well. Set aside.

3 Coat the large nonstick skillet with cooking spray again; heat over medium heat. Add onion; cook about 5 minutes or until tender, stirring occasionally. Stir in garlic, salt, and pepper. In a small bowl whisk together milk and flour until smooth. Add to onion mixture. Cook and stir until thickened and bubbly. Stir in wine and vegetables; heat through.

4 Place vegetables in serving dish; sprinkle with toasted crumb mixture.

Pan-Roasted Brussels Sprouts

START TO FINISH 30 minutes
MAKES 12 servings

NUTRITION FACTS per serving

CALORIES 61
TOTAL FAT 3 g (1 g sat. fat)
CHOLESTEROL 5 mg
SODIUM 128 mg
CARBOHYDRATE 7 g
FIBER 3 g
PROTEIN 3 g
EXCHANGES 1 Vegetable, ½ Fat

- 2 pounds Brussels sprouts, halved lengthwise
- 1 tablespoon rice oil or olive oil
- 7 cloves garlic, minced
- 2 tablespoons butter
- ½ bunch fresh thyme (about 10 sprigs)
- 1 large sprig fresh rosemary, halved
- 2 teaspoons fennel seeds
- ½ teaspoon salt
- 1 tablespoon sherry or white wine vinegar

1 In a large saucepan cook Brussels sprouts, uncovered, in enough lightly salted boiling water to cover for 3 minutes; drain well. Pat dry with paper towels.

2 Place a very large heavy skillet over high heat for 1 to 2 minutes. Reduce heat to medium. Add oil and garlic; cook and stir for 2 minutes. Add 1 tablespoon of the butter. Increase heat to medium-high; carefully arrange half the sprouts, cut sides down, in the hot skillet. Top with half the thyme, rosemary, fennel seeds, and salt. Cook, uncovered, for 3 to 4 minutes or until the sprouts are well browned. Remove sprouts from pan. Repeat with remaining butter, sprouts, thyme, rosemary, fennel seeds, and salt.

3 Return all sprouts to skillet; add sherry. Quickly toss to distribute flavors.

Make-Ahead Directions: Cook, drain, and dry Brussels sprouts as directed in Step 1. Place in a covered container and store in the refrigerator

Corn Bake

PREP 30 minutes **BAKE** 1 hour
STAND 10 minutes **OVEN** 350°F
MAKES 16 servings

- Nonstick cooking spray
- 1 cup chopped red sweet pepper (1 large)
- ½ cup chopped onion (1 medium)
- 1 15.25-ounce can no-salt-added whole kernel corn, drained
- 1 14.75-ounce can no-salt-added cream-style corn
- 1 8.5-ounce package corn muffin mix
- ⅓ cup refrigerated egg product
- 1 8-ounce carton light sour cream
- ½ cup reduced-fat shredded sharp cheddar cheese (2 ounces)

1 Preheat oven to 350°F. Coat a large skillet with cooking spray. Heat over medium heat. Cook red pepper and onion in hot skillet until tender. Cool slightly. Lightly coat a 2-quart rectangular baking dish with cooking spray; set aside.

2 Meanwhile, in a large bowl combine whole corn, cream-style corn, corn muffin mix, and egg product. Stir in cooled vegetables. Transfer mixture to prepared baking dish.

3 In a small bowl combine sour cream and cheese. Spoon in small mounds on top of corn mixture. Bake about 1 hour or until set. Let stand for 10 minutes before serving.

NUTRITION FACTS per serving

CALORIES 134
TOTAL FAT 4 g (2 g sat. fat)
CHOLESTEROL 7 mg
SODIUM 155 mg
CARBOHYDRATE 22 g
FIBER 1 g
PROTEIN 4 g
EXCHANGES 1½ Starch, ½ Fat

Broccoli with Goat Cheese and Walnuts

START TO FINISH 30 minutes
MAKES 6 servings

NUTRITION FACTS per serving

CALORIES 105
TOTAL FAT 7 g (2 g sat. fat)
CHOLESTEROL 4 mg
SODIUM 212 mg
CARBOHYDRATE 9 g
FIBER 3 g
PROTEIN 5 g
EXCHANGES 1½ Vegetable, 1½ Fat

- 1 pound broccoli, trimmed and cut into 1-inch pieces
- ½ cup buttermilk
- 1 tablespoon snipped fresh Italian (flat-leaf) parsley
- 1 tablespoon Dijon mustard
- 2 teaspoons extra virgin olive oil
- 1 teaspoon snipped fresh thyme
- 1 teaspoon red wine vinegar
- 1 clove garlic, minced
- ¼ teaspoon kosher salt
- ⅛ teaspoon ground nutmeg
- ⅛ teaspoon freshly ground black pepper
- ½ cup thinly slivered red onion
- ¼ cup coarsely chopped walnuts, toasted (see note, page 275)
- 1 ounce semisoft goat cheese (chèvre) or feta cheese, crumbled

1 In a covered large saucepan cook broccoli in a small amount of lightly salted boiling water for 6 to 8 minutes or until crisp-tender. Drain and set aside.

2 In a large bowl whisk together buttermilk, parsley, mustard, olive oil, thyme, red wine vinegar, garlic, kosher salt, nutmeg, and pepper. Add the broccoli and red onion; stir gently to coat. Top with walnuts and goat cheese.

Make-Ahead Directions: Prepare as directed, except do not top with walnuts and goat cheese. Cover and chill up to 4 hours. To serve, top with walnuts and goat cheese.

Orange and Fennel Salad with Citrus Vinaigrette

START TO FINISH 25 minutes
MAKES 6 servings

NUTRITION FACTS per serving

CALORIES 93
TOTAL FAT 5 g (1 g sat. fat)
CHOLESTEROL 0 mg
SODIUM 76 mg
CARBOHYDRATE 12 g
FIBER 3 g
PROTEIN 2 g
EXCHANGES 1½ Vegetable, ½ Fruit, 1 Fat

- 1 medium fennel bulb
- 4 cups torn romaine lettuce
- 2 cups torn radicchio (½ of a small head)
- 1½ teaspoons finely shredded orange peel (set aside)
- 2 medium oranges, peeled and sectioned
- 1 small red onion, halved and thinly sliced
- 3 tablespoons white wine vinegar
- 2 tablespoons olive oil
- 2 tablespoons water
- 2 cloves garlic, minced
- 1 teaspoon sugar
- ⅛ teaspoon salt
- ⅛ teaspoon black pepper

1 Snip enough of the fennel leaves to equal 1 teaspoon; reserve for dressing. If desired, save additional fennel leaves for garnish. Cut off and discard fennel stalks. Remove any wilted outer layers of the fennel bulb; cut a thin slice from the base of the bulb. Cut bulb into quarters lengthwise. Thinly slice quarters; set aside.

2 On a large serving platter arrange romaine, radicchio, orange slices, onion slices, and fennel slices. Set aside.

3 For dressing, in a small bowl combine the reserved snipped fennel leaves, the vinegar, olive oil, the water, garlic, orange peel, sugar, salt, and pepper; whisk together until well mixed. To serve, spoon dressing over salad. If desired, garnish with fennel leaves.

Note: To make a creamy dressing, whisk 1 tablespoon light mayonnaise or salad dressing into the dressing in Step 3.

Ginger Ale Salad

PREP 20 minutes **CHILL** 7 hours 30 minutes
MAKES 9 servings

NUTRITION FACTS per serving

CALORIES 108
TOTAL FAT 0 g (0 g sat. fat)
CHOLESTEROL 0 mg
SODIUM 115 mg
CARBOHYDRATE 26 g
FIBER 1 g
PROTEIN 2 g
EXCHANGES 1½ Other Carbo.

- 1 6-ounce package sugar-free, low-calorie lemon-flavor gelatin
- 1 cup water
- 2 cups ginger ale, chilled
- 2 cups assorted fruit (such as drained canned pineapple [do not use fresh pineapple], raspberries, sliced strawberries, fresh or canned peaches or pears, quartered fresh apricots, or halved seedless grapes)
- ⅓ cup sliced celery
- 2 tablespoons finely chopped crystallized ginger
- Frozen whipped dessert topping, thawed (optional)
- Chopped nuts, toasted (see note, page 275) (optional)

1 In a medium saucepan combine gelatin and water; heat and stir until gelatin is dissolved. Stir in ginger ale. Chill about 1½ hours or until partially set (the consistency of unbeaten egg whites). Fold in fruit, celery, and ginger.

2 Pour into a 2-quart square baking dish. Cover and chill about 6 hours or until firm.

3 To serve, cut into squares. If desired, top each serving with whipped topping and nuts.

Rosemary-Chive Parker House Rolls

PREP 30 minutes **RISE** 1 hour 30 minutes
BAKE 12 minutes **OVEN** 375°F
MAKES about 30 rolls

- 3 to 3½ cups all-purpose flour
- 1 package active dry yeast
- 3 tablespoons snipped fresh chives
- 1 tablespoon snipped fresh rosemary
- ¾ cup water
- ¼ cup butter
- 1 teaspoon sugar
- ½ teaspoon salt
- 1 egg
- ¼ cup mashed potatoes
- 3 tablespoons butter, melted

1 In a large mixing bowl combine 1 cup of the flour, yeast, chives, and rosemary. In a small saucepan heat and stir the water, ¼ cup butter, sugar, and salt until warm (120°F to 130°F) and butter is almost melted. Add butter mixture to flour mixture. Add egg and mashed potatoes. Beat with an electric mixer on low to medium for 30 seconds, scraping bowl constantly. Beat on high for 3 minutes. Use a wooden spoon to stir in as much of the remaining flour as possible.

2 Turn dough out onto a lightly floured surface. Knead in enough of the remaining flour to make a moderately stiff dough that is smooth and elastic (6 to 8 minutes). Shape dough into a ball. Place in a lightly greased bowl, turning once to grease surface. Cover; let rise in a warm place until double in size (about 1 hour).

3 Punch dough down. Turn dough out onto a lightly floured surface. Cover; let rest for 10 minutes. Grease 2 large baking sheets; set aside. Roll dough to ¼-inch thickness. Using a floured 2½-inch biscuit cutter, cut dough into rounds. Brush with some of the melted butter. Reroll scraps as necessary.

4 To shape rolls, fold dough rounds in half, making the crease slightly off center. Place rolls, larger halves on top, 2 inches apart on prepared baking sheets. Cover; let rise until nearly double in size (about 30 minutes).

5 Preheat oven to 375°F. Lightly brush tops of rolls with the remaining melted butter. Bake for 12 to 15 minutes or until golden. Serve warm.

NUTRITION FACTS per roll

CALORIES 75
TOTAL FAT 3 g (2 g sat. fat)
CHOLESTEROL 14 mg
SODIUM 66 mg
CARBOHYDRATE 10 g
FIBER 0 g
PROTEIN 2 g
EXCHANGES ½ Starch, ½ Fat

Fruit Stollen

PREP 35 minutes **RISE** 2 hours 15 minutes
BAKE 20 minutes **OVEN** 350°F
MAKES 2 loaves (24 servings)

NUTRITION FACTS per serving

CALORIES 113
TOTAL FAT 2 g (1 g sat. fat)
CHOLESTEROL 5 mg
SODIUM 72 mg
CARBOHYDRATE 21 g
FIBER 1 g
PROTEIN 2 g
EXCHANGES 1½ Starch

- 1 package active dry yeast
- ¼ cup warm water (105°F to 115°F)
- ½ cup fat-free milk
- ¼ cup granulated sugar
- ¼ cup butter
- ½ teaspoon salt
- 3 to 3½ cups all-purpose flour
- ¼ cup refrigerated or frozen egg product, thawed, or 1 egg, lightly beaten
- ½ cup raisins
- ¾ cup diced mixed candied fruits and peels (4½ ounces)
- Sifted powdered sugar

1 In a large mixing bowl dissolve yeast in the warm water; let stand for 5 minutes. Meanwhile, in a small saucepan heat and stir milk, granulated sugar, butter, and salt just until warm (105°F to 115°F) and butter starts to melt. Add 1⅓ cups of flour, the milk mixture, and egg product to yeast mixture. Beat with an electric mixer on low for 30 seconds, scraping sides of bowl constantly. Beat on high for 3 minutes more. Stir in raisins, candied fruits, and as much of the remaining flour as possible with a wooden spoon.

2 Turn dough out onto a lightly floured surface. Knead in enough remaining flour to make a moderately soft dough that is smooth and elastic (3 to 5 minutes). Place dough in a greased bowl, turning once to grease surface of dough. Cover and let rise in a warm place until double (about 1½ hours).

3 Punch dough down. Divide dough in half. Cover and let rest for 10 minutes. Grease a large baking sheet; set aside. Press or roll each half of dough to a 9×5-inch oval. Without stretching, fold lengthwise in half; press edges to lightly seal. Place loaves on prepared baking sheet. Cover and let rise until nearly double (about 45 minutes).

4 Preheat oven to 350°F. Bake about 20 minutes or until bread is golden brown and sounds hollow when lightly tapped. Remove from baking sheet and cool on wire racks. Sprinkle with powdered sugar before serving.

Nuts-About-Cranberries Tart

PREP 45 minutes **BAKE** 31 minutes
OVEN 450° F/375°F **MAKES** 12 servings

NUTRITION FACTS per serving

CALORIES 165
TOTAL FAT 9 g (4 g sat. fat)
CHOLESTEROL 15 mg
SODIUM 62 mg
CARBOHYDRATE 20 g
FIBER 2 g
PROTEIN 3 g
EXCHANGES 1 Other Carbo., 2 Fat

- 1 recipe Rich Pastry
- ¼ cup packed brown sugar
- 2 tablespoons butter
- 1 cup fresh cranberries
- 1 medium pear, cored and chopped
- ⅓ cup lightly salted pistachio nuts
- ⅓ cup sliced almonds
- ½ teaspoon vanilla

1 Preheat oven to 450°F. On a lightly floured surface use your hands to slightly flatten the Rich Pastry dough. Roll dough from center to edges into a 15×6-inch rectangle. Transfer dough to an ungreased 13¾×4-inch tart pan with a removable bottom. Ease pastry into tart pan, being careful not to stretch pastry. (Or roll dough from center to edges into a 10-inch circle. Wrap pastry around rolling pin. Unroll into an ungreased 9-inch tart pan with removable bottom.) Press pastry into the fluted sides of the tart pan. Trim pastry even with edges of pan. Line pastry with a double thickness of foil. Bake for 8 minutes. Remove foil. Bake for 3 to 4 minutes more or until set and dry. Cool crust in pan on wire rack. Reduce oven temperature to 375°F.

2 For filling, in a medium saucepan combine brown sugar and butter. Cook and stir over medium heat until combined. Add cranberries and pear; cook and stir until bubbly. Remove from heat. Stir in pistachio nuts, almonds, and vanilla. Spoon filling into cooled crust, spreading evenly. Place tart pan on a baking sheet.

3 Bake for 20 to 25 minutes or until juices are bubbly around edges and pastry is golden brown. Cool in pan on a wire rack. Remove sides of pan. Using 2 wide spatulas, remove tart from bottom of pan; transfer to a serving platter.

Rich Pastry: In a medium bowl combine 1 cup all-purpose flour, ¼ cup whole wheat pastry flour or whole wheat flour, and 1 tablespoon granulated sugar. Using a pastry blender, cut in ¼ cup butter until pieces are pea size. In a small bowl combine 2 tablespoons refrigerated or frozen egg product, thawed, and 2 tablespoons ice water. Gradually stir water mixture into flour mixture until moistened. (If necessary, stir additional cold water, 1 teaspoon at a time, into mixture to moisten.) Shape dough into a ball.

Raisin-Pumpkin Tart

PREP 40 minutes **BAKE** 43 minutes
COOL 1 hour **CHILL** 2 hours
OVEN 450°F/375°F **MAKES** 12 servings

NUTRITION FACTS per serving

CALORIES 213
TOTAL FAT 11 g (4 g sat. fat)
CHOLESTEROL 49 mg
SODIUM 151 mg
CARBOHYDRATE 23 g
FIBER 1 g
PROTEIN 6 g
EXCHANGES ½ Starch, 1 Other Carbo., ½ Medium-Fat Meat, 2 Fat

- 1 recipe Oil Pastry
- 1 8-ounce package reduced-fat cream cheese (Neufchâtel), softened
- 1 egg yolk
- 1 tablespoon honey
- ¼ cup finely chopped sliced almonds, toasted (see note, page 275)
- ¼ cup snipped golden raisins
- 1 cup canned pumpkin
- 1 5-ounce can evaporated fat-free milk (⅔ cup)
- ¼ cup sugar
- 1 egg
- 1 egg white
- 2 teaspoons pumpkin pie spice

1 Preheat oven to 450°F. On a well-floured surface use your hands to flatten Oil Pastry. Roll from center to edge into a circle 12 inches in diameter. Ease pastry into a 10-inch tart pan with removable bottom, being careful not to stretch pastry. Press pastry against edge of pan. Trim edges. Do not prick. Line pastry with a double thickness of heavy foil. Bake for 8 minutes. Remove foil. Bake for 5 minutes more. Remove from oven. Reduce oven temperature to 375°F.

2 Meanwhile, in a medium mixing bowl combine cream cheese, egg yolk, and honey; beat with electric mixer on low to medium until combined. Stir in chopped almonds and raisins; set aside. In a medium bowl stir together pumpkin, evaporated milk, sugar, whole egg, egg white, and pumpkin pie spice; set aside. Carefully spoon cream cheese mixture into hot baked pastry shell; spread evenly. Pour pumpkin mixture over cream cheese layer; spread evenly.

4 Bake for 30 to 35 minutes or until set. Cool on wire rack for 1 hour. Chill for 2 hours. To serve, remove side of pan; lift tart from pan bottom with a large spatula and slide onto a platter. If desired, garnish with *sliced almonds.*

Oil Pastry: In a bowl mix 1⅓ cups all-purpose flour and ¼ teaspoon salt. Add ⅓ cup vegetable oil and 3 tablespoons fat-free milk all at once. Stir lightly with a fork. Form into a ball.

Gingerbread Tea Cake

PREP 25 minutes **BAKE** 40 minutes
OVEN 350°F **MAKES** 18 servings

NUTRITION FACTS per serving

CALORIES 166
TOTAL FAT 6 g (0 g sat. fat)
CHOLESTEROL 0 mg
SODIUM 108 mg
CARBOHYDRATE 26 g
FIBER 0 g
PROTEIN 2 g
EXCHANGES 1 Other Carbo., ½ Fat

- Nonstick cooking spray
- 2⅓ cups all-purpose flour
- 1½ teaspoons baking powder
- 1 teaspoon ground ginger
- 1 teaspoon ground cinnamon
- ½ teaspoon baking soda
- ¼ teaspoon salt
- ¼ teaspoon ground cloves
- ½ cup canola oil
- ¼ cup granulated sugar
- 1¼ cups cold water
- ⅔ cup full-flavor molasses
- ½ cup refrigerated or frozen egg product, thawed, or 2 eggs, lightly beaten
- Powdered sugar (optional)

1 Preheat oven to 350°F. Lightly coat a 13×9×2-inch baking pan with cooking spray; set aside. In a medium bowl stir together flour, baking powder, ginger, cinnamon, baking soda, salt, and cloves; set aside.

2 In a large bowl whisk together oil and sugar until combined. Add the cold water, molasses, and egg product; whisk until combined. Add flour mixture all at once to water mixture, whisking just until smooth. Pour into prepared pan.

3 Bake for 40 to 45 minutes or until a wooden toothpick inserted near center comes out clean. Cool completely on a wire rack. If desired, sprinkle with powdered sugar.

Note: To match photo, lay kitchen string in a decorative pattern on top of the cooled cake. Sprinkle cake with powdered sugar. Remove strings to reveal the pattern.

Chocolate Chip Pumpkin Bars

PREP 20 minutes **BAKE** 25 minutes
OVEN 350°F **MAKES** 36 bars

NUTRITION FACTS per bar

CALORIES 90
TOTAL FAT 4 g (1 g sat. fat)
CHOLESTEROL 0 mg
SODIUM 77 mg
CARBOHYDRATE 12 g
FIBER 1 g
PROTEIN 2 g
EXCHANGES 1 Other Carbo., ½ Fat

Nonstick cooking spray
1 cup all-purpose flour
1 cup whole wheat flour
¾ cup granulated sugar
½ cup finely chopped pecans or walnuts (optional)
2 teaspoons baking powder
1 teaspoon ground cinnamon
½ teaspoon baking soda
½ teaspoon salt
1 cup refrigerated or frozen egg product, thawed, or 4 eggs, lightly beaten
1 15-ounce can pumpkin
½ cup canola oil
¼ cup fat-free milk
⅓ cup miniature semisweet chocolate pieces
2 tablespoons miniature semisweet chocolate pieces
1½ to 2 teaspoons powdered sugar (optional)

1 Preheat oven to 350°F. Lightly coat a 15×10×1-inch baking pan with cooking spray; set aside. In a large bowl stir together all-purpose flour, whole wheat flour, granulated sugar, nuts (if desired), baking powder, cinnamon, baking soda, and salt.

2 In a medium bowl combine egg product, pumpkin, canola oil, and milk. Add pumpkin mixture and the ⅓ cup chocolate pieces to flour mixture; stir just until combined. Spread the batter evenly in the prepared pan. Sprinkle with the 2 tablespoons chocolate pieces.

3 Bake about 25 minutes or until a wooden toothpick inserted in the center comes out clean. Cool in pan on a wire rack. If desired, sprinkle lightly with powdered sugar. Cut into bars.

Gingerbread Cookies

PREP 35 minutes **CHILL** 2 hours
BAKE 4 minutes per batch **OVEN** 375°F
MAKES 36 (3-inch) cookies

NUTRITION FACTS per cookie

CALORIES 73
TOTAL FAT 2 g (1 g sat. fat)
CHOLESTEROL 3 mg
SODIUM 73 mg
CARBOHYDRATE 12 g
FIBER 0 g
PROTEIN 1 g
EXCHANGES 1 Other Carbo.

- ¼ cup butter, softened
- ¼ cup 50% to 70% vegetable oil spread
- ½ cup packed brown sugar
- 2 teaspoons ground ginger
- 1 teaspoon baking soda
- 1 teaspoon ground cinnamon
- ¼ teaspoon salt
- ¼ teaspoon ground cloves
- ¼ cup full-flavor molasses
- ¼ cup refrigerated or frozen egg product, thawed, or 1 egg
- 2 cups all-purpose flour
- ¾ cup white whole wheat flour or whole wheat flour
- 1 recipe Cream Cheese Frosting

1 In a large mixing bowl combine butter and vegetable oil spread; beat with an electric mixer on medium to high for 30 seconds. Add brown sugar, ginger, baking soda, cinnamon, salt, and cloves. Beat until well mixed, scraping bowl occasionally. Beat in molasses and egg product (mixture will look curdled). Add all-purpose flour and whole wheat flour, beating just until combined. Divide dough in half. Cover and chill dough for 2 to 3 hours or until easy to handle.

2 Preheat oven to 375°F. On a lightly floured surface roll dough, half at a time, to ⅛-inch thickness. Using a 2- to 3-inch gingerbread person cookie cutter, cut out shapes. Place 1 inch apart on lightly greased cookie sheets.

3 Bake for 4 to 6 minutes or until edges are firm and centers are set. Cool on cookie sheets on wire racks for 1 minute. Transfer to wire racks; cool. Pipe Cream Cheese Frosting onto cookies. If desired, decorate with small *candies.*

Cream Cheese Frosting: In a large mixing bowl beat 4 ounces reduced-fat cream cheese (Neufchâtel), softened, and 1 teaspoon vanilla with an electric mixer on medium until smooth. Beat in 3 to 3½ cups powdered sugar to make piping consistency. If necessary, stir in milk or additional powdered sugar to reach desired consistency. If desired, tint frosting with food coloring. Makes about 1¼ cups.

Almond Meringue Kisses

PREP 25 minutes **STAND** 30 minutes
BAKE 12 minutes **DRY** 1 hour **OVEN** 300°F
MAKES about 36 cookies

NUTRITION FACTS per cookie

CALORIES 13
TOTAL FAT 0 g (0 g sat. fat)
CHOLESTEROL 0 mg
SODIUM 11 mg
CARBOHYDRATE 3 g
FIBER 0 g
PROTEIN 0 g
EXCHANGES Free

- 2 egg whites
- 1 teaspoon almond extract
- ¼ teaspoon cream of tartar
- ⅛ teaspoon salt
- ½ cup sugar
- 1 tablespoon cornstarch
- Food-safe silver, blue, or gold luster dust and/or unsweetened cocoa powder (optional)

1 Let egg whites stand in a medium mixing bowl at room temperature for 30 minutes. Preheat oven to 300°F. Line 2 large cookie sheets with parchment paper; set aside.

2 Add almond extract, cream of tartar, and salt to egg whites. Beat with an electric mixer on medium to high until soft peaks form (tips curl). In a small bowl combine sugar and cornstarch. Gradually add the sugar mixture to the egg white mixture, about 1 tablespoon at a time, beating on high until stiff peaks form (tips stand straight).

3 Transfer egg white mixture to a disposable piping bag fitted with a large closed star tip. Pipe 1½-inch "kisses" on prepared cookie sheets, leaving 1 inch between kisses.

4 Place cookie sheets on separate oven racks; bake for 12 minutes. Turn off oven; let cookies dry in oven with door closed for 1 hour. Carefully lift cookies off parchment paper. Transfer to wire racks; cool completely.*

5 If desired, use a new paintbrush or a pastry brush used only for food to lightly brush luster dust on cookies or sprinkle with cocoa powder.

***Note:** Store cookies in a single layer in an airtight container as soon as they are cool. Seal and store at room temperature up to 4 days.

Chapter 18

Index & Metric

How Recipes Are Analyzed

The Better Homes and Gardens® Test Kitchen uses nutrition-analysis software to determine the nutritional value of a single serving of a recipe. Here are some factors to keep in mind regarding each analysis:

- Analyses do not include optional ingredients.
- The first serving size listed is analyzed when a range is given. For example, if a recipe makes 4 to 6 servings, the Nutrition Facts are based on 4 servings.
- When ingredient choices (such as butter or margarine) appear in a recipe, the first one mentioned is used for analysis.
- When milk is a recipe ingredient, the analysis has been calculated using fat-free (skim) milk unless otherwise noted.
- The exchanges, listed for every recipe along with the Nutrition Facts, are based on the exchange list developed by the American Dietetic Association and the American Diabetes Association.

NUTRITION NOTE

Note on Sodium: For this cookbook, the goal was to keep the sodium levels at a reasonable level that would allow you to stay under the recommended limit of 2,400 mg a day. But for recipes that have high-sodium ingredients, such as ham or other processed foods, the sodium levels are relatively high—1,000 mg or more. This only occurs in a few recipes but it is something to watch for if you have hypertension and have been told to follow a low-sodium diet.

A

G

H

I-J

Q

R

S

T

U-V

W

Y

Z

METRIC INFORMATION

The charts on this page provide a guide for converting measurements from the U.S. customary system, which is used throughout this book, to the metric system.

Product Differences

Most of the ingredients called for in the recipes in this book are available in most countries. However, some are known by different names. Here are some common American ingredients and their possible counterparts:

- Sugar (white) is granulated, fine granulated, or castor sugar.
- Powdered sugar is icing sugar.
- All-purpose flour is enriched, bleached or unbleached white household flour. When self-rising flour is used in place of all-purpose flour in a recipe that calls for leavening, omit the leavening agent (baking soda or baking powder) and salt.
- Light-color corn syrup is golden syrup.
- Cornstarch is cornflour.
- Baking soda is bicarbonate of soda.
- Vanilla or vanilla extract is vanilla essence.
- Green, red, or yellow sweet peppers are capsicums or bell peppers.
- Golden raisins are sultanas.

Volume and Weight

The United States traditionally uses cup measures for liquid and solid ingredients. The chart below shows the approximate imperial and metric equivalents. If you are accustomed to weighing solid ingredients, the following approximate equivalents will be helpful.

- 1 cup butter, castor sugar, or rice = 8 ounces = ½ pound = 250 grams
- 1 cup flour = 4 ounces = ¼ pound = 125 grams
- 1 cup icing sugar = 5 ounces = 150 grams

Canadian and U.S. volume for a cup measure is 8 fluid ounces (237 ml), but the standard metric equivalent is 250 ml.

1 British imperial cup is 10 fluid ounces.

In Australia, 1 tablespoon equals 20 ml, and there are 4 teaspoons in the Australian tablespoon.

Spoon measures are used for smaller amounts of ingredients. Although the size of the tablespoon varies slightly in different countries, for practical purposes and for recipes in this book, a straight substitution is all that's necessary. Measurements made using cups or spoons always should be level unless stated otherwise.

Common Weight Range Replacements

IMPERIAL / U.S.	METRIC
½ ounce	15 g
1 ounce	25 g or 30 g
4 ounces (¼ pound)	115 g or 125 g
8 ounces (½ pound)	225 g or 250 g
16 ounces (1 pound)	450 g or 500 g
1¼ pounds	625 g
1½ pounds	750 g
2 pounds or 2¼ pounds	1,000 g or 1 Kg

Oven Temperature Equivalents

FAHRENHEIT SETTING	CELSIUS SETTING*	GAS SETTING
300°F	150°C	Gas Mark 2 (very low)
325°F	160°C	Gas Mark 3 (low)
350°F	180°C	Gas Mark 4 (moderate)
375°F	190°C	Gas Mark 5 (moderate)
400°F	200°C	Gas Mark 6 (hot)
425°F	220°C	Gas Mark 7 (hot)
450°F	230°C	Gas Mark 8 (very hot)
475°F	240°C	Gas Mark 9 (very hot)
500°F	260°C	Gas Mark 10 (extremely hot)
Broil	Broil	Grill

***Electric and gas ovens may be calibrated using celsius. However, for an electric oven, increase celsius setting 10 to 20 degrees when cooking above 160°C. For convection or forced air ovens (gas or electric), lower the temperature setting 25°F/10°C when cooking at all heat levels.**

Baking Pan Sizes

IMPERIAL / U.S.	METRIC
9×1½-inch round cake pan	22- or 23×4-cm (1.5 L)
9×1½-inch pie plate	22- or 23×4-cm (1 L)
8×8×2-inch square cake pan	20×5-cm (2 L)
9×9×2-inch square cake pan	22- or 23×4.5-cm (2.5 L)
11×7×1½-inch baking pan	28×17×4-cm (2 L)
2-quart rectangular baking pan	30×19×4.5-cm (3 L)
13×9×2-inch baking pan	34×22×4.5-cm (3.5 L)
15×10×1-inch jelly roll pan	40×25×2-cm
9×5×3-inch loaf pan	23×13×8-cm (2 L)
2-quart casserole	2 L

U.S. / Standard Metric Equivalents

⅛ teaspoon = 0.5 ml
¼ teaspoon = 1 ml
½ teaspoon = 2 ml
1 teaspoon = 5 ml
1 tablespoon = 15 ml
2 tablespoons = 25 ml
¼ cup = 2 fluid ounces = 50 ml
⅓ cup = 3 fluid ounces = 75 ml
½ cup = 4 fluid ounces = 125 ml
⅔ cup = 5 fluid ounces = 150 ml
¾ cup = 6 fluid ounces = 175 ml
1 cup = 8 fluid ounces = 250 ml
2 cups = 1 pint = 500 ml
1 quart = 1 litre